exercises in
elementary
algebra

second
edition

exercises in elementary algebra

second edition

J. Richard Lux
and Richard S. Pieters
PHILLIPS ACADEMY
ANDOVER

Independent School Press

Wellesley Hills   Massachusetts

808182
34567890

PRINTED IN THE UNITED STATES OF AMERICA

0-88334-087-9

CONTENTS

FRACTIONS

LINEAR EQUATIONS

WORD PROBLEMS

EXPONENTS AND RADICALS

QUADRATIC EQUATIONS

RELATIONS AND FUNCTIONS

GRAPHS

RIGHT TRIANGLE TRIGONOMETRY

ELEMENTARY STATISTICS

EXERCISES AND EXAMINATIONS

PREFACE

Every algebra teacher needs some supplementary material, but the teacher of small classes of college preparatory students requires a large and interesting supply. We have attempted to provide him with the best of the traditional drill problems as well as exercises on structure, sets, inequalities, functions and other modern topics. Most of these problems are new, but some are an up-to-date revision of a set of exercises that have been used for over thirty years. Once known as *Exercises in First Year Algebra* by George K. Sanborn, they were later revised by Winfield M. Sides and Evan A. Nason under the title *George K. Sanborn's Exercises in First Year Algebra with Reviews and Examinations*. We share their desire to provide drill to develop manipulative skills, but feel that it is also possible to bring a modern emphasis in notation and vocabulary to the traditional topics as well as to add the new ones that have recently filtered down into elementary algebra. We hope to accomplish this in the following ways.

1. *Adequate and carefully graded lists of oral exercises.*—Almost every section is introduced by a large number of oral problems, designed to furnish classroom drill and to prepare the student for the written work which follows. The student is led to discover generalizations through a step-by-step approach.

2. *An unusually wide range of topics.*—The exercises cover all the topics suggested by groups such as SMSG for this level. Many second-year topics are presented at a degree of difficulty suitable for the first-year student. Long lists of miscellaneous problems in each section teach the student to use the basic types to make a scientific and orderly analysis in the solution of an original problem.

3. *A comprehensive collection of review exercises and examinations.*—There are review exercises at the end of each large general section as well as review exercises, mid-year examinations, final examinations, and NAIS examinations. All the exercises and examinations have been tested in the classroom.

We are very happy to be able to carry on and extend the work of three great teachers.

GEORGE K. SANBORN
EVAN A. NASON
WINFIELD M. SIDES

We are also grateful for the advice and assistance of all the members of the Phillips Academy Mathematics Department, and cherish the understanding of two math widows, Ann and Norma.

Andover, Mass.   J. Richard Lux
July 5, 1969   Richard S. Pieters

PREFACE TO THE SECOND EDITION

The first edition of this exercise book has been used in many classrooms. This second edition has benefited from the criticisms and suggestions of the teachers and students who have used the book.

The major changes are:

1. Worked examples are included in most of the written exercises.

2. The problem sets have been carefully rearranged in an effort to have the problem difficulty gradually increase from easy to hard in each exercise.

3. Problems have been included whose solutions can best be found by the use of hand-held calculators which are now being used in many classrooms.

4. Some of the more difficult problems have been omitted. They will be included in the next book in this series: *Exercises in Algebra and Trigonometry*. Exercises involving computer programming will also be included in this next book.

5. All the problems, except those in some sample final examinations, have had the units changed to the metric system.

6. Multiple choice and true-false exercises have been added in various sections. The reviews and examinations have been updated by the inclusion of some recent examinations.

7. The book contains answers to the odd numbered problems in all exercises as well as the answers to all the problems in the review and examination sections. An answer key to all problems is available in a separate booklet. The authors have checked the exercises and their answers carefully, but it is inevitable that some errors are still present. We would be grateful to anyone who will send such errors to the publisher.

We are particularly thankful to Ann Lux and Norma Pieters for their careful typing of an often illegible manuscript. We are also grateful to the Independent School Press for their support and encouragement.

July 5, 1977

J. R. L.
R. S. P.

exercises in
elementary
algebra

second
edition

FUNDAMENTAL OPERATIONS

Exercise 1. Numerical Substitution

Oral

When $a = 0$, $b = 1$, $c = -2$, and $d = 3$, give the value of:

1. $b + c$ **2.** $a + b + c + d$ **3.** $d + b - c$

4. $3b + 2c - d$ **5.** $3b + 4c - 3d$ **6.** $bc + bd$

7. $ac + 2bd + cd$ **8.** $b^2 + c^2 + d^2$ **9.** $bc^2 - 2bc$

10. $c^2d^2 + b^3c^3$ **11.** $a^2 + d^3$ **12.** $abc + 2bc^2d$

13. $b^5 + c^4 + d^2$ **14.** $b^2cd - bc^2$ **15.** $b^3 - c^3$

16. $\dfrac{b + d}{d}$ **17.** $\dfrac{2d - bc}{2b}$ **18.** $\dfrac{b - c}{d}$

19. $\dfrac{a}{d}$ **20.** $\dfrac{d - b + c}{4c}$ **21.** $\dfrac{ab^3 + ac^3}{d}$

Written

When $a = 1$, $b = 2$, $c = 5$, $d = 6$, and $m = 0$, give the value of:

Example: $\dfrac{b^2c + a^2b^2}{2bc - 4ab}$

First substitute the values, then do the computations.

$$\frac{(2)^2(5) + (1)^2(2)^2}{2(2)(5) - 4(1)(2)} = \frac{20 - 4}{20 - 8} = \frac{16}{12} = \frac{4}{3}$$

1. $ad^2 + 5bc$ **2.** $a^2bc^2 - 3ad + a^4$ **3.** $mabc + 3a^2b^2c^2$

4. $b^2cd - abc^2$ **5.** $a^4b^3c + bcd$ **6.** $ma^3 + 4cd - ad$

7. $\dfrac{ab^2}{2} + 5c$ **8.** $\dfrac{md}{3} + \dfrac{4cd}{b}$ **9.** $\dfrac{ac}{d} + a$

10. $\dfrac{a^2}{c} + 3a^2b$ **11.** $\dfrac{ab^2}{a} - \dfrac{a^5d}{b}$ **12.** $\dfrac{c + d}{d} + \dfrac{d - c}{a}$

13. $\dfrac{d^2 - a^2b^2}{a^2b^2}$ **14.** $\dfrac{mcd + 3abc}{d^2 - 4b^2}$ **15.** $\dfrac{a^2d^2 - 9b^2}{abcd}$

If $a = -1$, $b = 6$, $c = \frac{1}{3}$, $x = 3$, and $d = -2$, find the value of:

Example: $(3a + b^2c) \div [2x - (b \div d)]$

If there are parentheses in the problem, you may have to add brackets or braces to make the substitutions.

$$[3(-1) + (6)^2(\tfrac{1}{3})] \div \{2(3) - [6 \div (-2)]\} =$$
$$[-3 + 12] \div \{6 - [-3]\} =$$
$$9 \div 9 = 1$$

16. $bc + (b \div x)$

17. $abx - b^2d$

18. $a^2 + b^2 + c^2$

19. $a \times c \times b \div x$

20. $a^2x^2 + bc$

21. $-a^2 + 3bd$

22. $4b + (5x \div a)$

23. $(a + b + x) \div (da)$

24. $a^3 + bd^2 \div (cx)$

25. $-2a + 7bc$

26. $-2ad + 4d^3 - 9bc$

27. $\dfrac{b^2 + x^2}{27c}$

28. $4x - (2b + 5a)$

29. $3(abx - 4dx)$

30. $\dfrac{3a + bd}{5x}$

31. $(2b + 3a)^2 \div (3x)$

32. $(4c \div ad) + c$

33. $a^5 + a^4 - a^3 - a^2 + a - 1$

34. $\dfrac{d^3 + ba}{x - 2d}$

35. $\dfrac{c^2x^2 + ab^2 + a^2}{dx}$

36. $(a + b)(b + x) \div (x - d)$

37. $[(3x + 3c) \div (b + a)] \div (b + 2x)$

38. $(b \div c) - abc - bx^2$

39. $[d \div (c \times a)][b - (x \div c)]$

40. $\dfrac{(a + d)(a + x)}{abcd}$

41. $\dfrac{c}{2} + \dfrac{12}{b} + \dfrac{d}{a}$

42. $\dfrac{b^2}{x + 15c} + \dfrac{a^3}{dc}$

43. a^3d^2bcx

44. $\left(-5c \div \dfrac{1}{b}\right) + 3d^3$

45. $(a^3 \div c) + (d^3 \div c) + (c^2 \times b)$

Exercise 2. Addition

Give the algebraic sum of:

1. $5x$
   $7x$

2. $17ab$
   $9ab$

3. $9d$
   $-4d$

4. $7\frac{3}{4}$
   $-2\frac{1}{4}$

5. $-2xy$
   $6xy$

6. $-4c^2d$
   $-3c^2d$

7. $3mn$
   $-3mn$

8. $10i$
   $-3i$
   $2i$

9. $-3a$
   $-5a$
   $2a$

10. $-6x$
    $3x$
    $-5x$

11. $-3abc$
    $-2abc$
    $-4abc$

12. $-2\frac{1}{2}$
    $3\frac{1}{2}$
    -1

13. $a + 2b$
    $3a + 4b$

14. $x - 2y$
    $2x + 7y$

15. $-3m + 2$
    $m - 5$

16. $4a - 3b$
    $-4a + 7b + 2c$

17. $2l + 3m - \ \ n$
    $6l - 4m - 2n$

18. $2a + 3b - \ \ c$
    $-3a + \ \ b - 2c$
    $-4a - 2b - 5c$

19. $-7x$ and $4x$

20. $a + b$ and $2a - 3b$

21. $8mn$, $-3mn$, and $2mn$

22. $-a - 13b$ and $-4a + 6b$

23. $a + c$, $2a - c$, and $-7 + 2xy$

24. $a - 3c$ and $a - 2b$

25. $xy + 3 + 2a$ and $-a + 3c$

26. $2ab - 4xy + 3cd$ and $-xy - 7ab$

27. $a - b + 2c$ and $-6a + 3b - d$

28. $2x - 4\frac{1}{2}$ and $3\frac{1}{2} + 2y$

29. $-3l + 2m - 4n$ and $-n + 2l - 2m$

30. $a - b$, $b - c$, and $c + d$

Give the algebraic sum of:

1. $3a - 2b + c$
$-2a + 4b - 6c$

2. $-2x - 2\frac{1}{4} + 6y$
$14x - 1\frac{1}{2}$

3. $7l + m - 2n + p$
$- 6m - 5p$

4. $3.2a + 5.3b$
$-1.6a - 6.5b$

5. $x^2 - 3x + 2$
$-7x^2 + 4x - 6$

6. $r + 3s - 7t$
$2a + 8s - 4t$

7. $x^3 + 5x^2 - x + 7$
$- 4x^2 + 15x - 18$
$-9x^3 - 14x^2 - 13x + 9$

8. $x^2 + 3xy - 9y^2$
$-4x^2 - 17y^2$
$- 4xy + 7a$
$15x^2 - 19xy - 20a$

Example: $3xy + x^2 - 2y^2$, $2x^2 - 5y^2 - 2xy$, and $y^2 - x^2$.

Be sure to arrange your work with similar terms in the same column.

$$x^2 + 3xy - 2y^2$$
$$2x^2 - 2xy - 5y^2$$
$$-x^2 \qquad + y^2$$
$$\overline{2x^2 + xy - 6y^2}$$

9. $ax + 7y$, $14m - 16ax - 13y$, and $-31m - 19y - 6ax$

10. $3a - 7b$, $12a + 5c$, and $-17b - 36c + 5a$

11. $x^3 - 4x^2 - 3x + 2$, $x^3 - 4x - 9$, and $x^2 - 6x + 1$

12. $-2x^2 + 3x^3 - 7x + 4$, $-x^3 + 4 - 7x^2 - 4x$, and $5x^2 - 3x - 4$

13. $7\frac{1}{2} + 6.1x - 3y$, $2\frac{1}{2} - 3.2x - 6.5y$, and $-3\frac{1}{2} - 1.8x$

14. $ax - by - cm$, $14by - 17ax$, $13ax$, $-3by$, and $-17cm + 6ax$

15. $13ax^2 - 9a^2x + 2ax$, $4a^2x$, $-3ax^2 - 7ax$, and $-3ax^2$

16. $5x^3 + x^2y - 3xy^2$, $2xy^2 + 3y^3 - 4x^2y$, and $2y^3 - xy^2 - 2x^3$

Exercise 3. Collecting Similar Terms

Oral

Simplify:

1. $a + b - 3c - 2a - 2c + b$
2. $ab + 2cd - 2ab + xy - 3cd$
3. $ax^2 - 2ax - 3x^2 + 2ax^2 - a^2 + 3ax$
4. $-ab + 3 + 2a - 2ab - 4 - 5a$
5. $-a^2x + ax - 3a^2x - ax^2 - 4ax$
6. $x^3 - 4x - 5x^3 + 3 - 4x^2 - x - 7$
7. $m^2 - 3n^2 - m^2n - 2m^2 + 3n^2 - 2mn^2$
8. $xy - 2x^2y - xy^2 - 3x^2y - 4xy - xy^2$
9. $-a^2b^2 - a^2b - 5a^2b^2 - 4ab^2 + 3a^2b$
10. $6.5 + 2am - 3mn - 4ma - 4.2$

Written

Simplify:

Example: $9x^2 - 7x + 5 + 15x - 14x^2 - 6 + 20x^2 - 40x$

Collect the coefficients of the like powers.

$$9x^2 - 7x + 5 + 15x - 14x^2 - 6 + 20x^2 - 40x =$$
$$(9x^2 - 14x^2 + 20x^2) + (-7x + 15x - 40x) + (5 - 6) =$$
$$15x^2 - 32x - 1$$

1. $a^2 - 4b^2 + 7ab - 6b^2 + 2a^2 - 14ab - 8b^2$
2. $3.5 + 7x - 9x^2 - 2\frac{1}{2} - 4x - 8 - 6x^2 - 17x$
3. $x^2 - 4y^2 + 3xy + 4y^2 - 16xy + 3 + 7y^2 - 18 + xy$
4. $2m^2 + 9m^2n^2 + 4n^2 - 3m^2n^2 - 19m^2 - 14n^2m^2 - 8n^2$
5. $2a^2b + 3a^2 - 4ab^2 - 6a^2b - 5b^2 - 9b^2 - 11a^2b + 8a^2$
6. $-2m^2n + 4m^2 - 5m^2n^2 - 3m^2n - 4n^2 + 2mn^2 - 4m^2 - 6m^2n^2$
7. $ax + 3by + 5mn - 4b^2y^2 - 3ax - 3by + 2ax - 4by^2 - 12mn$
8. $7x^2y + 3xy^2 - 2yx^2 - 6y^2x - 3x^2y - 7xy^2 + 4yx^2$
9. $-11abc + 3ac + 4acb - 4bc - 7ac + 6bc + 5ab + 4ac$
10. $15x^3 - 7x^2y - 4xy + 3x^2 - xy^2 - 8x^2y + 4x^2 - 9x^3 - 16xy - 3xy^2$

Exercise 4. Subtraction

Oral

Subtract the expression in the lower line from that in the upper line.

1. $16a$	**2.** $13xy$	**3.** $4.5b$	**4.** $14x$
$\underline{7a}$	$\underline{8xy}$	$\underline{3.6b}$	$\underline{-x}$

5. $17a^2b$	**6.** $7\frac{1}{2}$	**7.** $-4ab$	**8.** $-17x$
$\underline{-3a^2b}$	$\underline{-5\frac{1}{2}}$	$\underline{-4ab}$	$\underline{-8x}$

9. $-12mn$	**10.** $6.2a$	**11.** $65n$	**12.** $1\frac{3}{4}x$
$\underline{4mn}$	$\underline{-3.8a}$	$\underline{-17n}$	$3\frac{3}{4}x$

13. $-1.4rs$	**14.** $.02ab$	**15.** $-72abc$	**16.** $.31xy$
$\underline{6.8rs}$	$\underline{-.07ab}$	$\underline{-96abc}$	$\underline{-.07xy}$

17. $7a + 4b$	**18.** $6x - 9y$	**19.** $4ab - 6xy$	**20.** $.3a + .4b$
$\underline{8a + 3b}$	$\underline{-2x + 4y}$	$\underline{7ab - 4xy}$	$\underline{1.2a - .7b}$

21. $a - 2b$	**22.** $-3b + 2c$	**23.** $-4x - y - 3a$	
$\underline{3a + c}$	$\underline{-2b - 3c}$	$\underline{-6x - y - 4b}$	

24. $-4m + 3n - 5$	**25.** $a + 2b - m$
$\underline{-6m + 13}$	$\underline{-3a + 4b - n}$

Subtract:

26. $18 + x$ from $25 - 7x$

27. $-7x + 3y$ from $x - 2y$

28. $a + 2b - c$ from $b - 2c$

29. $-5m + 2n$ from $5m + 3$

30. $-s - c$ from $2c - b$

31. From $x^2 - 2x + 8$ take $2x^2 - 4x - 2$.

32. From $-6a^2 - 2b^2$ take $6a^2 - 4c^2$.

33. From $m^3 - 3m^2 - 6$ take $-3m^2 - 4m$.

34. From $4\frac{1}{2} + 7.5b$ take $3\frac{1}{4} - b - .2c$.

35. From $-ab - 4ac + 2bc$ take $4ac - ab$.

Example: Subtract the sum of $5x$ and $-3y$ from their difference.

Difference: $5x - (-3y) = 5x + 3y$
Sum: $5x + (-3y) = \underline{5x - 3y}$
$$6y$$

1. From $-16m + 18n - 19p$ subtract $17m - 37n + 46p$.

2. From $a^2 - 13a - 72$ subtract $-14 + 19a^2 - 4a$.

3. From $.9x^2 - 1.6x - .72$ subtract $3.4x^2 + .91 - .4x$.

4. From $-6ab + 25ac - 3bc$ subtract $-3bc - 4cd + 19ab$.

5. From $-37y^2 + 62y^3 - 13$ subtract $-57y + 16.5 - 18y^3 + 14y^2$.

6. From $a + b + 4c - 5a$ subtract $6a - 4b + 3c - a$.

7. From the difference between $5a$ and $7b$ subtract $-4a - 16b$.

8. From the sum of $2x - 3y$ and $-7x + 4y$ subtract $13x - 6y$.

9. From the sum of $5m$ and $-3n$ subtract their difference.

10. From $-7ab - 3bc$ take the difference between $4bc$ and $-6ac$.

11. Subtract $x^2 - 2xy + y^2$ from $-3y^2 + 4.6xy - x^2$.

12. Subtract $6a^3 + 3a - 5a^2 - 19$ from $-37 + 4a^3 - 17a^2 + 22a$.

13. Subtract $-27x^2 + 13ax - 16a^2x$ from $19ax^2 - 18ax - 41x^2$.

14. Subtract $5ax^2 - 15a^2x - 31a^2x^2$ from $-14x^2a - 19xa^2 + 2x^2a^2$.

15. Subtract the sum of $-3m$ and $-6p$ from their difference.

16. Subtract the sum of $x + 2y$ and $-9y - 4z$ from $6x - 13z$.

17. Subtract the difference between $19a + 21x$ and $13x - y$ from $14a - 17x$.

18. Subtract the sum of $-a + b$ and $3a - 4b$ from their difference.

19. Subtract the sum of $16m - 9n + 17p$ and $-4n + 3a$ from their difference.

20. Subtract the difference of $6x - 2y + 3z$ and $2x - 2y - 3z$ from their sum.

Oral

Perform the indicated multiplications:

1. 6×13 **2.** $7 \cdot 5 \cdot a$ **3.** $-4 \cdot 12b$

4. $8 \times (-11m)$ **5.** $(4x)(7a)$ **6.** $(-3a)(13)$

7. $-14(2x)$ **8.** $11(-10ab)$ **9.** $(-6)(-11)$

10. $(-3a)(-12b)$ **11.** $(-16m)^3$ **12.** $a^2 \cdot a^3$

13. $-b^2 \times ab$ **14.** $(-m^2n)(mn^3)$ **15.** $(8x^3y^2)(-xy^2)$

16. $\frac{1}{2}(-14a)$ **17.** $3 \times 2 \times 7$ **18.** $(2a)(6)(5b)$

19. $(-4)(a)(2b)$ **20.** $(-a)(-b)(c)$ **21.** $(-a)(-b)(-c)$

22. $(-3a)(-2a)(4b)$ **23.** $-2x(y^2)(-2x)$ **24.** $(-m)(-2n)a$

25. $-2a(a^2)3a$ **26.** $(-4ab)(-9b^2)a^2$ **27.** $-.3(.2a^2)$

28. $\frac{1}{2} \cdot \frac{3}{4} \cdot a \cdot b$ **29.** $\frac{1}{3}x \cdot 9x^3y^2$ **30.** $(-a)(-b)(-c)(-d)$

31. $2(a + b)$ **32.** $-7(x + y)$ **33.** $(m + n)2a$

34. $-a(b - c)$ **35.** $-3x(-2x - 3)$ **36.** $a^2y^2(2a - 3y)$

37. $7 \cdot 4(a - b)$ **38.** $(-6)(-2)(x + y)$ **39.** $a(a - b)b$

40. $7 \times 2(m - n)a$ **41.** $(ab - ac - bd)(-a)$ **42.** $-3xy(x - 2y + a)$

43. $(3)^2 \times (2)^2$ **44.** $(-2)^2 \cdot (-3)$

Written

Perform the indicated multiplications:

1. $(-16a)(-32b)(-5c)$ **2.** $(.32m - .19n)(-.9mn)$

3. $(6a^2 - 14a - 91)(-8a^2)$ **4.** $-\frac{2}{3}a(-\frac{1}{2}a^2 + \frac{3}{4}ab)$

5. $(2a^2 - 3ab + 9b^2)(-\frac{1}{3}ab)$ **6.** $(4a)^2(-3a)^3$

7. $(-3)^2(-a)^3(-b)^4(-abc)^2$ **8.** $(-2)^3(-a^2)(-b)^2(-a)^3$

Example: Multiply: $(3x^2 - y^2 - 4xy)(2x - 5y)$

Arrange each multiplier in decreasing order of the exponents of one of the letters. This example uses a vertical format, the next one will use a horizontal one.

$$\begin{array}{r} 3x^2 - 4xy - y^2 \\ 2x - 5y \\ \hline 6x^3 - 8x^2y - 2xy^2 \\ - 15x^2y + 20xy^2 + 5y^3 \\ \hline 6x^3 - 23x^2y + 18xy^2 + 5y^3 \end{array}$$

Example: Multiply: $(x + a - b)(x - 2a - 3b)$

The horizontal format uses the form of the distributive law.

$$(x + a - b)(x - 2a - 3b) =$$
$$x(x - 2a - 3b) + a(x - 2a - 3b) - b(x - 2a - 3b) =$$
$$x^2 - 2ax - 3bx + ax - 2a^2 - 3ab - bx + 2ab + 3b^2 =$$
$$x^2 - ax - 4bx - 2a^2 - ab + 3b^2$$

9. $(a - b - c)(x - 2y)$ 10. $(a^2 + 2ab - b^2)(a - b)$

11. $(x + y)(x^2 - xy + y^2)$ 12. $(a + b - c)(a - c)$

13. $(5a - 3b)(-3a - 7b)$ 14. $(x^3 - 2x^2 - 3x + 3)(x - 2)$

15. $(x^3 + 2x^2 + x + 3)(x + 2)$ 16. $(4x^3 - 3x^2 + 2x - 1)(2x + 1)$

17. $(x^3 + x^2y + xy^2 + y^3)(x - y)$ 18. $(a^3 - a^2b + ab^2 - b^3)(a + b)$

19. $(a^3 + 3a^2b + 5ab^2 + 4b^3)(3a + 2b)$

20. $(4r^3 - 8r^2s + 3rs^2 + 8s^3)(2r - 7s)$

21. $(a^5 - a^4 + a^3 - a^2 + a - 1)(a + 1)$

22. $(x^4 + x^3y + x^2y^2 + xy^3 + y^4)(x - y)$

23. $(x^2 - x + 1)(x^2 - 3 + 2x)$

24. $(x^3 + x^2 - 1)(x^2 - x - 3)$

25. $(a^5 - 7a^3 + 13)(-3a^3 - 5a - 4)$

26. $(x^2 - 2xy + y^2)(x^2 + 2xy - y^2)$

27. $(m^4 - 3m^2 + 5m^3 - 4m)(2 + m - m^2)$

28. $(3a^4 - a - a^2 + 1)(1 - 2a^2 + a)$

Example: Multiply: $(m + 2)(m + 3)(m^2 - 1 + m)$

First multiply what you can by inspection, then multiply out the rest.
$$(m + 2)(m + 3)(m^2 - 1 + m) = (m^2 + 5m + 6)(m^2 + m - 1)$$

$$
\begin{array}{r}
m^2 + 5m + 6 \\
\underline{m^2 + m - 1} \\
m^4 + 5m^3 + 6m^2 \phantom{{}+ m - 6} \\
+ m^3 + 5m^2 + 6m \phantom{{}- 6} \\
\underline{ - m^2 - 5m - 6} \\
m^4 + 6m^3 + 10m^2 + m - 6
\end{array}
$$

29. $a^2(a + 3b)(-2b - 6a)$ 30. $(x^2 - x - 2)(x - 1)(x + 1)$

31. $(-3)(-5a - 5c)(-4c + 3a)$ 32. $(x + 2y)(x + 3y)(x - y)$

33. $(a + b)^2(a - b)^2$ 34. $(2a + 3b)^3$

9

Exercise 6. Division

Oral

Perform the indicated divisions:

1. $51 \div 3$
2. $48 \div 7$
3. $10a \div 5$
4. $12a \div 3a$
5. $18 \div -6$
6. $-132 \div 11$
7. $-24 \div -8$
8. $0 \div 4$
9. $0 \div -3a$
10. $16ab \div -2a$
11. $-27abc \div 27c$
12. $9ab \div -12ab$
13. $-14x^3 \div 7x^2$
14. $32x^3y^2 \div 8xy$
15. $-.4x \div .2$
16. $-.8ab \div -2b$
17. $7abc \div 7abc$
18. $\frac{1}{2} \div \frac{3}{2}$
19. $-\dfrac{a}{3} \div \dfrac{b}{3}$
20. $-9x^2y^3 \div -3xy^3$
21. $-12ab \div 4a$
22. $16m^2n \div (-4mn)$
23. $\dfrac{2x}{3y} \div \dfrac{3x}{2y}$
24. $7x^2y^2 \div 7xy$
25. $-4m \div -\frac{1}{3}$
26. $-90x^2y^3a^4 \div -15xy^3a$
27. $-\dfrac{4a}{9} \div -4a$
28. $-.09x \div -.03$
29. $(6a \times 5b) \div 2ab$
30. $4\frac{1}{2}x^2 \div \frac{1}{2}x$
31. $(3a + 9b) \div 3$
32. $(x^3 + x^2 - x) \div x$
33. $(27ab - 9abc + 3ac) \div (-3a)$
34. $(.2ab - .4ac - .6a^2) \div (.2a)$
35. $(4x^2y^3 - 2x^3y^2 - 8x^3y) \div (-2xy)$
36. $(5a - 25a^2 - 15ab) \div (5a)$
37. $(-4x^3y + 4xy - 8xy^2) \div (-4xy)$
38. $(\frac{1}{2}a - \frac{1}{4}b - \frac{1}{6}c) \div \frac{1}{2}$
39. $(.5 - .15x + .2y) \div .5$
40. $(-x - 3x^2 - x^3 + x^4) \div (-x)$
41. $(\frac{1}{3}xy - \frac{2}{3}x^2y - \frac{4}{9}xy^2) \div (\frac{2}{3}xy)$
42. $(4x^8 - 20x^5 + 13x^4) \div (-4x^3)$
43. $2(a + b) \div (a + b)$
44. $(3x + 3y) \div (x + y)$
45. $ab(m + n) \div -a(m + n)$

Written

Perform the indicated divisions:

1. $-1.2ab \div .4a$

2. $-\dfrac{8a}{9} \div \dfrac{2x}{3}$

3. $(\frac{2}{3}xy^5 - 1\frac{1}{3}xy^3 + \frac{4}{9}x^2y) \div (\frac{1}{3}xy)$

4. $(-8m^2n^2 + 18m^3n^2 - 4mn^2) \div (-4mn^2)$

5. $-16m^2n \div .4mn$

6. $.07x^3 \div .1x^2$

Example: $(3x^2 + x + 2x^3 + 6) \div (x + 2)$.

Arrange in descending powers of x.

$$
\begin{array}{r}
2x^2 - x + 3 \\
x + 2 \overline{\smash{)}2x^3 + 3x^2 + x + 6} \\
\underline{2x^3 + 4x^2} \\
-x^2 + x \\
\underline{-x^2 - 2x} \\
3x + 6 \\
\underline{3x + 6}
\end{array}
$$

Ans. $2x^2 - x + 3$.

Example: $(x^3 + xy^2 - 2y^3) \div (x - 2y)$.

In arranging the problem leave blank spaces for missing powers. If there is a remainder, be sure to indicate it as part of the answer.

$$
\begin{array}{r}
x^2 + 2xy + 5y^2 \\
x - 2y \overline{\smash{)}x^3 + xy^2 - 2y^3} \\
\underline{x^3 - 2x^2y} \\
+ 2x^2y + xy^2 \\
\underline{2x^2y - 4xy^2} \\
5xy^2 - 2y^3 \\
\underline{5xy^2 - 10y^3} \\
+ 8y^3
\end{array}
$$

Ans. $x^2 + 2xy + 5y^2 + \dfrac{8y^3}{x - 2y}$

7. $(x^2 + 3x - 10) \div (x + 5)$

8. $(x^2 + 12x + 32) \div (x + 4)$

9. $(2a^2 + 10a + 12) \div (a + 3)$

10. $(5m^2 + 3m - 2) \div (m + 1)$

11. $(6x^2 - 13x + 6) \div (3x - 2)$

12. $(-x^2 + 8x - 12) \div (x - 2)$

13. $(2x^2 - 11x + 15) \div (-x + 3)$

14. $(2a^2 - 7a + 6) \div (2a - 3)$

11

15. $(6x^2 - xy - 15y^2) \div (3x - 5y)$

16. $(9s^2 - 16t^2) \div (3s - 4t)$

17. $(a^2 + 7ab - 30b^2) \div (a - 3b)$

18. $(x^2 - 12xy - 28y^2) \div (x - 14y)$

19. $(2m^2 - 13mn + 21n^2) \div (2m - 7n)$

20. $(a^3 - 4a^2 + 7a - 6) \div (a - 2)$

21. $(2p^3 - p^2 - 7p + 6) \div (p - 1)$

22. $(x^3 + 3x^2 + 3x + 1) \div (1 + x)$

23. $(14x + x^3 - 11x^2 + 8) \div (x - 2)$

24. $(m^3 - 3m^2 - 3m + 5) \div (m^2 - 2m - 5)$

25. $(x^2 - 2x - 3) \div (x - 1)$

26. $(2x^2 - 5xy + y^2) \div (2x - y)$

27. $(x^3 - x + 1) \div (x - 2)$

28. $(m^3 - 3) \div (m + 3)$

29. $(x^2 + 3x - 12) \div (x + 5)$

30. $(m^3 + 7m - 4m^2 - 3) \div (m - 2)$

31. $(5m^3 - 7m^2n + 5mn^2 - 3n^3) \div (5m^2 - 2mn + 3n^2)$

32. $(4x^2 + 4ax + a^2 - 16) \div (2x + a - 4)$

33. $(a^2 - 6ab + 9b^2 + a - 3b - 2) \div (a - 3b - 1)$

34. $(12x^4 - 15x^2 + 3) \div (4x^2 - 1)$

35. $(x^3 - y^3) \div (x - y)$

36. $(32x^5 + y^{10}) \div (2x + y^2)$

37. $(23x^2 - 14 + x - 6x^3) \div (2x^2 - 7 - 5x)$

38. $(6x^3 - 7x^2y - xy^2 - y^3) \div (2x - 3y)$

Exercise 7. Parenthesis Removal

Oral

Remove the parenthesis in each of the following examples:

1. $3a + (5a)$
2. $8 - (6)$
3. $4 - (-3)$
4. $x + (a + b)$
5. $x - (a + b)$
6. $a - (b - c) + a$
7. $a - (-b - c)$
8. $3ab - (-5ab)$
9. $4a + (1 - 2a) + 2$
10. $3x - (2 + 4x) - 3$
11. $a + b - (a + b)$
12. $3a + 2b - (a + b)$
13. $4m - (-3 - m)$
14. $-(x + y) + (x - y)$
15. $x + [x - (x + 2)]$
16. $a - \{a + (2a - 1)\}$
17. $3x + 2(x + 1)$
18. $-5 - 3(7)$
19. $8 - 4(-2)$
20. $a + 1 - 2(a + 1)$
21. $2x - 7 - 3(x + 1)$
22. $-4a + 5(1 - a)$
23. $6x - 7(-x - 2)$
24. $x^2 - x + x(x - 1)$

Written

Simplify:

Example: $a - \{-a + [-a - (a - 1)]\}$.

In general work from inside out. Be particularly careful when a minus sign is in front of the parenthesis, bracket or brace.

$$a - \{-a + [-a - a + 1]\} =$$
$$a - \{-a + [-2a + 1]\} =$$
$$a - \{-a - 2a + 1\} =$$
$$a - \{-3a + 1\} =$$
$$a + 3a - 1 =$$
$$4a - 1$$

1. $8x^2 - x + (x^2 - 4x - 2) + 5$
2. $3m - 2n - (14m + 5n) - 12m$
3. $8p - 17 - (-12p - 31) + 6p - 4$
4. $-7a + 2(-a - 3) + 5 - 4a$
5. $(8y^2 - 3)3 - 2 + 4y^2$
6. $-(a - 2b) - 3a - (-7a + 6b)$
7. $4x^2 - 3y^2 - (14x^2 - 3xy - 7y^2)$
8. $(7 - 3)(a - 2) - 4(a + 2)$
9. $1.8x - (2.4x - .05) + .3$
10. $-4m - (-.3m) + (-2m + .5m)$

11. $5\frac{1}{3}a - (2\frac{2}{3}a - 4\frac{1}{2}) + \frac{3}{2}$

12. $-(-7a + 3b - 18c) - (7a - 3b + 18c)$

13. $x^3 - 3x^2 - (2 - x^2) - (-x^3 - 3x)$

14. $a + [-3a - (19a - 3) + 7a]$ 15. $-3m - [4m - (2m - 9n) + 4n]$

16. $-[-4p^2 + 3p - (7p + 2p^2 - 6)]$

17. $-x^2 - [(x - 7) - (18 - 4x) - x^2]$

18. $13a - [-(7 + 5a) + (18a - 3)]$

19. $-[-(-19y - 8) - 14y - (3 + 2y)]$

20. $4ab - (ab + 1) - [-(1 - 3ab)] - 14$

21. $-5x - \{15x^2 - 13x - (8x - 19) + 3x^2\} - 8$

22. $-\{3 + [2p - (3p - 7)] - 4p - 11\}$

23. $9a^2 - [3a - (7a^2 + 3a)] - [2 + (15a - 2)]$

24. $-4xy - \{x^2 - [3y^2 - 4x^2]\} - (-4xy + 3y^2)$

25. $-2(a - 3b) + 3[3a - 2b - (4b + 3a)]$

26. $2.5 - \{.07 - [6.91 + (3 - .9)]\}$

27. $-9a^2 - 3a(-a - 2) - [4a^2 - a(2 - 5a)]$

28. $-\{[(2a - 3b) - 13a] - 9b + [-(7a - 2b) - 6a] - 4a\}$

29. $2a + 3b - (2a - 3b) - [(a - b) - (a + b)] - \{-[-(3a - 4b)]\}$

30. $-[-x^2 - (3x + 1) - 13x^2] + (x^2 - 3x - 2) - \{9x - [-(-8x + x^2) - 3]\}$

Exercise 8. Parenthesis Insertion

Oral

Enclose the last three terms in parentheses preceded by a minus sign:

1. $7 + a - b + x - y$

2. $a^3 + 5a^2 - 3a - 1$

3. $9m^2 - 3mn - 3n^2 + mn^2$

4. $.04a - .001b + 1.23c - .0143d$

5. $9a^2b - 3ab + 4ab^2 - 9a^2b^2$

6. $18rs + 3r^2 - 4s^2 + 14s$

7. $x^4 - 3x^3 + 4x^2 - 9x - 17$

8. $m - n - 1 - m + n + 1$

9. $4\frac{1}{2}a + x - 3 + 4\frac{1}{4}a^2 + ax - 3a$

10. $.013x^3 - 1.02x^2 + .0012x - 10.03$

11. $am - an - ap - bm + bn + bp$

12. $.6\frac{1}{3}a - .07\frac{2}{3}b + 9.001 - 6\frac{1}{2}x$

13. $3x + 9y - 4z - 3ax - 9ay + 4az$

14. $3a \times 2b - 7 + 5ab \times 2 - 6a$

15. $-x^2 + 17xy - 9y^2$

16. $-(a + b) + (x - y) - (c - d)$

14

Indicate by the use of the parenthesis that:

1. $a + 7b - c$ is added to $3a - 2b + 7c$
2. $-3x + 2y - 4$ is added to $x - 7y + 9$
3. the sum of $3a$ and $2b$ is added to their difference
4. $a - 3b + 2$ is subtracted from $13a - 4b + 16$
5. $-m + 13m^2 + 9$ is subtracted from $m^2 - 8m + 2$
6. the sum of $a + 3c$ and 4 is subtracted from their difference
7. the difference of $9a$ and $7m$ is subtracted from their sum
8. the sum of $5a + 2$ and $2 + 3a$ is subtracted from their difference
9. $a + b - c$ is multiplied by $a - b + c$
10. $2r^2 + 3r - 7$ is multiplied by $-r + 3$
11. $x - y$ is multiplied by the product of 3 and $x - y$
12. $m + n - 1$ is divided by $m + n$
13. $a + b + 3a + 3b$ is divided by $-a - b$
14. the product of $a - 3$ and $a + 2$ is added to $-3a$
15. the product of $a - 5$ and $-2a + 7$ is subtracted from the product of $a - 9$ and $-4a + 1$

Collect the coefficients of x, y, and z in each of the following:

Example: $2ax - 3ay + 3bx - 6by + 5cx + 8cy$

To enclose terms in parentheses preceded by a minus sign, change the sign of each term enclosed.

$$2ax - 3ay + 3bx - 6by + 5cx + 8cy =$$
$$(2ax + 3bx + 5cx) - (3ay + 6by - 8cy) =$$
$$(2a + 3b + 5c)x - (3a + 6b - 8c)y$$

16. $ax - bx + cx + ay - by - cy$
17. $3z + 4x + ax - 2az - 2bx + 5bz$
18. $5x + 4y - 2mx + 3z - ay + bz$
19. $4mz - 3ax + 5az + 4mx - 13z + 11x$
20. $-2y - 8x + 2z - ay + az + 2ax$
21. $-3a^2x + 4b^2y - 10ax - 18by - 2z + az$
22. $x + 3y - 2px - 2py + 7ax - 4ay$

Collect the coefficients of x, y, and z in each of the following:

23. $-y + ay - 3x + a^2y - 4ax + 17a^2x$

24. $-ax + \backslash z - bx + ay - az - cx - by$

25. $a^2by - ab^2x - 3abz - ab^2y + 7a^2bx + 14z - 3ay$

When $A = 2x^2 - 3x - 2$, $B = 4x^2 - 7$, and $C = 3x - 5x^2 + 1$, find the value of each of the following:

Example: $C - (B - A)$

$$(3x - 5x^2 + 1) - [(4x^2 - 7) - (2x^2 - 3x - 2)] =$$
$$(3x - 5x^2 + 1) - (4x^2 - 7 - 2x^2 + 3x + 2) =$$
$$(3x - 5x^2 + 1) - (2x^2 + 3x - 5) =$$
$$3x - 5x^2 + 1 - 2x^2 - 3x + 5 =$$
$$6 - 7x^2$$

26. $A - B$ **27.** $C - A + B$ **28.** $A - B - C$

29. $2A - 4B$ **30.** $-A + 2C$ **31.** $A - (B + C)$

32. $B - (C - A)$ **33.** $2A - (-B - C)$ **34.** $C - 2(A - B)$

Exercise 9. Short Multiplication

Oral

Find the following indicated squares of the sum of two numbers:

1. $(a + b)^2$ **2.** $(x + 1)^2$ **3.** $(m + n)^2$

4. $(x + 3)^2$ **5.** $(a + 2)^2$ **6.** $(5 + x)^2$

7. $(a + 2b)^2$ **8.** $(2x + 1)^2$ **9.** $(2c + d)^2$

10. $(ab + 2)^2$ **11.** $(4 + xy)^2$ **12.** $(3a + 2c)^2$

13. $(5x + 4y)^2$ **14.** $(1 + 3cd)^2$ **15.** $(2a + bc)^2$

16. $(x^2 + y)^2$ **17.** $(7a + 3b^2)^2$ **18.** $(a^2b + 2ab^2)^2$

19. $(x + \frac{1}{3})^2$ **20.** $(\frac{1}{2}x + 1)^2$

Find the following indicated squares of the difference of two numbers:

21. $(x - y)^2$ **22.** $(a - 1)^2$ **23.** $(a - b)^2$

24. $(a - 4)^2$ **25.** $(3 - k)^2$ **26.** $(r - 8s)^2$

27. $(7m - n)^2$ **28.** $(2c - 5d)^2$ **29.** $(ab - 9)^2$

30. $(x^2 - y)^2$ **31.** $(a^2b - 4c)^2$ **32.** $(3x^3y^2 - 2xy^3)^2$

33. $(\frac{5}{2}a - 2b)^2$ **34.** $(\frac{1}{3} - \frac{1}{2}xy)^2$

Find the following products of the sum and the difference of two numbers:

35. $(a + b)(a - b)$ **36.** $(x + 4)(x - 4)$

37. $(2a + b)(2a - b)$ **38.** $(a^2 - 3)(a^2 + 3)$

39. $(xy - 8)(xy + 8)$ **40.** $(7 - b)(7 + b)$

41. $(3a + 9b)(3a - 9b)$ **42.** $(4x^2y - a)(4x^2y + a)$

43. $(9m^3 + n^3)(9m^3 - n^3)$ **44.** $(x^5 - 12)(x^5 + 12)$

45. $(ab - \frac{1}{3})(ab + \frac{1}{3})$ **46.** $(\frac{1}{2}mn + p)(\frac{1}{2}mn - p)$

47. $(\frac{4}{9}a^4 - \frac{1}{3}b)(\frac{4}{9}a^4 + \frac{1}{3}b)$ **48.** $(1 - 11r^2s)(1 + 11r^2s)$

49. $(abc + .2)(abc - .2)$ **50.** $(.01p^2 - .5a)(.01p^2 + .5a)$

Find the following products of the form $(x + a)(x + b)$:

51. $(a + 2)(a + 1)$ **52.** $(x + 3)(x + 5)$ **53.** $(p + 7)(p + 4)$

54. $(b^2 + 2)(b^2 + 3)$ **55.** $(ab + 9)(ab + 1)$ **56.** $(x + 2y)(x + y)$

57. $(2x + 1)(2x + 3)$ **58.** $(m + 5n)(m + 3n)$ **59.** $(x - 4)(x - 5)$

60. $(a - 3)(a - 1)$ **61.** $(p - 7)(p - 6)$ **62.** $(xy - 2)(xy - 9)$

63. $(a^2 - 4)(a^2 - 8)$ **64.** $(a + 3)(a - 5)$ **65.** $(x - 7)(x + 3)$

66. $(ax - 9)(ax + 4)$ **67.** $(p + 2q)(p + 5q)$ **68.** $(x - 4y)(x + 3y)$

69. $(b - 5c)(b - 7c)$ **70.** $(y^2 - 16)(y^2 + 2)$ **71.** $(rs - 14)(rs - 5)$

72. $(x^3 + 7)(x^3 - 10)$ **73.** $(a^4 - b)(a^4 + 4b)$

74. $(x^2y^2 - 5)(x^2y^2 - 13)$

Written

Find the following indicated squares:

1. $(3a + \frac{1}{3}b)^2$ **2.** $(\frac{1}{2}ab + 2)^2$ **3.** $(9x^2 + ab^2)^2$

4. $(\frac{3}{4}m + \frac{1}{3}n)^2$ **5.** $(x^4 + 7y^2)^2$ **6.** $(a + .1)^2$

7. $(x + .2y)^2$ **8.** $(.1p + .2q)^2$ **9.** $(5 + .03a)^2$

10. $(.4x + .2ay)^2$ **11.** $(abc + 3x)^2$ **12.** $(a^5 + 3a^3)^2$

13. $(3r^2s + 7rs^3)^2$

Example: $[x - 2y + 2]^2$

To square an expression with three terms, first group two of them together.

$$[(x - 2y) + 2]^2 = (x - 2y)^2 + 2(x - 2y)(2) + 2^2$$
$$= x^2 - 4xy + 4y^2 + 4x - 8y + 4 \quad \textbf{Ans.}$$

14. $[(a + b) + 1]^2$ **15.** $[(x + y) + 3]^2$ **16.** $[(x + 2y) + 1]^2$

17. $[(2x + a) + 5]^2$ **18.** $[(a + b) + c]^2$ **19.** $[(2m + 3n) + 4]^2$

20. $[(4p + 2q) + \frac{1}{2}]^2$ **21.** $[(2r + 5s) + .1]^2$ **22.** $[x + y + 1]^2$

23. $(2a + b + 3)^2$ **24.** $(4x + 3a + 5)^2$ **25.** $(r + s + 3t)^2$

26. $(\frac{4}{5}a - \frac{5}{2}bc)^2$ **27.** $(1\frac{1}{2}m - 2n)^2$ **28.** $(2a - .3b)^2$

29. $(.08c - .1d)^2$ **30.** $(.4a^2 - 6ab)^2$ **31.** $(\frac{1}{2}p - .2q)^2$

32. $[(x + y) - 1]^2$ **33.** $[(a - b) - 1]^2$ **34.** $[(m + n) - 3]^2$

35. $[(2p + q) - 5]^2$ **36.** $[(a - 2b) - 4]^2$ **37.** $[1 - (a + b)]^2$

38. $[3 - (2a + b)]^2$ **39.** $[x + y - z]^2$ **40.** $[x - 2a + 4]^2$

41. $[m + 3n - 6]^2$

Perform the indicated multiplications:

Example: $(x - 2y + 3)(x - 2y - 3)$

$[(x - 2y) + 3][(x - 2y) - 3] = (x - 2y)^2 - 9 = x^2 - 4xy + 4y^2 - 9$

42. $[(a + b) + c][(a + b) - c]$

43. $[(7x + 2y) - 9a][(7x + 2y) + 9a]$

44. $[(2a - b) - 9][(2a - b) + 9]$ **45.** $[(x^2 + y) - a^2][(x^2 + y) + a^2]$

46. $(a + b + 7)(a + b - 7)$ **47.** $(2x - y - a)(2x - y + a)$

48. $[a + (x + y)][a - (x + y)]$

49. $[11r + (2a + m)][11r - (2a + m)]$

50. $(4p + 2q - r)(4p + 2q + r)$

51. $(1 + a + b)(1 - a - b)$

52. $[(3m^2 - 2n) - (a + b)][(3m^2 - 2n) + (a + b)]$

53. $(2 - a + b)(2 + a + b)$

54. $(.2a - .3b + 8c)(.2a - .3b - 8c)$

55. $[(m - n^2) + (a^2 - b)][(m - n^2) - (a^2 - b)]$

56. $(x + \frac{1}{2})(x + \frac{3}{2})$ **57.** $(a + \frac{1}{4})(a + \frac{7}{4})$ **58.** $(a - \frac{3}{2})(a + \frac{1}{2})$

59. $(m + \frac{2}{3})(m - \frac{1}{3})$ **60.** $(x - 3)(x - \frac{1}{2})$ **61.** $(y - \frac{1}{5})(y + 5)$

62. $(p + .2)(p + .3)$ **63.** $(x - .3)(x + .8)$ **64.** $(m + .9)(m + .4)$

65. $(a + 4)(a + .1)$ **66.** $(a - .7)(a + 3)$ **67.** $(p - .4q)(p + .2q)$

68. $(x + m)(x + n)$ **69.** $(a + b)(a - c)$

70. $(y + 2p)(y + 3q)$ **71.** $(x - a)(x + 2b)$

Example: $[(a + 2b) - 3c][(a + 2b) + 2c]$

$$(a + 2b)^2 - c(a + 2b) - 6c^2 = a^2 + 4ab + 4b^2 - ac - 2bc - 6c^2$$

72. $[(x + y) + 3][(x + y) + 4]$ **73.** $[(a + b) + 7][(a + b) - 2]$

74. $(r + s + .3)(r + s + .7)$ **75.** $[x + 2(y + 1)][x + 3(y + 1)]$

76. $[(2x - y) + 3][(2x - y) - 5]$ **77.** $[(x - 2y) + 5][(x - 2y) - 1]$

78. $(3x - y + z)(3x - y - 2z)$ **79.** $[3x - y + z][3x - 2y + z]$

80. $[2x + y - z][2x - 2y - z]$

Exercise 10. Miscellaneous Short Multiplication

Oral

Give the following products:

1. $(ax + 9)(ax - 9)$ **2.** $(3p - 7q)^2$

3. $(ab + 5)(ab - 1)$ **4.** $(3r + 4)(3r - 2)$

5. $(.2mn + .1p)^2$ **6.** $(4 - 2a)(4 - 5a)$

7. $(15m - 10n)(15m + 10n)$ **8.** $(\frac{5}{2} - 2b)^2$

9. $(2x + a)(a + 2x)$ **10.** $(7a - 3)(3 + 7a)$

11. $(.2 - .3x)^2$ **12.** $(5a - 2b)(5a + 7b)$

13. $(x - 9y)(2y + x)$ **14.** $\left(\frac{3x}{2} - a\right)\left(\frac{3x}{2} + 2a\right)$

15. $(4x - 11y)(4x - y)$ **16.** $(2x + 1)(x + 2)$

17. $(3a - 2)(a - 3)$ **18.** $(-x - 8)(-x + 8)$

19. $(-x + 3)^2$ **20.** $\left(-\frac{x}{2} + 3\right)\left(2 - \frac{x}{2}\right)$

21. $(a + 2b + x)(a + 2b - x)$

22. $(a - 2c + b)(a + 2c + b)$

23. $(2m + n + 1)(2m + n - 3)$

24. $(a + x + 2y)^2$

25. $(a - 3b + 4)^2$

26. $(1 + p - 3q)(1 + p - 7q)$

27. $(a + m + 2n)(a + 2n + m)$

28. $(2x - 3y - 5)^2$

Written

Find the following products:

1. $(\frac{1}{2}x + .04y)^2$

2. $(3\frac{1}{3}a^2 - 4\frac{1}{2}b^2)^2$

3. $(a^3 - 9)(a^3 + 3\frac{1}{3})$

4. $(13x^2y^5 - .06)^2$

5. $(2x + .3)(2x - .01)$

6. $(x + 9)(11x - 10)$

7. $(2m + n)(2m - 3p)$

8. $(-3a - 5)(-3a - 5)$

9. $(27 - x^2)(-x^2 + 27)$

10. $(17r^2 - s^3)(s^3 - 17r^2)$

11. $(-a - bc)(-bc + a)$

12. $(.13a - x)(x + .13a)$

13. $(2a - b)(b - 2a)$

14. $(3x^2 + 2b)(b - 7x^2)$

15. $(13m - 17n)(12m + 5)$

16. $[4 + (x + y)][4 - (x + y)]$

17. $[3 + (a + 2b)]^2$

18. $[a + (m - 3)]^2$

19. $[2x - (a - y)][2x + (a - y)]$

20. $[1 - (a - b)]^2$

21. $(3a - b + \frac{1}{2})^2$

22. $(2a - 3m + 4)(2a + 3m + 4)$

23. $(-m + n - a)(m + n + a)$

24. $[a + 2(x + 1)][a - 2(x + 1)]$

25. $(4a - 9b - 7c)^2$

26. $(-3a^2 + 2m - 8n)^2$

27. $(-4x - 3y - 5a)^2$

28. $(x - .2 + .1y)^2$

29. $(2\frac{1}{2} + 2y - \frac{1}{2}x)^2$

30. $(3m + 9n + 6p)(3m + 6p - 9n)$

31. $(7a - b + 3c)(7a - 3c - b)$

32. $[x^2 - (9y + 1)][x^2 + (9y + 1)]$

33. $[3b - c - 2d][3b + c + 2d]$

34. $(7x + y - 13)(7x + y - 9)$

35. $(9p - 4q - 8)(9p - 4q + 2)$

36. $(13 - 2a - 3b)(13 + 2a - 3b)$

37. $(-19 + 8x - 4y)(-19 - 8x - 4y)$

38. $(x - y + 1)(x + y - 1)$

39. $(2a - b + 3c)(2a + b - 3c)$

40. $(4m - 3n + 2p)(2p + 4m + 3n)$

41. $(x + 7y - 4)(4 - 7y + x)$

42. $(ax + by + cz)^2$

43. $(-m - n - 3)(m + n - 3)$

44. $[3(a + b) - 14][3(a + b) + 10]$

45. $[(2a + b) + (x + 3y)][(2a + b) - (x + 3y)]$

46. $[(3x - a) - (y - b)][(3x - a) + (y - b)]$

47. $(m - 3n + p + 7q)(m - 3n - p - 7q)$

48. $(4a - 5b - x + y)(4a - 5b + x - y)$

49. $(6a - x + 3y - 2b)(x + 6a - 2b - 3y)$

50. $(2x - y + 3a - b)(2x + y + 3a + b)$

Exercise 11. Elementary Set Notation

Oral

Specify each of the following sets by listing its elements.

1. {the letters in the word *algebra*}
2. {the whole numbers less than 6}
3. {the whole numbers between 2 and 8}
4. {the multiples of 3 between 1 and 10}
5. {the vowels in the word *multiple*}
6. {the three digit numbers less than 105}
7. {the letters in the word *Mississippi*}
8. {the positive multiples of 6 which are less than 50}
9. {the prime numbers between 7 and 11}
10. {the even prime numbers}

State a rule which describes each of the following sets.

11. {2, 3, 4}
12. {2, 4, 6, 8}
13. {Alaska, California, Hawaii, Oregon, Washington}
14. {$\frac{1}{2}$, $\frac{1}{3}$, $\frac{1}{4}$, $\frac{1}{5}$}
15. {$\frac{1}{2}$, $\frac{2}{3}$, $\frac{3}{4}$, $\frac{4}{5}$}
16. {a, e, i, o, u}
17. {2, 7, 12, 17, . . .}
18. {2, 4, 8, 16, . . .}
19. {3, 9, 27, 81}
20. {11, 22, 33, . . ., 99}

Given: $A = \{1, 2, 3, 4\}$; $B = \{0, 1\}$; $C = \{1\}$.
Determine if each of the following is true or false.

Example: (a) $2 \in A$ is true because 2 is in set A.
      (b) $2 \subseteq A$ is false because 2 is not a set.
      (c) $\varnothing \in A$ is false because the empty set is not an element of set A.
      (d) $\varnothing \subseteq A$ is true because the empty set is a subset of every set.

21. $1 \in A$ 22. $1 \subseteq A$ 23. $\{1\} \in A$
24. $\{1\} \subseteq A$ 25. $\{1\} \in C$ 26. $\{1\} \subseteq C$
27. $1 \in B$ 28. $1 \subseteq B$ 29. $0 \in B$
30. $0 \subseteq B$ 31. $\varnothing \in B$ 32. $\varnothing \subseteq B$
33. $B \subseteq C$ 34. $C \subseteq B$ 35. $C \subseteq A$

36. $B \subseteq A$ 37. $C \in A$ 38. $3 \in A$

39. $3 \subseteq A$ 40. $\{3\} \in A$ 41. $\{3\} \subseteq A$

42. $\{1\} \in B$ 43. $\{1\} \subseteq B$ 44. $\varnothing \in C$

45. $\varnothing \subseteq C$ 46. $A \cap B = C$ 47. $B \cup C = A$

48. $\varnothing \cap B = B$ 49. $\varnothing \cup A = A$ 50. $C \subseteq \varnothing$

Given: $M = \{1, 2, 3, 4\}$; $N = \{1, 3, 5\}$; $P = \{0, 2\}$.
State the elements in each of the following sets:

51. $M \cap N$ 52. $M \cup N$ 53. $M \cap P$

54. $M \cup P$ 55. $N \cap P$ 56. $N \cup P$

57. $M \cap (N \cup P)$ 58. $M \cup (N \cup P)$ 59. $\varnothing \cup M$

60. $\varnothing \cap M$ 61. $\varnothing \cup P$ 62. $\varnothing \cap P$

Written

Express each of the following sets both by listing its elements (roster method) and by using the set builder notation (rule method).

Example: Describe the set of whole numbers less than 4 using each of the two methods.

Roster: $\{0, 1, 2, 3\}$
There are many ways to state a rule.

Rule: $\{x \,|\, 0 \leq x \leq 3 \text{ and } x \text{ is an integer}\}$,
    or $\{x: -1 < x < 4 \text{ and } x \text{ is an integer}\}$,
    or $\{x \in W : x < 4\}$ where $W = \{0, 1, 2, \ldots\}$

1. The set of positive integers less than 5.

2. The set of prime numbers not greater than 13.

3. The set of positive multiples of 11 that are less than 100.

4. The set of two digit numbers such that the sum of the digits is 5.

5. The set of integers greater than $\sqrt{2}$ which are also less than $\sqrt{7}$.

6. The set of natural numbers which are less than 20.

7. The set of positive integers less than 40 which are multiples of 6 but not multiples of 9.

8. The set of even integers greater than -10 but not more than 10.

9. The set of the four smallest natural numbers.

10. The set of prime numbers divisible by 21.

Describe each of the following sets either by the roster method or the rule method whichever is easier.

11. The set of your current mathematics teachers.

12. The set of students in your school.

13. The set of New England States.

14. The set of integers that are equal to their squares.

15. The set of integers such that the sum of the integer and itself is equal to the square of the integer.

Describe each of the following sets.

Exercises **16–30** involve sets with an infinite number of elements, therefore no roster can be complete and the rule method should be used.

Example: (a) $\{2, 4, 6, 8, \ldots\} = \{x \,|\, x = 2n$ where n is a positive integer$\}$.
(b) $\{40, 50, 60, 70, \ldots\} = \{10x : x > 3$ and x is an integer$\}$.

16. $\{1, 2, 3, 4, \ldots\}$ **17.** $\{1, 3, 5, 7, \ldots\}$

18. $\{0, -1, -2, -3, \ldots\}$ **19.** $\{\frac{1}{2}, \frac{1}{3}, \frac{1}{4}, \frac{1}{5}, \ldots\}$

20. $\{1, \frac{1}{3}, \frac{1}{5}, \frac{1}{7}, \ldots\}$ **21.** $\{3, 6, 9, 12, \ldots\}$

22. $\{3, 9, 27, 81, \ldots\}$ **23.** $\{5, 10, 15, 20, \ldots\}$

24. $\{2, 3, 5, 7, 11, \ldots\}$ **25.** $\{1, 5, 9, 13, \ldots\}$

26. $\{0, 1, 8, 27, 64, \ldots\}$ **27.** $\{0, 1, 4, 9, 16, \ldots\}$

28. $\{1, 2, 5, 10, 17, \ldots\}$ **29.** $\{\frac{1}{3}, \frac{3}{5}, \frac{5}{7}, \frac{7}{9}, \ldots\}$

30. $\{2, \frac{4}{3}, \frac{6}{5}, \frac{8}{7}, \ldots\}$

If $A = \{1, 2, 3, 4\}$; $B = \{1, 3, 5, 7\}$; $C = \{2, 4, 6\}$
List the elements of the following sets.

Example: $B \cap (A \cup C)$

Since $A \cup C = \{1, 2, 3, 4, 6\}$, therefore $B \cap (A \cup C) = \{1, 3\}$.

31. $A \cup B$ **32.** $A \cup C$ **33.** $B \cup C$

34. $A \cap B$ **35.** $A \cap C$ **36.** $B \cap C$

37. $A \cup (B \cap C)$ **38.** $A \cap (B \cup C)$

39. $(A \cup B) \cap (A \cup C)$ **40.** $(A \cap B) \cup (A \cap C)$

41. $(A \cup C) \cap (A \cap B)$

Given: $X = \{-1, 0, 1\}$; $Y = \{\varnothing, 1\}$; $Z = \{2, \{1\}\}$
Determine if each of the following is true or false.

42. $\varnothing \in X$ **43.** $\varnothing \subseteq X$ **44.** $\varnothing \subseteq Y$

45. $\varnothing \in Y$ **46.** $1 \in X$ **47.** $1 \subset X$

48. $\{1\} \in X$ **49.** $\{1\} \subseteq X$ **50.** $1 \in Y$

51. $\{1\} \in Y$ **52.** $\{1\} \in Z$ **53.** $\{1\} \subseteq Z$

Given: $A = \{2, 4, 6\}$; $B = \{3, 4, 6\}$; $C = \{2, 6\}$
Determine if each of the following is true or false.

54. $C \subseteq A$ **55.** $A = B \cup C$ **56.** $A \subseteq (B \cup C)$

57. $A \cap B = C$ **58.** $(A \cap B) \subseteq C$ **59.** $C \subseteq (A \cap B)$

60. $(A \cap B) \cap C = \varnothing$ **61.** $A \cap (B \cup C) = A$ **62.** $(A \cap B) \cup C = A$

Venn diagrams may be used to illustrate unions and intersections of sets.

Example: Use a Venn diagram to picture $A \cap B$ and $(A \cup B) \cap C$.

(a) A

$A \cap B$

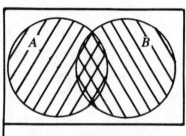

(b) $A \cup B$

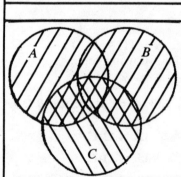

$(A \cup B) \cap C$

Draw a Venn diagram to picture each set.

63. $A \cup B$ **64.** $A \cap (B \cap C)$

65. $A \cap (B \cup C)$ **66.** $(A \cap B) \cup C$

67. $(A \cup B) \cup C$ **68.** $A \cup (B \cap C)$

69. $(A \cap B) \cup (B \cap C)$ **70.** $(A \cap C) \cup (B \cap C)$

71. $(A \cup C) \cap (B \cup C)$

$X = \{n \mid n$ is a positive integer$\}$, and
$Y = \{m : m$ is rational and $-10 < m < 10\}$
Determine whether or not the set given in each case is a subset of X, or Y, or both, or neither.

72. $A = \{\frac{2}{2}, \frac{3}{2}, \frac{4}{2}\}$ **73.** $B = \{0, 1, 2, 3\}$

74. $C = \{x \mid x$ is a prime greater than 10$\}$

75. $D = \{x^2 - 5 \mid x$ is an integer less than $-2\}$

76. $E = \{t : t$ is greater than $\sqrt{3}$ and less than 1$\}$

Determine the elements of set A from the other given information.

77. $A \cup B = \{1, 2, 3, 4\}$, $A \cap B = \varnothing$, and $B = \{1\}$

78. $B \subseteq A$ and $A \cup B = \{1, 2\}$

79. $1 \notin B$, $B \neq \varnothing$, $A \cap B = \varnothing$, and $A \cup B = \{1, 2\}$

80. $C = \{1, 3\}$, $A \cap B = \{3\}$, $A \cup B = \{2, 3, 4\}$, and $B \cup C = \{1, 2, 3\}$.

Use the following number lines as indicated in each problem.

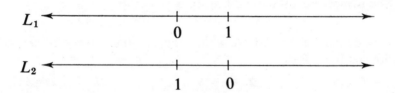

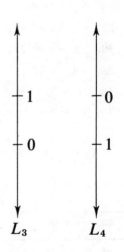

81. On L_1 plot the set of points $\{2, -1, 3, -2, 4\}$.

82. On L_2 plot the set of points $\{-1, -2, 2, 0\}$.

83. On L_3 plot 2, 3, -2, 1.

84. On L_4 plot -1, -2, -3, 0.

85. On L_1 plot $2\frac{1}{2}$, -0.7, $\frac{1}{3}$.

86. On L_2 plot $-\frac{2}{3}$, -0, $\frac{4}{5}$, .08.

87. On L_3 plot the points whose coordinates are positive integers less than 4.

88. On L_4 indicate the points whose coordinates are negative integers greater than -3.

89. On L_1 sketch the set of points whose coordinates are numbers greater than 3.

90. On L_1 sketch the set of points whose coordinates are numbers less than or equal to 1.

Exercise 12. Variables and Equations (Open Statements)

Oral

Identify the variable, if one is present, in each of the following statements.

1. $x + 3 = 5$
2. Wilt is tall.
3. A senator is going in.
4. πr^2 is greater than 7.
5. $\{2x : x \text{ is an integer}\}$
6. She has my ring.
7. $4 + 3 = 5 - 2$
8. $t \in \{1, 2, 3\}$
9. $\{x\} \subseteq \{1, 10\}$
10. $5n = 7$
11. He is older than I.
12. Sam is younger than Tom.
13. $x^2 = 9.$
14. $a^2 = -4.$
15. $2m + 3 = 5.$
16. $(x + 2)^2 = x^2 + 4x + 4.$
17. $(n + 2)^2 = 4n + 4.$
18. John Jones is a senator.
19. _____ is a Federal judge.
20. She is more beautiful than her sister.

If the domain of the variable is the set of positive integers, determine the solution set in each case.

21. $x + 5 = 7$
22. $11 = 6 + x$
23. $x - 2 = 13$
24. $9 = x - 4$
25. $x + 7 = 3$
26. $x + 10 = -2$
27. $x - 13 = -9$
28. $-15 = x - 3$
29. $-x = -13$
30. $-x - 6 = 25$
31. $5x = 15$
32. $2x - 3 = 9$
33. $-4x = 12$
34. $3x = -9$
35. $-6x = -18$
36. $2x + 3x = 9 - 4$
37. $5x - 2x + 1 = 7$
38. $3x - 4x = 15$
39. $9x + 4 = 3x + 16$
40. $-3x + 5 = 5x - 11$

Determine the integers in the solution set of each of the following.

41. $2x = 17$
42. $3x = x - 4$
43. $\dfrac{x}{2} = 7$
44. $\dfrac{3x}{5} = 9$
45. $-\dfrac{x}{5} = -4$
46. $3y - 9 = 16$
47. $2m - 3 = 5m - 9$
48. $4 + 3a = 5a - 8$
49. $3x = 15 - 5x$
50. $x + 1 = 3 + x$

Written

In each of the following the domain of the variable is $D = \{-1, 0, 1\}$. Find the solutions of each equation.

Example: $x^2 + x = 0$.

Substitute each member of the domain and see if it satisfies the equation.

$$(-1)^2 + (-1) = 1 - 1 = 0 \quad \text{Yes}$$
$$0^2 + 0 = 0 \quad \text{Yes}$$
$$1^2 + 1 = 2 \quad \text{No}$$

Therefore $\{-1, 0\}$ is the solution set.

1. $x = 1$
2. $3x^2 = 3$
3. $5x = 15$
4. $x^2 - 3x = 0$
5. $2x = 2$
6. $x^2 = x$
7. $x^3 = x^2$
8. $3x^3 - 2x - 1 = 0$
9. $x^3 + 3x + 2 = 0$
10. $x^2 + 1 = 0$

11. $5x - [x - 2(x - 17)] = -4$
12. $3 - x - [3x - (7 - 13x)] = -(x - 4)$
13. $-6(a - 5) - [9a + 3(a - 4)] - 3a = 0$
14. $5(x - 2) + 3 = 2[x - (2x - 7)]$
15. $-[2x - (8x - 1)] = 6 - [-(14 - x)]$

The replacement set for the variables in the following equations is the set of rational numbers. Determine the truth set in each case.

Example: $(x - 1)^2 - (2x - 1)^2 = 4 - 3x^2$

To solve an equation, find a subset of the domain which makes the equation a true statement. Remove parentheses, collect terms, and simplify until the truth set is obvious.

$$x^2 - 2x + 1 - (4x^2 - 4x + 1) = 4 - 3x^2$$
$$x^2 - 2x + 1 - 4x^2 + 4x - 1 = 4 - 3x^2$$
$$-3x^2 + 2x = 4 - 3x^2$$
$$2x = 4$$

Ans. $x = 2$

16. $4x - 6 = 2x + 8$

17. $2(x - 3) - 3(x - 2) = 0$

18. $5x - 8 = 2x - 17$

19. $2a - 3(5 - a) = 10$

20. $2x - 3 = 8$

21. $2(y - 3) = 3(y + 7)$

22. $5z - 8 = 2z + 3$

23. $3x^2 - 2x = x^2 - (2 - 2x^2)$

24. $x(x + 3) - 15 = x^2 + 2x - 10$

25. $y(3y - 2) = 3y^2 + 2y$

26. $4[2z - 8] = 0$

27. $3x + 2 = 4 + x + (1 + 2x)$

28. $(t + 3)(t - 2) - t(t + 4) = 0$

29. $s - \{ 3 - [2s + 3(s - 1)] + 5 \} = 2s$

30. $x(x + 1)^2 - x(x - 3)^2 = 2(2x + 1)^2$

31. $(2x + 3)^2 - x - 1 = (2x + 5)(2x - 5)$

32. $(3x + 1)^2 - (x - 3)^2 = 8x^2 + 32$

33. $(3x - .2)(3x + .2) - x(18x - .4) = -(3x - .6)^2$

34. $3x^2 - [x - 2(x + 3)(x - 2)] = 5x(x - 1)$

35. $x(3x - 2) = 3x^2 + 2x$

36. $.06(3a - 2) - .4(.2a - .3) = .013$

37. $(2x - 1)(3x + 2) - (3x - 1)^2 = -3x(x + 1)$

38. $2[x + 3(x - 5) - 1] = 3[-2(x + 2)]$

39. $(3 - x)(4 - 2x) - (7 - 2x)^2 = -2x^2 - 37$

40. $x(x + 1)^2 - x(x - 3)^2 = 2(2x + 1)^2$

Problems 41–48 are to be done using a hand calculator.

41. $43x + 47(23x - 19) = 22711$

42. $127x + 123(15x + 17) = 94775$

43. $19(17x - 12) - 23(18x - 71) = -9788$

44. $24(113x + 13) - 29(17x - 42) = -156019$

45. $23[17x - 19(21x - 37)] = 7383$

46. $38[25x - 32(57x - 83)] = -35796$

47. $(x + 127)^2 - (x - 483)^2 = 0$

48. $(52x - 31)^2 - (21x + 29)^2 = 2263x^2 + 30974$

More difficult linear equations may be found in Exercise 31, page 71.

Word problems leading to simple linear equations may be found in Exercises 36 through 45, pages 92-112.

Exercise 13. Properties of Number Systems

Oral

1. Count to five in base 2.
2. Count to ten in base 3.
3. Count to ten in base 6.
4. How do you test for even integers in base 2?
5. Does the same test work in base 3?

Give an example of each of the following.

6. A prime number greater than 23.
7. An integer less than $-\frac{22}{3}$.
8. A rational number that is neither positive nor negative.
9. A non-negative integer less than one.
10. An irrational number between 2 and 3.

State the law or property of the real number system which makes each of the following statements true for all replacements of the variables by numbers.

11. $x + (y + 3) = (x + y) + 3$
12. $(2x - \sqrt{3}) + -(2x - \sqrt{3}) = 0$
13. $x + (10 - 12 + 2) = x$
14. $(a + b)m + (a + b)n = (a + b)(m + n)$
15. $(m + n)(a + b) = (a + b)(m + n)$
16. $x + (3 + y) = (3 + y) + x$
17. $2x + 3x = (2 + 3)x$
18. $(2 - x) + (3 - 3) = 2 - x$
19. $(2 - x) + (x - 2) = 0$
20. $(x + y) + (m + n) = x + y + (m + n)$

One or more of the terms *positive, negative, zero, integer, rational*, and *irrational* can be used to describe each of the following numbers. In each case list all the terms which apply.

21. $\dfrac{1 - 2}{2}$

22. $\dfrac{2 + \frac{3}{2}}{\frac{1}{2}}$

23. $2^3 - 3^2$

24. $\dfrac{(1 - 2)(2 - 1)}{1 + 2}$

25. $\dfrac{(2 + 3 - 7)(3 - 7 + 2)}{9}$

26. $\sqrt{144}$

27. $\sqrt{250}$

28. $\sqrt{2} - \sqrt{3}$

29. $\sqrt{\dfrac{4}{49}}$

30. $\dfrac{5 - \sqrt{25}}{\sqrt{7}}$

Written

Example: Express 2013_4 as a decimal or base ten number.

$$2013_4 = 2 \cdot 4^3 + 0 \cdot 4^2 + 1 \cdot 4 + 3$$
$$= 128 + 0 + 4 + 3$$
$$= 135$$

1. Express in decimal form the number whose base five numeral is 10_5.

2. Express 100_7 as a decimal numeral.

3. Express 10_2 as a decimal numeral.

4. Change 2201_3 to a decimal numeral.

5. Express 144_{12} as a base 10 numeral.

Example: Change the base ten number 1234 to a base seven number.

$1234 = 176 \times 7 + 2$, so the units' digit is 2.

$176 = 25 \times 7 + 1$, so the sevens' digit is 1.

$25 = 3 \times 7 + 4$, so the forty-nines' digit is 4,

and the next digit is 3.

Therefore $1234_{10} = 3412_7$.

6. Change 100 in base ten to a binary numeral.

7. Write in base 10, the number whose base 5 numeral is 1234.

8. Write a base 8 numeral which is equivalent to one hundred seventy-four.

9. Express the decimal numeral 4496, in base 4.

10. Change 247_{10} to base 3.

Convert each of the following decimal numerals to a binary numeral.

11. 2   **12.** 31   **13.** 27   **14.** 113   **15.** $\frac{2}{3}$ **16.** 0.13

Convert the following decimals to hexadic (base 6) numerals.

17. 12   **18.** 17   **19.** 158   **20.** 521

Convert the following decimal numerals to duodecimals (base 12).

21. 15   **22.** 100   **23.** 247   **24.** 310   **25.** 852   **26.** 563

The following numbers have been written in the binary system.
Perform the indicated operations in that system.

27.   1110   **28.**   1011   **29.**   10011   **30.**   1111
     + 101   + 111   + 1101   − 101

31.   10011   **32.**   100000   **33.**   101   **34.**   1001
     − 101   − 1001   × 11   × 110

35.   1110   **36.** 10)‾1‾1‾0‾0   **37.** 11)‾1‾1‾1‾1   **38.** 101)‾1‾0‾0‾0‾1‾1
     × 101

39. $\dfrac{101 + 111}{11}$ **40.** $(11)^{10}$ **41.** $(101)^{11}$

Express each of the following as a repeating decimal.

Example: Use either long division or a hand calculator to determine the repeating sequence of digits.

$$\tfrac{2}{9} = .222\ldots = 0.\bar{2}$$

$$\tfrac{5}{99} = .050505\ldots = 0.\overline{05}$$

$$\tfrac{13}{7} = 1.857142857\ldots = 1.\overline{857142}$$

42. $\tfrac{2}{3}$ **43.** $\tfrac{5}{9}$ **44.** $\tfrac{6}{11}$ **45.** $\tfrac{11}{12}$

46. $\tfrac{14}{99}$ **47.** $\tfrac{57}{99}$ **48.** $\tfrac{120}{11}$ **49.** $\tfrac{5}{7}$

Express each repeating decimal as a fraction in simplest form.

Example: $1.4\overline{03}$

Let $x = 1.4\overline{03}$. Multiply both sides by the power of 10 needed to move the decimal point in front of the first block of repeating digits, in this case, 10.

$$10x = 14.\overline{03}$$

Now multiply by the power of 10 needed to move the decimal point to the end of the first block that repeats, in this case, 100.

$$1000x = 1403.\overline{03}$$

Now subtract the two equations.

$$\begin{aligned}1000x &= 1403.\overline{03} \\ 10x &= 14.\overline{03}\end{aligned}$$

$$990x = 1389$$

$$x = \frac{1389}{990} = \frac{463}{330}$$

31

50. $0.\bar{4}$ **51.** $0.\bar{7}$ **52.** $3.\bar{9}$

53. $0.\overline{21}$ **54.** $1.\overline{13}$ **55.** $0.\overline{52}$

56. $0.0\overline{45}$ **57.** $0.\overline{102}$ **58.** $1.\overline{213}$

59. $1.0\overline{428571}$

60. Each of the following statements is either true or false. State your conclusions and justify your answer with an example.

(a) Every rational number is a real number.

(b) Every real number is a rational number.

(c) The sum of any two integers is either positive or negative.

(d) The product of two irrational numbers is irrational.

61. If x and y can be replaced with any natural numbers, which of the following will *always* be:

(a) negative integers,

(b) rational numbers,

(c) irrational numbers.

     (i) $x^2 + y^2$ (ii) $\sqrt{x^2 + y^2}$ (iii) $x^2 - y^2$

     (iv) $\dfrac{x^2 - y^2}{y - x}$, $(x \neq y)$ (v) $\sqrt{625x}$

In the following problems, assume that the operations $+$, $-$, $\times$, and $\div$ are already defined on the real numbers.

Example: The operation $\$$ is defined for any two real numbers a and b by the formula $a\$ b = \dfrac{a + b}{3}$

(a) Is $\$$ a commutative operation?

     Yes, because $a\$ b = \dfrac{a + b}{3}$ and $b\$ a = \dfrac{b + a}{3}$.

Therefore $a\$ b = b\$ a$.

(b) Is $\$$ a closed operation on the whole numbers?

     No, because $2\$3 = \dfrac{2 + 3}{3} = \frac{5}{3}$ which is not a whole number.

(c) Solve for x: $x\$3 = 7\$5$.

$$\frac{x + 3}{3} = \frac{7 + 5}{3}$$

$$x + 3 = 12$$

$$x = 9$$

62. The operation $\oplus$ is defined for all real numbers as: $a \oplus b = \dfrac{a + b}{2}$.

    (a) Is $\oplus$ a commutative operation? Why?

    (b) Are the integers closed under $\oplus$? Why?

    (c) If $a \oplus b = 0$, what can you say about a and b?

    (d) Solve for x: $x \oplus 5 = 7$.

    (e) Simplify: $a \oplus (a \oplus (a \oplus a))$.

63. The operation $*$ is defined on the natural numbers by: $x * y = 2x + y$.

    (a) Is $2 * 3 = 3 * 2$? Show your work.

    (b) Is $2 * (3 * 4) = (2 * 3) * 4$? Show your work

    (c) Solve for x: $6 * x = 20$.

    (d) Simplify: $2 * \{1 * [(3 * 1) * 2]\}$.

    (e) Does $3 * x = 3$ have a solution? Why?

64. The operation $\#$ is defined so that $a \# b = 2(a - b)$ for any integers a and b.

    (a) Is $\#$ a commutative operation? Show your work.

    (b) Is $\#$ an associative operation? Show your work.

    (c) Solve for x: $3 \# x = 8$.

    (d) What can you say about a and b if $a \# b = 0$?

    (e) Solve for y: $(-2) \# (y \# 4) = 0$.

65. The additive operation, $\oplus$, is defined on the integers as follows: $a \oplus b = a + b + 4$.

    (a) Evaluate $3 \oplus 7$.

    (b) Is $\oplus$ commutative? Why?

    (c) Is $\oplus$ associative? Show work.

    (d) Determine the $\oplus$-identity.

    (e) What is the $\oplus$-inverse of 12?

    (f) Solve for x: $3 \oplus x = 12$.

66. The operation $\otimes$ is defined on the positive rational numbers by:

$$a \otimes b = \frac{1}{b} + \frac{1}{a}.$$

    (a) Express the commutative law for $\otimes$. Is it true for all the positive rational numbers?

(b) Express the associative law for $\otimes$. Is it true for all the positive rational numbers?

(c) Solve for x: $x \otimes 3 = 2 \otimes 6$.

67. The addition and multiplication tables for a finite number system of 5 symbols is given below.

+	0	1	2	3	4
0	0	1	2	3	4
1	1	2	3	4	0
2	2	3	4	0	1
3	3	4	0	1	2
4	4	0	1	2	3

×	0	1	2	3	4
0	0	0	0	0	0
1	0	1	2	3	4
2	0	2	4	1	3
3	0	3	1	4	2
4	0	4	3	2	1

(a) What is the zero element of the + operation? (identity)

(b) What is the negative of 2? (additive inverse)

(c) What is the unity element for ×? (multiplicative identity)

(d) What is the reciprocal of 4? (multiplicative inverse)

(e) Evaluate: $\dfrac{3 \times (2 + 4)}{3 + 4}$.

(f) Determine the two square roots of 1.

(g) Does 3 have a square root? Explain.

(h) Find the cube root of 2.

68. The additive operation $\oplus$, and the multiplicative operation $\odot$, are defined by the tables below.

$\oplus$	a	b	c
a	b	c	a
b	c	a	b
c	a	b	c

$\odot$	a	b	c
a	b	a	c
b	a	b	c
c	c	c	c

(a) Are the operations commutative? Show work.

(b) Are the operations associative? Show work.

(c) Does $\odot$ distribute over $\oplus$?

(d) Does $\oplus$ distribute over $\odot$?

(e) Which is the zero element? (additive identity)

(f) Which is the unity element? (multiplicative identity)

69. The symbol [x] denotes the greatest integer that is less than or equal to x, i.e., [3] = 3, $[\frac{7}{2}]$ = 3, $[\sqrt{2}]$ = 1, $[-\frac{1}{2}]$ = −1.

Find the value of each of the following:

(a) [8]

(b) $[\frac{2}{3}]$

(c) $[\frac{22}{7}]$

(d) $[\sqrt{3}]$

(e) $[-\pi]$

(f) $[-\sqrt{5}]$

(g) $[\frac{243}{17}]$

(h) $[\sqrt{140}]$

(i) $[\frac{4567}{4587}]$

(j) $[\frac{1}{2} - 100]$

70. Let the symbol ⟨x⟩ represent the smallest integer that is greater than x, i.e., ⟨3⟩ = 4, $\langle\sqrt{3}\rangle$ = 2, $\langle-\frac{5}{2}\rangle$ = −2.

Find the value of each of the following:

(a) ⟨0⟩

(b) ⟨4⟩

(c) ⟨π⟩

(d) $\langle-\frac{7}{8}\rangle$

(e) ⟨−2⟩

(f) $\langle\sqrt{5}\rangle$

(g) $\langle-\frac{984}{7}\rangle$

(h) $\langle\sqrt{256}\rangle$

(i) $\langle-2^5\rangle$

(j) $\langle\sqrt{120}\rangle$

71. Using the symbols defined in problems **69** and **70**, solve each of the following.

(a) x + ⟨3⟩ = [5]

(b) $[\pi] + x = \langle\frac{1}{2}\rangle - [\frac{1}{4}]$

(c) ⟨x⟩ = − [−x]

Exercise 14. Absolute Value

Oral

Express each of the following in simplest form without using absolute value signs.

1. $|-3|$

2. $|4 - 3|$

3. $|-17|$

4. $-|\frac{2}{3}|$

5. $|5 - 7|$

6. $|3 + 4|$

7. $|73 - 81|$

8. $|\frac{2}{3} - \frac{3}{4}|$

9. $|\frac{5}{6} - \frac{4}{5}|$

10. $-|-2|$

11. $|5 - 3| - |-2|$

12. $|-5| + |2 - 5 + 3|$

13. $|1 - \sqrt{2}|$

14. $|\pi - 5|$

15. $|.333 - \frac{1}{3}|$

16. $|\sqrt{3} - \sqrt{6}|$

17. $|\frac{1}{2} - \frac{1}{3}|$

18. $|.12304 - .12384|$

19. $|-3| \cdot |4|$

20. $|-\frac{1}{2}| \cdot |-6|$

21. $\left| \dfrac{-3}{2} \right|$

22. $\dfrac{|-3|}{2}$

23. $\dfrac{|2|}{|-3|}$

24. $\dfrac{1}{|2 - 3|}$

25. $\left| \dfrac{\pi}{2} - \pi \right|$

26. $-|-3| \cdot |6|$

27. $2 + |-2|$

28. $|-2 - (-3)|$

29. $|6| \div |-12|$

30. $\{|2| \div |3 - 4|\} \cdot |5|$

Find the values of x for which each of the following are true.

31. $|x| = 5$

32. $|x| = \frac{1}{2}$

33. $|x| = -1$

34. $x = |5|$

35. $x = |-1|$

36. $|x| = |-1|$

37. $|x| = |3|$

38. $|x + 1| = 0$

39. $|x - 1| = 0$

40. $|x| - 2 = 0$

Written

Solve for x:

Example: $|x - 2| = 5$.

Since there are two numbers, -5 and 5, whose absolute value is 5, there are *two* equations to solve.

$$x - 2 = 5 \text{ or } x - 2 = -5$$

$$x = 7 \text{ or } x = -3$$

1. $|x + 2| = 0$

2. $|x - 3| = 0$

3. $|x - 1| = 3$

4. $|x + 1| = 3$

5. $|2x| = 2$

6. $\left| \dfrac{x}{2} \right| = 3$

7. $|-2x| = 4$

8. $|-3x| = -6$

9. $\left| \dfrac{2x}{3} \right| = 4$

10. $|2x + 1| = 5$

11. $|x + 2| = 3$

12. $|2x| = 4$

13. $|3 - x| = 11$

14. $|\frac{1}{2} + x| = \frac{2}{3}$

15. $|x - \frac{1}{3}| = 2$

16. $|x - .01| = .1$

17. $\left| \dfrac{x}{3} \right| = 2$

18. $|5x| = 1$

19. $|2x| = |-2|$

20. $|2x + 1| = 3$

21. $|3x - 1| = 0$

22. $\left| 1 - \dfrac{x}{2} \right| = 1$

23. $\left| 3 - \dfrac{x}{3} \right| = 2$

24. $|4x - 7| = 3$

25. $|x| + 2 = |-3|$ **26.** $|2x - 3| = 5$ **27.** $|5 - 3x| = 7$

28. $5 + |-3x| = 7$ **29.** $|6 - 3x| + 2 = 11$ **30.** $|5 + 4x| = 3$

Graph on the number line the points with coordinates x, if x is an integer and:

31. $x = |3|$ **32.** $x = |-2|$ **33.** $|x| = 2$

34. $|-x| = 2$ **35.** $|x - 1| = 1$ **36.** $|x - 2| = 3$

37. $|x + 1| = 2$ **38.** $|x + 2| = 1$ **39.** $|x| = |-x|$

40. $|x| = x$

Exercise 15. Inequalities

Oral

State whether each of the following is true or false.

1. $2 < 4 - 1\frac{1}{2}$ **2.** $3 + 2 \leq 5$

3. $2(2 - \frac{1}{2}) \neq 24 \div 8$ **4.** $12 + 24 \neq 5(10 - 3)$

5. $2 + \dfrac{4 + 5}{3} \neq 4 - (-1)$ **6.** $\frac{1}{3} + \frac{1}{2} \geq 1$

7. $\dfrac{1}{7} + \dfrac{2}{3} \leq \dfrac{17}{20}$ **8.** $2 + \dfrac{3}{7} \neq \dfrac{17}{7}$

9. $\dfrac{0}{7} \neq \dfrac{0}{6}$ **10.** $(2 + 3)(4 - 5) > (4 + 2)(3 - 4)$

11. $\dfrac{243}{193} > \dfrac{244}{193}$ **12.** $\dfrac{567}{198} > \dfrac{567}{197}$

13. $\dfrac{16}{17} + \dfrac{2}{2} \neq \dfrac{18}{19}$ **14.** $\dfrac{2}{3} + \dfrac{3}{4} > \dfrac{5}{7}$

15. $\dfrac{3}{5} + \dfrac{4}{3} \neq \dfrac{3 + 4}{5 + 3}$ **16.** $2^{10} < 10^3$

17. $3 > 0 < 5$ **18.** $1 < \sqrt{2} < 3$

19. $1 > 2 > 3$ **20.** $-1 < -2 < -3$

Written

Determine the integers in the solution set of each of the following, and sketch the graph of each set on a number line.

Example; Determine the integers in the solution set of $x > -2$ and $x \leq 5$. Sketch the graph on a number line.

The integers satisfying *both* inequalities are those in the intersection of $\{-1, 0, 1, \ldots\}$ and $\{\ldots, 3, 4, 5\}$; that is, $\{-1, 0, 1, 2, 3, 4, 5\}$.

1. $x + 4 > 8$
2. $x - 2 \geq 3$
3. $2x + 1 \geq 5$
4. $x + 7 \leq 3$
5. $x - 2 < 1$
6. $x < 3$ and $x < 10$
7. $x \leq 3$ or $x \geq 7$
8. $x < -1$ or $x > 4$
9. $x \leq 6$ and $x \geq -1$
10. $x > 2$ and $x \leq 5$

Sketch on the real number line the points whose coordinates are the solutions of the following.

Example: $x \geq 4$ or $x < 2$.

The word "or" requires the union of the two sets.

11. $x + 2 \geq -3$
12. $x - 3 > -5$
13. $2x + 3 \leq 5$
14. $3x - 1 > 20$
15. $2x + 5 \leq 6$
16. $x \geq 3$ or $x < 2$
17. $x \geq -2$ and $x < 0$
18. $x + 3 \geq 7$ and $x - 1 \leq 6$
19. $x + 5 > 3$ or $x + 6 < 2$
20. $2x + 3 \geq 7$ or $x - 3 < -4$
21. $2 \leq x \leq 7$
22. $-2 \leq x \leq 2$ or $x > 5$
23. $0 \leq x \leq 3$ and $1 \leq x \leq 4$
24. $-2 < x < 1$ or $0 \leq x < 3$
25. $-3 < x < 3$ and $-4 \leq x \leq 5$

26. Given: $a > 0 > b$. Which of the following are true for *all* a and b which satisfy the given condition?

  (a) $a > b$ (b) $b^2 \geq b$ (c) $ab > b^2$ (d) $a > -a$

  (e) $b > -b$ (f) $a > b^2$ (g) $a^2 > ab$

27. Given: $a > b > 0$, answer problem **26**.

28. Given: a and b are any two real numbers, answer problem **26**.

29. Does $1 < \dfrac{2}{x}$ have the same solution set as $x < 2$? Explain.

30. Does $3x > 2x$ have the same solution set as $3 > 2$? Explain.

31. If $a > b$, for which values of x is $ax > bx$? Explain.

32. Determine which of the following are incorrect or meaningless applications of the inequality symbols.

  (a) $3 \leq x < 7$ (b) $-2 < x < -5$ (c) $3 > x < 0$

  (d) $3 < x < y < 7$ (e) $-3 < x > -4$ (f) $137 < x < 5^3$

Exercise 16. Absolute Value and Inequalities

Written

Example: $|x - 3| < \dfrac{3}{2}$

On the number line, $|x - a|$ represents the distance from the point whose coordinate is x to the point whose coordinate is a. Thus we want those points with integer coordinates that are less than $\frac{3}{2}$ of a unit from 3. These points are: 2, 3, 4.

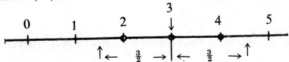

If x is an integer, graph the points such that:

  1. $|x - 2| < \frac{1}{2}$ 2. $|x| = -1$

  3. $|x - 2| \leq 1$ 4. $|x - \frac{3}{2}| \leq \frac{3}{2}$

  5. $|x + 3| \leq 2$

39

If x is a real number, graph the points with coordinates x.

Example: $|x + 2| \leq 3$.

Express $|x + 2|$ to represent a distance.

$$|x + 2| = |x - (-2)|$$

Therefore, $|x + 2| \leq 3$ is expressed as

$$|x - (-2)| \leq 3$$

This time we want *all* points that are 3 units or less from -2.

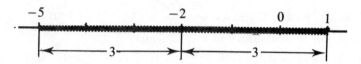

6. $|x| < 2$

7. $|x| \leq 2$

8. $x > 2$

9. $|x| > 2$

10. $|x - 1| < 3$

11. $|x - 1| \leq 3$

12. $|x - 3| < \frac{1}{2}$

13. $|2 - x| > 3$

14. $|2 + x| \geq \frac{1}{2}$

15. $|x - 5| \leq 2$

16. Is $|a| \cdot |b| = |ab|$ true for all a and b? Explain.

17. Is $|a + b| = |a| + |b|$ true for all a and b? Explain.

18. Does $|x| < 2$ have the same solution set as $-2 < x < 2$?

19. Does $1 < \dfrac{2}{|x|}$ have the same solution set as $-2 < x < 2$?

20. Does $|x| > 2$ have the same solution set as $x > 2$?

Exercise 17. Review Exercises on Fundamental Operations

Written

(A)

State whether each of the following is True or False.

1. The value of $x^3 - x^2 + 5x - 7$ when $x = -1$ is -14.

2. $\{x : x < 4 \text{ and } x \text{ is a positive integer}\}$ is the same set as $\{1, 2, 3, 4\}$.

3. The area of a rectangle m meters wide and $m + 3$ meters long is $m^2 + 3$ square meters.

4. The sum of x meters, y centimeters, and z millimeters is $100x + y + .01z$.

5. The simple interest on d dollars invested at r % for two years is $2dr$ dollars.

6. If B tons of coal cost D dollars, then you can buy KB/D tons for K dollars.

7. $(2x + 3)(5x - 9) = 10x^2 + 3x - 27$.

8. The solution set for $|x - 2| < 3$, where x is an integer, is $\{0, 1, 2, 3, 4, 5\}$.

9. $(3x - 4y)^2 = 9x^2 - 12xy + 16y^2$.

10. The base 5 numeral 234 is the decimal numeral 44.

11. If $A = \{1, 2, 3\}$; $B = \{2, 3, 4\}$; $C = \{1, 3, 5\}$; then $(A \cap B) \cup C = \{1, 2, 3, 4, 5\}$.

12. If the sum of m and $3n$ is subtracted from their difference, then the result is $6n$.

13. $|2 - |4 - 6|| \le |7 - 19| - |5 + 7|$.

14. If the sum of two numbers is s and one of them is y, then the other is $y - s$.

15. A man who can run 100 meters in m minutes will take $48m$ seconds to run 80 meters at the same rate.

16. $(8x + 11y^2)(8x - 11y^2) = 64x^2 - 121y^2$.

17. $ax - z + bx - ay + az + by = (a + b)x - (a + b)y + (a - 1)z$.

18. The solution set for $|7 - x| = 4$ is $\{3\}$.

19. If $x = 1$ and $y = -2$, then $x^3 - 2xy + y^3 = -3$.

20. $(a + b) + c = (a + c) + b$ is an example of the associative law for addition.

(B)

Multiple Choice: Select the correct answer for each of the following.

1. If $r = -3$, $s = 2$, and; $t = -2$, then the value of $r^2 + 2rs + rs^2 - t^3$ is

    (a) 7   (b) -7 (c) 17   (d) -25 (e) -23

2. $2a - [a - (2 - a)]$ simplifies to

    (a) $2a$ (b) 2   (c) $2a - 2$ (d) $2a + 2$ (e) $a - 2$

3. If P pencils cost C cents, the number of pencils you can buy for D dollars is

    (a) $\dfrac{DP}{C}$ (b) $\dfrac{DP}{100C}$ (c) $\dfrac{100DP}{C}$ (d) $\dfrac{CP}{D}$ (e) $\dfrac{CP}{100D}$

4. $(3x - 2y)^2 =$

    (a) $9x^2 + 4y^2$ (b) $9x^2 - 4y^2$ (c) $9x^2 - 6xy + 4y^2$

    (d) $9x^2 + 12xy + 4y^2$ (e) $9x^2 - 12xy + 4y^2$

5. The perimeter in meters of a rectangle 3 meters long and 75 centimeters wide is

    (a) 3.75   (b) 375   (c) 7.5   (d) 750   (e) 156

6. If x is an integer, the solution set of $|x - 3| < 2$ is

    (a) $\{1, 2, 3, 4\}$ (b) $\{2, 3, 4\}$

    (c) $\{2, 3, 4, 5\}$ (d) $\{2, 3\}$ (e) $\{1, 5\}$

7. $(2x - 1)(x + 2) =$

    (a) $2x^2 - 3x - 2$ (b) $2x^2 - 3x + 2$ (c) $2x^2 + 3x - 2$

    (d) $2x^2 + 3x + 2$ (e) $2x^2 + 5x - 2$

8. $A = \{2, 3, 4, 5, 6\}, \quad B = \{2, 4, 6\}, \quad C = \{2, 3, 4\}$.
Determine which one of the following is false.

    (a) $B \subseteq A$ (b) $A = B \cup C$ (c) $B \cap C = \{2, 6\}$

    (d) $C \cup (A \cap B) = \{2, 3, 4, 6\}$ (e) $\{3\} \subseteq (A \cap C)$

9. If $(2x - 3)(4x - 7) = 8x^2 + kx + 21$ for all x, then the value of k is

    (a) 26   (b) -26 (c) 2   (d) -2 (e) -12

10. The binary numeral 11101 written in decimal form is

    (a) 13   (b) 15   (c) 25   (d) 29   (e) 30

(C)

1. Subtract $2a^2b - ab^2 - 7$ from the sum of $-2ab - 2a^2b$ and $5ab - 7a^2b + 4ab^2$.

2. Simplify: $15 - \{(2x + 7) - [4(2x - 1) - 3(1 - 2x)]\}$.

3. When $r = -2$, $s = 1$, and $v = 0$; evaluate: $(-s)^5 + r^3v - r^3s^6$.

4. Multiply: $(2x^3 - 5x^2 + 4x - 1)(3 - 2x^2 - x)$.

5. Simplify: $\dfrac{6(x - 1)^3 - 4(x - 1)^2 - 2(x - 1)}{2(x - 1)}$.

6. (a) If a man drives at the rate of d kilometers per hour, how many hours will it take to drive t kilometers?

    (b) Find the width of a rectangle whose perimeter is p and whose length is 5.

(c) A boy purchased 3 pencils and 2 books. He paid c cents for each pencil, and each book cost $2.00 more than one pencil. How much change did he receive when he paid for his purchases with a $5.00 bill? ($c < 20$)

7. Divide $1 - 3x^2 - x^5 - x$ by $2x + 1 + x^2$.

8. For *all* replacements of x with integers, which of the following are natural numbers?

(a) $2x + 3$ (b) $10x - 1$ (c) $4x - 2 + 4(1 - x)$

(d) $x^2 + 7$ (e) $x + 3$ (f) $|x - 2| + 3$

9. Perform the following operations in base 7.

246	354	135	
+ 251	− 161	× 3	4$\overline{)125}$

10. (a) List the elements of the set A, if $A = \{a \mid a$ is a positive integer not greater than 7$\}$.

(b) Describe the set B in the form $B = \{x \mid \ldots\}$ if $B = \{2, 6, 10, 14, 18, \ldots\}$.

(D)

1. Subtract $4xy + 2ax^2 + ax - a^2$ from the sum of $3x^2 - x^2a + xy$, and $-3xy + a^2 - 3x^2$.

2. Show that $(x + 1)(x - 1) - x^2 - 4(x + 2)^2 = 8 - (2x + 1)^2$ is a true statement when $x = -2$.

3. Simplify: $x^3 - [x^2 - (1 - x)] - [1 + x^2 - (1 - x) + x^3]$.

4. Determine the integers in the solution set of: $|2x - 3| < 4$.

5. Divide $x^3 - 27$ by $x + 3$.

6. (a) Express in terms of M, R, and S, the time it will take for a girl to ride from her home to a town M kilometers away at R kilometers per hour and return home at S kilometers per hour.

(b) Express in terms of p the amount of salt that there will be in a mixture that is formed by putting p kilograms of a solution that is $12\frac{1}{2}\%$ salt together with p killograms of a solution that is $\frac{1}{4}$ salt.

7. If $a = -3$, and $b = -2$, which is greater $(a^3 - a^2 - a)$ or $(b^3 - b^2 - b)$ and by how much?

8. Give an example of each of the following.

(a) A positive number less than one, whose cube root is a rational number.

43

(b) A set of four irrational numbers between 1 and 2.

(c) A number whose square root and cube root are both rational numbers.

(d) An irrational number greater than 30.

(e) A subset of the non-positive integers greater than or equal to -1.

9. Each of the following is either true or false. State which and justify your answer.

(a) The set $\{0, 1, 2, \sqrt{9}, \frac{51}{17}\}$ is a subset of the set of positive integers.

(b) $(x + 3) + 7 = x + (3 + 7)$ for all replacements of x with real numbers.

(c) $a \cdot \dfrac{1}{a} = 1$ for all real numbers a.

(d) The set $\{\sqrt{x} \mid x$ is a natural number$\}$ is a subset of the irrational numbers.

(e) A number that has both 10 and 12 as factors must have 120 as a factor.

10. Define:

(a) an even integer

(b) a prime number

(c) the additive inverse (negative) of a number

(d) the multiplicative identity of a number system

(e) a rational number

FACTORING

Exercise 18. Common Monomial Factor

Oral

Factor:

1. $3a + 3b$
2. $2x + 6y$
3. $5x + 10$
4. $4m + 4$
5. $ma + mb$
6. $15x - 5y$
7. $-12a + 4b$
8. $-3m - 3n$
9. $2xa + 8xb$
10. $14abc - 7ab$
11. $a^2b - a^2c$
12. $a^4 - 3a^2$
13. $12x^2y - 15x^2$
14. $-13ab - 39ac$
15. $18a^4 - 27a^3$
16. $6a - 12a^5$
17. $14m^2n + 7mn^2$
18. $x^2y^3z - 2xy^2$
19. $2a - 2b$
20. $3xy + 9x^2$
21. $7x - 21y + 35z$
22. $x^4 - 5x^3 + 3x^2$
23. $2abc - 4abx - 12abd$
24. $x^2 + 3xy - x$
25. $45a^2b - 15ab^2 - 60ab$
26. $3ax^2 + 3a^2x^2 - 3ax$
27. $13 \times 5 + 7 \times 5 - 15 \times 5$
28. $236 \times 3 + 236 \times 11 - 236 \times 4$
29. $-a^2xy - a^2xz - a^2x^2$
30. $2a^2b^2c^3 - 2a^2b^3c^2 - 2a^3b^2$

Written

Factor:

Example: $6ax^2 + 6ax + 6a$

$\qquad 6a[x^2 + x + 1]$

1. $36a^2b^5 - 72a^4b^3 - 108a^3b^2$
2. $-8abx + 64aby - 112abz$
3. $13a^2by^2 - 65a^2b^2y - 39ab^2y^2$
4. $22m^5n^3 + 121m^2n^5 - 11m^2n^3$
5. $3p^2q^3 - 3p^3q^2 - 9p^2q^2$
6. $64x^6y^2 + 16x^4y^4 + 128x^2y^6$
7. $\pi x - \pi a + \pi b - \pi$
8. $3 - 27y + 9z$
9. $64x^6 - 32x^5 + 16x^4 - 8x^2$
10. $19a^5b^6c^4 - 57a^4b^6c^2 + 190a^3b^5c^3$
11. $2x(a + b) + 2(a + b)$
12. $213 \times 8 + 213 \times 7 - 213 \times 19$
13. $11 \times 14 \times 8 - 11 \times 14 \times 2 + 11 \times 14 \times 4$
14. $1235 \times 6 - 1235 \times 3 - 1235 \times 2$

15. $-31 \times 113 - 31 \times 27 - 31 \times 32$

16. $13(a + b) + 13(a - b) - 13a$

17. $2x(x + y) + 2x(x - y) + 2x(y - x)$

18. $3(x + y) + 5(x + y) - 19(x + y)$

19. $(x + y)(a + b) + (x + y)(a - b)$

20. $21(m + n) - 21(m - n) - 21(n - m)$

Exercise 19. Trinomial Square

Oral

Select the trinomial squares in the following examples:

1. $x^2 + 4x + 4$
2. $a^2 + 3a + 9$
3. $49x^2 - 140xy + 100y^2$
4. $8m^2 - 8m + 1$
5. $x^4 - 22x^2y^2 + 121y^4$
6. $-8x + 1 + 16x^2$
7. $x^9 + 4x^6 + 4$
8. $4a^{16} - 4a^4 + 1$
9. $9x^2y^2 + 24xya + 16a^2$
10. $14a^6 - 14a^3 + 1$
11. $(a + b)^2 + 2(a + b) + 1$
12. $1 - 2(x - y) + (x + y)^2$
13. $36x^4 + 81a^2 - 108x^2a$
14. $-2 + \dfrac{x^2}{y^2} + \dfrac{y^2}{x^2}$
15. $x^2 + 2xy + y^2$

Fill in the term that will make each of the following a square:

16. $x^2 + (\ ) + 4$
17. $9a^2 - (\ ) + 16$
18. $81x^4 + (\ ) + 9y^4$
19. $16a^4b^2 - (\ ) + 1$
20. $4x^2y^6 - (\ ) + 1$
21. $25x^2 + 10xy + (\ )$
22. $16a^2 - 16a + (\ )$
23. $4 - 4x^3y^3 + (\ )$
24. $81a^2 + 18ab^2c + (\ )$
25. $1 - 12x^3y^2 + (\ )$
26. $(\ ) + 4x + 1$
27. $(\ ) + 12a + 9$
28. $(\ ) + 6ab^2 + 9$
29. $(\ ) - 18a^2c^2 + c^4$
30. $(\ ) - 20x^3y + 4y^2$
31. $(\ ) - 12m^2 + 9m^4$

Factor:

32. $a^2 + 2ab + b^2$
33. $x^2 - 2xy + y^2$
34. $m^2 + 4m + 4$
35. $a^2 + 2a + 1$
36. $4p^2 - 4p + 1$
37. $9x^2 - 12x + 4$

38. $4a^2 + 36a + 81$

39. $9m^2 - 12mn + 4n^2$

40. $49 - 42k + 9k^2$

41. $25y^2 - 20y + 4$

42. $a^2 + 32ab + 256b^2$

43. $9x^2y^2 - 24xy + 16$

44. $49r^2 - 140rs + 100s^2$

45. $x^4 - 22x^2y^2 + 121y^4$

46. $49a^6 - 14a^3 + 1$

47. $64a^4b^4 + 48a^2b^2 + 9$

48. $81m^4n^2 - 18m^2n + 1$

49. $25x^6 - 20x^3y + 4y^2$

50. $1 - 12p^3q^2 + 36p^6q^4$

51. $81a^2 + 18ab^2c + b^4c^2$

52. $4a + 1 + 4a^2$

53. $144x^2 + y^2 - 24xy$

54. $-12x^2 + 4 + 9x^4$

55. $a^6 - 4a^3 + 4$

56. $25x^2 + 10xy + y^2$

57. $4a^2 + 4a + 1$

58. $36m^2 + 12mn + n^2$

59. $(a + b)^2 + 2(a + b) + 1$

60. $4 + 4(x + y) + (x + y)^2$

61. $(m + n)^2 - 6(m + n) + 9$

Written

Factor completely:

Example: $25x^2 + 16y^2 - 40xy$

Arrange in descending powers of x

$$25x^2 - 40xy + 16y^2$$

Perfect squares take the form $A^2 \pm 2AB + B^2 = (A \pm B)^2$. In this case, $A = 5x$ and $B = 4y$, thus the result is

$$(5x - 4y)^2$$

1. $169x^2 + 312xy + 144y^2$

2. $a^2b^8 - 28ab^4c^2 + 196c^4$

3. $81m^2 - 36mn + 4n^2$

4. $256y^6a^2 + 288y^3a + 81$

5. $-50p^2 + 1 + 625p^4$

6. $289 + 121q^2 - 374q$

7. $2ax^2 + 4axy + 2ay^2$

8. $18b^4 + 12b^2 + 2$

9. $x^4 - 8x^3 + 16x^2$

10. $a^5x^3 - 4a^3x^2 + 4ax$

11. $16x^2 - 24xy + 9y^2$

12. $8a^2 + 8ab + 2b^2$

Example: $16x^2 + 8x(a - b) + (a - b)^2$

This is of the form $A^2 + 2AB + B^2$ where $A = 4x$ and $B = a - b$. Thus it factors to

$$[4x + (a - b)]^2$$

$$\text{or} \quad (4x + a - b)^2$$

13. $(a + b)^2 - 32(a + b) + 256$

14. $4(x + y)^2 + 4(x + y) + 1$

15. $(a + b)^2 + 6c(a + b) + 9c^2$

16. $9 - 6(x + y) + (x + y)^2$

17. $16 + 24(m + n) + 9(m + n)^2$

18. $p^2 - 2p(m - n) + (m - n)^2$

19. $49 + 42(a - b) + 9(a - b)^2$

20. $(a + b)^2 + 6a + 6b + 9$

Exercise 20. Difference of Two Squares

Oral

Factor:

1. $a^2 - b^2$

2. $x^2 - 1$

3. $m^2 - 9n^2$

4. $16p^2 - 1$

5. $1 - 36a^2b^2$

6. $81p^2 - 4q^2$

7. $121 - a^4$

8. $a^2 - 49b^2c^2$

9. $144x^6 - y^4$

10. $64r^4s^2 - 25t^2$

11. $x^6y^4 - 121a^2$

12. $m^{12}n^6 - 4r^{10}$

13. $10x^2 - 810$

14. $16a^4 - 25b^2$

15. $36 - 49m^2$

16. $16 - 4x^2$

17. $81a^2 - 16b^2$

18. $1 - 25p^2$

19. $-a^8 + 4b^2$

20. $x^4 - y^4$

21. $1 - a^4$

22. $m^4 - 16$

23. $81x^4 - 16y^4$

24. $x^8 - 1$

25. $16 - a^8$

26. $(x + y)^2 - a^2$

27. $(a + b)^2 - 9c^2$

28. $4(m + n)^2 - 81$

29. $a^2 - (b + c)^2$

30. $(a + b)^2 - (x + y)^2$

Written

Factor completely:

Example: $405 - 80a^4b^4$.

Since $a^2 - b^2 = (a + b)(a - b)$, look for two perfect squares separated by a minus sign. First note the common factor 5.

$$405 - 80a^4b^4 = 5[81 - 16a^4b^4] = 5[9 + 4a^2b^2][9 - 4a^2b^2]$$

Now note that the third factor is again the difference of two squares.

Ans. $5[9 + 4a^2b^2][3 + 2ab][3 - 2ab]$

1. $225a^4b^6 - 169y^2$

2. $25a^6x^2 - 121b^4$

3. $144m^2 - 49n^2$

4. $128 - 2x^2y^2$

5. $a^6b^2 - a^2b^6$

6. $81x^4 - 16y^8$

7. $5x^3 - 125xy^2$

8. $256x^8 - y^8$

9. $32a^5 - 162ab^4$

10. $-a^4y^8 + 16b^4$ 11. $3m^3 - 108mn^6$ 12. $289 - 225p^{10}$

13. $8r^2 - 18s^4$ 14. $405 - 80a^4b^4$ 15. $32a^2x^4 - 32a^2y^4$

16. $a^4 - 2a^2b^2 + b^4$ 17. $x^4 - 18x^2 + 81$ 18. $64(a + b)^2 - 25$

19. $144x^2 - 25(m + n)^2$ 20. $9p^2 - (a - b)^2$

21. $x^4 - 16(m - n)^2$ 22. $169a^4 - 81(a + 1)^2$

23. $4(x + 2)^2 - 441a^2$ 24. $(a^2 + 2ab + b^2) - 64c^2$

25. $(x^2 - 6x + 9) - 121y^2$ 26. $16a^2 - (x^2 + 2xy + y^2)$

27. $25x^2 - (4a^2 + 8ab + 4b^2)$ 28. $256a^2 - (b^2 - 6bc + 9c^2)$

29. $(4a^2 - 4a + 1) - y^2$ 30. $3x^2 - (3b^2 - 6ab + 3a^2)$

Exercise 21. Expresssions of the Form $x^2 + bx + c$

Oral

Factor:

1. $a^2 + 3a + 2$ 2. $x^2 + 5x + 6$ 3. $x^2 + 8x + 15$

4. $p^2 + 5p + 4$ 5. $m^2 + 11m + 28$ 6. $a^2 - 3a + 2$

7. $n^2 - 7n + 12$ 8. $x^2 - 9x + 20$ 9. $y^2 - 13y + 42$

10. $a^2 - 19a + 90$ 11. $x^2 + x - 2$ 12. $b^2 - 3b - 4$

13. $a^2 - 2a - 15$ 14. $x^2 + 4x - 21$ 15. $x^2 - x - 30$

16. $x^2 + 3xy + 2y^2$ 17. $m^2 + 8mn + 15n^2$ 18. $p^2 + 7pq + 10q^2$

19. $a^2 - 3ab - 10b^2$ 20. $b^2 + 5bc - 14c^2$ 21. $x^2 - 9ax + 18a^2$

22. $a^2b^2 + 10ab + 9$ 23. $x^2y^2 - 11xy + 18$ 24. $b^4 + 5b^2 + 6$

25. $y^4 - 14y^2 - 32$ 26. $x^6 - 3x^3 - 70$ 27. $a^2 + 5a + 6$

28. $x^2 + 4x - 5$ 29. $y^2 + 5y - 24$ 30. $x^2y^2 - 18xy + 65$

31. $(x + y)^2 - 3(x + y) + 2$ 32. $(m + n)^2 + 7(m + n) - 18$

33. $(a - b)^2 - 13(a - b) - 30$ 34. $(a + b)^2 - 5x(a + b) + 6x^2$

Written

Factor completely:

Example: $x^2 - 10x + 16$

The factors of 16 are: 1 and 16, or 2 and 8, or 4 and 4. The plus in front of the 16 implies that both factors have the same sign and add to give 10. In this case, the factors are 2 and 8. The minus in front of the 10 implies that both are minus.

Ans. $(x - 2)(x - 8)$

Example: $x^2 - 2x - 15$

The factors of 15 are: 1 and 15, or 3 and 5. The minus in front of the 15 implies that the factors are opposite in sign and subtract to give 2. In this case the factors are 3 and 5. The minus in front of the 2 implies that the larger factor gets the minus sign.

Ans. $(x - 5)(x + 3)$

1. $x^2 + 12x + 35$
2. $x^2 - 13x + 40$
3. $x^2 - 7x + 6$
4. $a^2 + 15a + 56$
5. $m^2 + 16m + 63$
6. $x^2 + 3x - 40$
7. $a^2 + 8a - 20$
8. $x^4 + 3x^2 - 10$
9. $x^2 + 3x - 54$
10. $x^2 - 9x + 20$
11. $x^4 - 19x^2 + 88$
12. $x^4 - 10x^2 + 21$
13. $x^2 - 3x - 108$
14. $x^2 - 2x - 323$
15. $x^2 - 3x - 154$
16. $a^2b^2 - 20abc - 69c^2$
17. $m^3 - 7m^2 - 78m$
18. $3x^2 - 18x - 48$
19. $a^4 - 4a^2 + 3$
20. $p^4 - 4p^2q^2 + 3q^4$
21. $x^4 - 13x^2 + 36$
22. $ax^4 - 5ax^2y^2 + 4ay^4$
23. $5x^4y^4 - 90x^2y^2 + 325$
24. $20p - 9p^2 + p^3$
25. $92 - 42x - 2x^2$
26. $a^2 + 2a - 35$
27. $p^2 - 2pq - 63q^2$
28. $x^2 + 5x - 24$
29. $a^2 - 12a + 35$
30. $m^4 - 9m^2 - 112$
31. $3a^3 - 9a^2 - 84a$
32. $2y^4 - 4y^2 - 126$
33. $4a^4b^2 - 12a^2bc - 72c^2$
34. $x^4 + 8x^2 - 9$

Exercise 22. Expressions of the Form $ax^2 + bx + c$

Written

Factor completely:

Example: $6x^2 + 43x - 15$

The last term is negative so use trial and error to find factors of 6 and 15 such that the cross products *subtract* to give 43. If the last term had been

50

positive, the cross products should *add* to give the coefficient of the middle term.

$$6x^2 + 43x - 15 = (2x \quad 15)(3x \quad 1)$$

The larger product is given the sign of the middle term.

$$= (2x + 15)(3x - 1)$$

Example: $15x^2 - 33x + 6$

Remove the common factor 3.

$$3(5x^2 - 11x + 2)$$

The factors of 5 and 2 whose cross products add to 11 are 5 and 1, and 1 and 2.

$$3(5x \quad 1)(x \quad 2).$$

Since both signs are the same, we have

$$3(5x - 1)(x - 2).$$

1. $2x^2 + 3x + 1$ 2. $6a^2 + 5a + 1$ 3. $2m^2 + 5m + 2$

4. $3x^2 + 13x + 4$ 5. $2q^2 - 9q + 7$ 6. $3y^2 - 8y - 3$

7. $6a^2 + 7ab + 2b^2$ 8. $-x^2 + 5x + 14$ 9. $-6x^2 + 7x + 3$

10. $2x^2 - 3x - 2$ 11. $3x^2 + 2x - 1$ 12. $4x^2 - 11x + 6$

13. $5x^2 - 11x + 2$ 14. $56x^2 + 9x - 2$ 15. $56x^2 + 26x - 1$

16. $16x^2 + 2x - 3$ 17. $6x^4 - 13x^2 + 6$ 18. $8x^6 + 2x^3 - 1$

19. $4x^4 + 3x^2 - 1$ 20. $16 - 28a + 10a^2$ 21. $25a^2 + 25ab - 14b^2$

22. $12m^2 + 17m + 6$ 23. $10y^3 - 19y^2 + 6y$ 24. $7x^4 - 27x^2 - 4$

25. $9a^4 - 13a^2 + 4$ 26. $18m^2 + 9m - 14$ 27. $8 - 14x + 5x^2$

28. $70 - 2a - 12a^2$ 29. $3a^4b^2 + a^2bc - 2c^2$ 30. $72x^2 + 50x - 50$

31. $15x^2 + 24x - 12$ 32. $55x^4 - x^2 - 2$ 33. $12x^2 - 25x + 12$

34. $24x^2 + 18x + 3$ 35. $6x^2 + 7xy + 2y^2$ 36. $21x^2 + xy - 2y^2$

Exercise 23. Grouping to Get a Common Factor

Oral

Factor:

1. $2(a + b) + 3(a + b)$
2. $x(a + b) + y(a + b)$
3. $m(x + y) - n(x + y)$
4. $a(p + q) - (p + q)$
5. $x(a - b) - 3(a - b)$
6. $mx + my + nx + ny$
7. $am - an + bm - bn$
8. $bp - bq + p - q$
9. $ay - ax + 3y - 3x$
10. $a(m + n) - 3m - 3n$
11. $mx + my - nx - ny$
12. $an - am - 3n + 3m$
13. $a^2 + a + ab + b$
14. $x^2 + px - xy - py$
15. $am - bn + an - bm$
16. $ap + q + aq + p$
17. $am - an + bm - bn + cm - cn$
18. $(x + y)^2 + (x + y)$
19. $(a + b)^2 - a - b$
20. $m^2 + 2mn + n^2 + 2m + 2n$

Written

Factor completely:

Example: $3ax - 6a - x + 2$

$$(3ax - 6a) - (x - 2) =$$
$$3a(x - 2) - (x - 2) =$$
$$3a(x - 2) - 1(x - 2) =$$
$$(x - 2)(3a - 1)$$

1. $2ax + 2bx + 2ay + 2by$
2. $2am + bn - 2an - bm$
3. $x^3 + x^2 - x - 1$
4. $a^2m - a^2n - b^2m + b^2n$
5. $6ax - 3bx - 2ay + by$
6. $2ab - 2b - 3a + 3$
7. $5pm + 5qm - 5pn - 5qn$
8. $ax^2 + ax - 3xy - 3y$
9. $3(a + b) + (4 - x)(a + b)$
10. $(a^2 - b^2) + (a + b)^2$
11. $(a - b)(x - y) - ax + ay$
12. $(x + y)(x - y) - ax - ay$
13. $a^2 - 2ab + b^2 - 5a + 5b$
14. $m^2 - n^2 - am - an$
15. $a^2x^2 - a^2y^2 - x^2 + y^2$
16. $(x - y)^3 + xy(x - y)$
17. $(3 + x)(m - n) + (2 - x)(m - n)$
18. $(a + 1)(a - 3) - a^2 + 1$
19. $x^2 - x - 2 + 2(x - 2)$
20. $a^2x + a^2y + a^2z - 4x - 4y - 4z$

21. $ma - mb - na + nb - a + b$ **22.** $(a^2 - 1) + (a - 1)^2 - (a - 1)$

23. $ax + 2b - bx - 2a - ay + by$ **24.** $a^2 - 2ab + b^2 - 4(b - a)$

25. $a^2b - a^2c - ab + ac - 2b + 2c$ **26.** $2a^2 - 2b^2 - 4(a^2 - 2ab + b^2)$

27. $mx + ny + my + nx + m + n$ **28.** $7a^3 - 7a + 7a^2 - 7$

29. $3ax - 3ay + 2bx - 2by + 3az + 2bz$

30. $m^2 + 2m + 1 - 2(m + 1) - 3(m + 1)(m - 1)$

Exercise 24. Sum and Difference of Two Cubes

Written

Factor:

Examples: $x^3 - y^3 = (x - y)(x^2 + xy + y^2)$
and $x^3 + y^3 = (x + y)(x^2 - xy + y^2)$

Note that the second factor is *not* a perfect square.

1. $a^3 - b^3$ **2.** $a^3 - 8b^3$ **3.** $8a^3 + b^3$

4. $27x^3 - y^3$ **5.** $y^3 + 27z^3$ **6.** $a^3 + 1$

7. $a^9 + 1$ **8.** $a^3 - 1$ **9.** $x^6 - y^6$

10. $a^6 + b^6$ **11.** $64a^6 - 1$ **12.** $8x^3 + 1$

13. $27y^6 - 1$ **14.** $a^3 - b^6$ **15.** $xy^4 - x^4y$

16. $125a^6 - b^3$ **17.** $8a^5 + 27a^2b^3$ **18.** $2x^3 - 16$

19. $64a^3 - 8b^3$ **20.** $5a^3b^3 - 40a^3$ **21.** $8m^3 - 27p^3$

Exercise 25. Miscellaneous

Oral

Factor completely: (Some are prime)

1. $a^2 - b^2$ **2.** $16a^2 - 25b^2$ **3.** $5x^2 - 45y^2$

4. $a^2 - a - 2$ **5.** $x^2 - 10x + 16$ **6.** $x^2 - 10x + 9$

7. $x^2 - 10x - 11$ **8.** $x^2 - 6x + 9$ **9.** $x^2 - 9x - 22$

10. $4x^2 + 12xy + 9y^2$ **11.** $2a^2 + 12a + 18$ **12.** $6 - x - x^2$

13. $x^2 - (a + b)^2$ **14.** $4 + 8y + 16y^2$ **15.** $a^4 - 16$

16. $4m^2 - 4m$ 17. $x^2 + x + 1$ 18. $m - n + 2m - 2n$

19. $(a^2 - b^2) + (a - b)$ 20. $2x^2 - x - 1$ 21. $a^4 + a^3 - a^2$

22. $4a^2 + 5$ 23. $2a^2 - 5a + 3$ 24. $a^4 + 16$

25. $100m^2 - 40mn + 4n^2$ 26. $a^2 - a - 6$ 27. $x^2 + 11x + 30$

28. $25a^2y^2 - 16y^2$ 29. $(x^3 + x^2) + (x + 1)$ 30. $5 + 4x - x^2$

31. $4m^3n - 4mn^3$

32. $a(a + b - 1) - ac(a + b - 1)$

Written

Factor completely: (Some may be prime).

1. $x^2 + 16x + 64$ 2. $x^2 + x - 6$

3. $12x^2 + 11x + 2$ 4. $36a^2 - 49b^2$

5. $a^3 - 8$ 6. $a^4 - 81$

7. $4x^2 + 7x - 36$ 8. $6x^2 - x - 77$

9. $a^2b^2 + 19a^2b - 42a^2$ 10. $16 + a^3b^3$

11. $(a^2 + ac) + (3ab + 3bc)$ 12. $(4x^2 - 25y^2) + (2x - 5y)$

13. $p^4 - 17p^2 + 16$ 14. $(a + b)^2 + 2(a + b) + 1$

15. $(x + a)(y - b) - (x - a)(y - b)$ 16. $(a - 1)(a^2 - 2) + (a - 1)a$

17. $4ab - 4ac - 8b^2 + 8bc$ 18. $x^2 - x - 110$

19. $121a^4 - 44a^2 + 4$ 20. $10a^2 + 28a - 6$

21. $-1 - a + 6a^2$ 22. $a^4 - (a - 2)^2$

23. $16x^4 - 8x^2 + 1$ 24. $a^4 - 6a^2 + 9 - 4a^2$

25. $9p^2 - 13p + 4$ 26. $(a^2 - 9) - (a^2 - 6a + 9)$

27. $256x^2 - 288x + 81$ 28. $(a^2 - 2)^2 - (2a - 1)^2$

29. $8a^2 + 29a - 12$ 30. $-x^2 + 3x + 108$

31. $m^4 + 2m^3n + m^2n^2 - m^2$ 32. $a^8 - 2a^6 + a^4$

33. $4(x - y)^2 - 169$ 34. $9a^2 - 18ab + 9b^2 - x^2$

35. $a^{12}x^4 - a^4x^{12}$ 36. $4a^4 - 37a^2 + 9$

37. $1 - a - b + ab$ 38. $4 - 5x - 6x^2$

39. $9m^2 - 4n^2 + 3m - 2n$ 40. $a(a - 1)(a - 2) + (a - 1)$

41. $12x^4 - ax^3 - 6a^2x^2$ 42. $x^2 - 4y^2 - 3x + 6y$

43. $3p^3 - p^2 - 10p$ 44. $x^2 + 16 - y^2 - 8x$

45. $x^4 - 2ax^2 + a^2 - 1$

46. $m^2 - y^2 - 4a^2y^2 + 4ay^2$

47. $(a - b)^2 - a(b - a)$

48. $(a + b)^2(a - b) - (a^2 - b^2)$

49. $4(x - y)^2 + 12x - 12y + 9$

50. $16a^4 - 81b^8$

51. $8a^3 - b^3$

52. $a^5 - ab^4$

53. $(x^2 - y^2) + (x - y)^2$

54. $(b^2 - 4b + 4) - a^2$

55. $x(x + 2)(2x - 1) - (x + 2)$

56. $(a + b)^2 - (a - b)^2$

57. $(x^3 - 2x^2) + (3x - 6)$

58. $4x^2 + 12xy + 9y^2$

59. $x^2 - x - 3$

60. $10 - x - 3x^2$

61. $6x^2 - 7xy + 2y^2$

62. $96 - 20x - x^2$

63. $x^2(a - 1) + x(a - 1) - 6(a - 1)$

64. $a(a - 1)(a + 2) - 8(a - 1)$

65. $(a - 1) + (a - 1)^2$

66. $x^2 - (3 - a)^2$

67. $x^2 - (9 + 6a + a^2)$

68. $m^2 - (9 - 6a + a^2)$

69. $c^2 - (a^2 + 2ab + b^2)$

70. $(16y^2 - 8xy + x^2) - 16$

71. $x^3 + 1$

72. $m^3 - 27$

73. $a^4 - 2a^2 + 1$

74. $a^6 - 1$

75. $a^4 + 2a^2b^2 + b^4$

76. $(x^2y + 4xy) - (4z + xz)$

77. $xy^3 - 2xy^2 + 5xy - 10x$

78. $x^2 + 8r - r^2 - 16$

79. $a^4 - (2a - 3)^2$

80. $a^4 - [4a^2 - 12a + 9]$

81. $x^4 - 6x^2 + 9$

82. $m^2(x - y) - m(x - y)^2$

83. $x^2(x - y) - x(x - y)^2$

84. $a^3 + 3a^2 + 3a + 9$

85. $m^3 - m^2 + m - 1$

86. $x^3 - x^2 - x + 1$

87. $(3a - b)^2 - (a - b)^2$

88. $(3x - y)^2 - (x + y)^2$

89. $(x + y)^2(x - y) - (x + y)(x - y)^2$

90. $(a - 4)^2 + (a - 4) - 12$

91. $12 + x^2y^4 - x^4y^8$

92. $27x^3 + y^9$

93. $a^6b^3 - x^{12}$

94. $(a + 1)^3 + 8$

95. $64 + x^2$

96. $6 - 13mn + 6m^2n^2$

97. $x^4 - x^2y^2 - x^2 + y^2$

98. $4a^3 - a^2 - 8a + 2$

99. $x^2 - 2xy + y^2 - 16a^2$

100. $6x^2 - 7xy + 2y^2$

FRACTIONS

Exercise 26. Reduction

In each problem assume that the domain of the variable excludes division by zero.

Oral

Reduce to lowest terms:

1. $\frac{10}{15}$

2. $\frac{9}{27}$

3. $\frac{24}{72}$

4. $\dfrac{8x}{24}$

5. $\dfrac{ab}{ac}$

6. $\dfrac{7ax}{21a}$

7. $\dfrac{14ab}{21ab}$

8. $\dfrac{abc}{2ac}$

9. $\dfrac{-4bx}{4x}$

10. $\dfrac{6a^2m}{-9a^2}$

11. $\dfrac{m^2n^2}{m^2n}$

12. $\dfrac{-3x^2}{-6x^3}$

13. $\dfrac{x^2y^3}{4xy}$

14. $\dfrac{x^5a^4b}{x^2ab^2}$

15. $\dfrac{13mn^2x}{39m^2n^2x^2}$

16. $\dfrac{28x^4y^4}{12x^2y^4}$

17. $\dfrac{-17a^2b^2x}{-17a^2b^2x}$

18. $\dfrac{-2(a+b)}{9(a+b)}$

19. $\dfrac{a(x+y)}{b(x+y)}$

20. $\dfrac{4a(m-n)}{9a(m-n)}$

21. $\dfrac{12(a-b)}{24(a+b)}$

22. $\dfrac{(a+b)(a-b)}{2(a+b)}$

23. $\dfrac{-4x(x-y)}{(x-y)^2}$

24. $\dfrac{(a+b)^3}{(a+b)^2}$

25. $\dfrac{m^2-n^2}{m-n}$

26. $\dfrac{a^2+2ab+b^2}{3(a+b)}$

27. $\dfrac{x^2-y^2}{x^2-2xy+y^2}$

28. $\dfrac{-3(a-b)}{21a-21b}$

29. $\dfrac{-2x+2y}{-8x+8y}$

30. $\dfrac{a-b}{b-a}$

Written

Reduce to lowest terms:

Examples: Only non-zero *common factors* may be divided out. Always start by factoring numerator and denominator.

(a) $\dfrac{4x^2r}{8x^2 - 12x^3r} = \dfrac{4x^2r}{4x^2(2 - 3xr)} = \dfrac{r}{2 - 3xr}$

(b) $\dfrac{a^2 + 4a + 3}{a^2 + 2a - 3} = \dfrac{(a + 3)(a + 1)}{(a + 3)(a - 1)} = \dfrac{a + 1}{a - 1}$

Sometimes the sign of a factor must be changed.

(c) $\dfrac{(x - y)^2}{y^2 - x^2} = \dfrac{(x - y)^2}{-(x^2 - y^2)} = \dfrac{(x - y)^2}{-(x - y)(x + y)} = \dfrac{x - y}{-(x + y)} = -\dfrac{x - y}{x + y}$

1. $\dfrac{132a^4b^5x^2}{324a^2b^6x^3}$

2. $\dfrac{164a^2b^3 - 8a^3b^2}{4a^2b^2}$

3. $\dfrac{-4a^3 - 4a^2b}{-4(a + b)}$

4. $\dfrac{x^2 - 9y^2}{2x^2 - 12xy + 18y^2}$

5. $\dfrac{(x - a)(x - b)}{(x^2 - a^2)(x - b)}$

6. $\dfrac{(a - b)(c - d)}{-3(b - a)}$

7. $\dfrac{36m^2 - 12m + 1}{48m - 8}$

8. $\dfrac{45(x - y)^3}{54(x^2 - y^2)(x - y)}$

9. $\dfrac{a^2 - 2a - 15}{4a - 20}$

10. $\dfrac{am + an + bm + bn}{m^2 - n^2}$

11. $\dfrac{3a^2 - 6ab + 3b^2}{12a^2 + 12ab - 24b^2}$

12. $\dfrac{2x^2 + 5x - 3}{2x^2 - 7x + 3}$

13. $\dfrac{(a - x)(b - x)}{(x - a)(x - b)}$

14. $\dfrac{x^4 - 16}{(x - 2)(x^2 + 4)}$

15. $\dfrac{(2a - b)(x - y)}{y^2 - x^2}$

16. $\dfrac{-a^2 + 2ab - b^2}{b^2 - a^2}$

17. $\dfrac{(x + h)^2 - x^2}{h}$

18. $\dfrac{9 - h^2}{h^2 - 7h + 12}$

19. $\dfrac{(x^2 + x - 6)(x - 3)}{(x - 2)(x^2 - 9)}$

20. $\dfrac{(a - 2)^2 - (a - 2)}{a^2 - 5a + 6}$

21. $\dfrac{6x^2 + 7x - 3}{18x^2 - 12x + 2}$

22. $\dfrac{-x^2 + 4x + 5}{x^2 - 25}$

23. $\dfrac{x^2 - (a + b)^2}{a^2 - (x + b)^2}$

24. $\dfrac{a^2 - 8a + 15}{12 - 7a + a^2}$

25. $\dfrac{3x^2 + 7xy - 6y^2}{3x^2 - 11xy + 6y^2}$

Exercise 27. Addition and Subtraction

In each problem assume that the domain of the variables excludes division by zero.

Oral

Find the lowest common multiple:

1. 12, 9, 8

2. 2, 3, 5, 7

3. 4, 6, 3^2, 2

4. $3a$, $2b$, $12a$

5. $9x^3$, $24x^2y^2$, $8y^3$ 6. $7a^2bc^3$, $4ab^5c^2$, $14a^3b^2c$

7. $2a(x + y)$, $3a(x - y)$ 8. $5a^2b(a - b)$, $3a(a - b)^2$

9. $(a + b)^2$, $(a - b)^2$, $(a^2 - b^2)$ 10. $b - a$, $a - b$

Change to improper fractions:

11. $7\frac{9}{11}$ 12. $-9\frac{3}{8}$ 13. $1 + \dfrac{2}{x}$

14. $2 - \dfrac{3}{a}$ 15. $-m - \frac{1}{3}$ 16. $a^2 - 2a + \frac{1}{3}$

17. $2 - \dfrac{1}{a + b}$ 18. $x^2 - x - \dfrac{5}{x}$ 19. $2a - 3 + \dfrac{a - 2}{a}$

20. $x + 2 - \dfrac{a + b}{x - 2}$

Change to fractions having the same denominators:

21. $\dfrac{c}{7ab}$, $\dfrac{b}{2ac}$, $\dfrac{a}{bc}$ 22. $\dfrac{1}{a + b}$, $\dfrac{2}{a - b}$, $\dfrac{4a}{a^2 - b^2}$

23. $\dfrac{1}{a - b}$, $\dfrac{-1}{b - a}$, $\dfrac{3}{b - a}$ 24. $\dfrac{x - 1}{(x + 1)^2}$, $\dfrac{x}{x^2 - 1}$

Simplify:

25. $\frac{1}{2} + \frac{2}{3} - \frac{1}{6}$ 26. $\frac{3}{7} - \frac{3}{2} - \frac{9}{14}$ 27. $\dfrac{1}{a} + \dfrac{1}{b} - \dfrac{1}{c}$

28. $\dfrac{a}{b} - \dfrac{b}{a} + \dfrac{2}{ab}$ 29. $\dfrac{1}{a - b} - \dfrac{1}{a + b}$ 30. $\dfrac{1}{a - b} - \dfrac{1}{b - a}$

31. $\dfrac{a}{b(a + b)} + \dfrac{b}{a(a + b)}$ 32. $\dfrac{1}{a^2 - b^2} + \dfrac{1}{a^2 - 2ab + b^2}$

33. $\dfrac{x - 2}{x - 1} - \dfrac{2}{x - 1} - \dfrac{1}{1 - x}$

Written

Simplify:

Example: $\dfrac{a}{a - 1} - a + \dfrac{1}{a^2 - a} + \dfrac{1}{a}$

58

Factor each denominator in order to determine the *least common denominator*, (L.C.D.).

$$\frac{a}{a-1} - a + \frac{1}{a(a-1)} + \frac{1}{a}$$

Indicate the multiplications needed to change each into a fraction with the L.C.D.

$$\frac{a^2 - a^2(a-1) + 1 + (a-1)}{a(a-1)}$$

Do the indicated multiplications being careful with minus signs.

$$\frac{a^2 - a^3 + a^2 + 1 + a - 1}{a(a-1)} = \frac{-a^3 + 2a^2 + a}{a(a-1)}$$

Factor the numerator and reduce.

$$\frac{a(-a^2 + 2a + 1)}{a(a-1)} = \frac{-a^2 + 2a + 1}{a-1}$$

1. $\dfrac{7}{3abc^2} - \dfrac{6}{3ab^2c} + \dfrac{3}{4a^2bc}$

2. $\dfrac{x+3}{2x^2} - \dfrac{x+2}{4x} + \dfrac{6}{3x}$

3. $\dfrac{2}{a-1} - \dfrac{3}{a+1} - \dfrac{4a}{a^2-1}$

4. $\dfrac{2x}{x^2-9} - \dfrac{x}{x^2-3x-18}$

5. $a + 4b - \dfrac{a^2 + 16b^2}{a+4b}$

6. $\dfrac{1}{x} - \dfrac{3}{x-3} + \dfrac{4}{x+1}$

7. $\dfrac{5x}{x-1} + 4 - \dfrac{3x}{x+1}$

8. $x + y - \dfrac{(x+y)^2}{x-y} + x - y$

9. $\dfrac{1}{x^2-7x+6} - \dfrac{3}{x^2-6x+5}$

10. $\dfrac{x^2}{x^2-1} + \dfrac{x}{x+1} + \dfrac{x}{x-1}$

Example: $\dfrac{x^2}{x^2-1} + \dfrac{x^2-1}{(x+1)^2} + \dfrac{1}{1-x}$

Make sure all the denominators have the same order. Factor -1 out of the denominator of the last fraction and change the sign in front.

$$\frac{x^2}{x^2-1} + \frac{x^2-1}{(x+1)^2} - \frac{1}{x-1}$$

Factor and simplify where possible.

$$\frac{x^2}{(x+1)(x-1)} + \frac{(x+1)(x-1)}{(x+1)(x+1)} - \frac{1}{x-1} =$$

$$\frac{x^2}{(x+1)(x-1)} + \frac{x-1}{x+1} - \frac{1}{x-1} =$$

$$\frac{x^2 + (x-1)^2 - (x+1)}{(x+1)(x-1)} =$$

$$\frac{x^2 + x^2 - 2x + 1 - x - 1}{(x+1)(x-1)} = \frac{2x^2 - 3x}{(x+1)(x-1)}$$

11. $\dfrac{m-2}{m+2} - \dfrac{2m^2+3}{m^2-4} - \dfrac{m+2}{2-m}$

12. $\dfrac{a}{a-1} - \dfrac{a^2}{1-a^2} + \dfrac{3a}{a+1}$

13. $\dfrac{2a-b}{3a-3b} - \dfrac{a+3b}{4a+4b} + \dfrac{4ab}{a^2-b^2} - \dfrac{5}{12}$

14. $\dfrac{3x}{2x-1} - \dfrac{-2x^2-x}{1-4x^2} - \dfrac{4x}{2x+1}$

15. $\dfrac{2}{x^2-5x+6} - \dfrac{4}{x^2-3x+2} + \dfrac{1}{x^2-4x+3}$

16. $\dfrac{3}{a} - \dfrac{4a+1}{a^2-5a+4} + \dfrac{5}{a-1} - \dfrac{2}{4-a}$

17. $\dfrac{3-a}{4} - 1 + \dfrac{2-3a}{1-a} - a + \dfrac{1}{a-1}$

18. $\dfrac{5}{12m-12} - \dfrac{3}{16m+16} - \dfrac{9-11m}{8m^2-8}$

19. $\dfrac{a-2}{a^2-4a-4} - \dfrac{a+2}{a^2+4a+4}$

20. $\dfrac{x-1}{4x^2-9} - \dfrac{x}{2x^2-x-3} + \dfrac{2x-3}{2x^2+5x+3}$

21. $\dfrac{x+2}{x(x-1)^2} - \dfrac{x+3}{x^2(x-1)} - \dfrac{3}{x^4-2x^3+x^2}$

22. $\dfrac{1}{a^3(a-2)} - \dfrac{1}{a^2(a-2)^2} + \dfrac{a-2}{a^2(a-2)^3}$

23. $\dfrac{1}{a(a-b)} + \dfrac{1}{b(b-a)} + \dfrac{1}{4ab}$

24. $\dfrac{1}{2a} - \dfrac{1}{2b} + \dfrac{1}{a-b} - \dfrac{1}{a+b} - \dfrac{b-a}{2ab}$

25. $3 + \dfrac{x-y}{y} + \dfrac{x}{x-y} + \dfrac{y}{y-x} + \dfrac{1}{x}$

26. $\dfrac{1}{-a^2 + 4a - 3} + \dfrac{2}{a^2 - 9} - \dfrac{3}{9 - 6a + a^2}$

27. $\dfrac{1}{4(2x-1)} - \dfrac{3x}{2(2x-1)^2} + \dfrac{x}{(2x-1)^3}$

Example: $\dfrac{2}{x+1} + \dfrac{3}{x-1} + \dfrac{4}{x+2} + \dfrac{5}{x-2}$

If there are many different denominators, it is wise to look for convenient ways to group them in pairs and add separately.

$$\frac{2(x-1) + 3(x+1)}{(x+1)(x-1)} + \frac{4(x-2) + 5(x+2)}{(x+2)(x-2)} =$$

$$\frac{2x - 2 + 3x + 3}{x^2 - 1} + \frac{4x - 8 + 5x + 10}{x^2 - 4} =$$

$$\frac{5x + 1}{x^2 - 1} + \frac{9x + 2}{x^2 - 4} =$$

$$\frac{(5x+1)(x^2 - 4) + (9x+2)(x^2 - 1)}{(x^2 - 1)(x^2 - 4)} =$$

$$\frac{5x^3 + x^2 - 20x - 4 + 9x^3 + 18x^2 - 9x - 2}{(x^2 - 1)(x^2 - 4)} =$$

$$\frac{14x^3 + 19x^2 - 29x - 6}{(x^2 - 1)(x^2 - 4)}$$

28. $\dfrac{2}{2m+3} - \dfrac{2}{2m-3} + \dfrac{1}{m-3} - \dfrac{1}{m+3}$

29. $\dfrac{b-x}{(a-b)(x-y)} - \dfrac{1}{b-a} - \dfrac{1}{y-x}$

30. $\dfrac{1}{(a-1)(a-2)} + \dfrac{1}{(1-a)(3-a)} - \dfrac{1}{(2-a)(a-3)}$

31. $\dfrac{1}{m^2 - m} + \dfrac{1}{m^2} - \dfrac{1}{m^2 - 2m + 1} - \dfrac{1}{m^3 - m^2}$

32. $\dfrac{a + b}{a^2 + ab - 2b^2} + \dfrac{a - b}{2b^2 + 3ab + a^2} - \dfrac{a + 2b}{b^2 - a^2}$

33. $x + \dfrac{2}{3 - x} + 3 + \dfrac{4}{3 + x}$

34. $\dfrac{3}{a} - \dfrac{1}{b} - \dfrac{2b - a}{ab} - \dfrac{3}{a^2 - ab} + \dfrac{1}{b^2 - ab} - \dfrac{4}{a^2 - b^2}$

Example: $\left(\dfrac{1 + x}{2} + \dfrac{x}{x - 1}\right) + \left(\dfrac{1}{1 - x} - \dfrac{x}{2}\right)$

Fractions with the same denominator should be added together first.

$$\dfrac{1 + x}{2} + \dfrac{x}{x - 1} + \dfrac{1}{1 - x} - \dfrac{x}{2} =$$

$$\dfrac{1 + x - x}{2} + \dfrac{x}{x - 1} - \dfrac{1}{x - 1} =$$

$$\dfrac{1}{2} + \dfrac{x - 1}{x - 1} = \dfrac{1}{2} + 1 = \dfrac{3}{2}$$

35. $\dfrac{1}{m - n} - \left(\dfrac{m}{m^2 - 2mn + n^2} + \dfrac{n}{m^2 - n^2}\right)$

36. $\dfrac{x - 2}{(x - 1)(x - 3)} + \dfrac{1 - x}{(x - 2)(4 - x)}$

37. $\dfrac{2}{a} - \left(3 - \dfrac{4a}{b}\right) - \dfrac{2}{a} - \left(\dfrac{1}{a - b} - \dfrac{1}{b - a}\right)$

38. $\dfrac{p - 6}{2p - 6} - \left(\dfrac{p + 3}{3p^2 - 27} - \dfrac{2p}{12 - 4p}\right)$

39. $\left(x - \dfrac{1}{x - 1} + 2\right) - \left(x + 1 - \dfrac{1}{x + 1}\right)$

40. $3\left(\dfrac{1}{a} - \dfrac{1}{b}\right) + \dfrac{a + 5b}{ab} - 2\left(\dfrac{1}{b} - \dfrac{1}{a}\right)$

41. $\dfrac{2}{a^2 - 5a} - \left[\dfrac{a + 1}{a^3 - 5a^2} - \dfrac{a - 3}{a(a - 5)^2}\right]$

42. $\dfrac{1}{x} - \left[\dfrac{1}{x - 1} - \left(\dfrac{2}{x} - \dfrac{1}{x - x^2}\right)\right]$

43. $\dfrac{a}{a - 1} - \left[\dfrac{3}{a} - \left(\dfrac{a + 1}{1 - a^2} + \dfrac{1}{a + 1} \right) \right] + \dfrac{3}{a}$

44. $\dfrac{m}{m + 2} + 1 - \left[\dfrac{6m - 1}{3} - 2m - \left(\dfrac{2m + 5}{m - 2} - \dfrac{1}{3} \right) \right]$

45. $\left(\dfrac{a}{a - 1} - \dfrac{a + 1}{a} \right) - \left[\dfrac{1}{a} - \left(\dfrac{2}{1 - a} - \dfrac{3}{a} \right) - \dfrac{2}{a(a - 1)} \right]$

Exercise 28. Multiplication and Division

In each problem assume that the domain of the variables excludes division by zero.

Oral

Multiply and divide as indicated:

1. $\frac{3}{4} \times 7$

2. $3 \times \frac{5}{6}$

3. $a \times \dfrac{a}{b}$

4. $\frac{3}{4} \times x^2$

5. $\dfrac{x}{y} \times (-2x)$

6. $\left(-\dfrac{1}{a} \right)(-3)$

7. $\frac{1}{6} \cdot \frac{5}{2}$

8. $\dfrac{a}{b} \cdot \dfrac{c}{d}$

9. $\dfrac{-2}{3} \cdot \dfrac{-4}{5}$

10. $\dfrac{a^2 b}{c^2 d} \cdot \dfrac{cd}{ab}$

11. $\frac{6}{7} \div 2$

12. $\frac{9}{5} \div 3$

13. $\frac{2}{3} \div 5$

14. $-\frac{8}{9} \div 16$

15. $\frac{9}{8} \div (-6)$

16. $\dfrac{3a}{b} \div a$

17. $\dfrac{a^2}{5b^2} \div a^3$

18. $\dfrac{ax}{3} \div 2a$

19. $3 \div \frac{1}{2}$

20. $4 \div \frac{2}{5}$

21. $\dfrac{2ab}{3} \cdot \dfrac{6}{ac}$

22. $\frac{1}{12} \cdot \frac{3}{4}$

23. $2 \cdot \frac{1}{3} \cdot \frac{1}{2}$

24. $\dfrac{a}{b} \cdot \dfrac{c}{d} \cdot \dfrac{b}{c}$

25. $x \div \dfrac{2}{x}$

26. $-1 \div \dfrac{a}{b}$

27. $2m \div \dfrac{m}{-3}$

28. $\dfrac{a}{b} \div \dfrac{a}{b}$

29. $\dfrac{a}{b} \div \dfrac{b}{a}$

30. $\dfrac{3m}{n} \cdot \dfrac{n^2}{9m^2} \cdot \dfrac{m}{2n}$

31. $\dfrac{m + n}{3} \cdot \dfrac{9a}{m + n}$

32. $\dfrac{3(a - b)}{2c} \cdot \dfrac{4a}{a - b}$

33. $\dfrac{3a^2}{b^2} \div \dfrac{2a}{b}$

34. $(-\frac{1}{3}) \div (-\frac{4}{9})$

35. $\dfrac{4a}{5} \div \left(-\dfrac{2a}{b}\right)$

36. $\dfrac{(a - b)(a + b)}{a^2 + b^2} \cdot \dfrac{2}{a^2 - b^2}$

37. $\dfrac{x - y}{2ab} \cdot \dfrac{4a}{y - x}$

38. $\dfrac{a - b}{c - d} \cdot \dfrac{d - c}{b - a}$

39. $\dfrac{x + y}{a} \div \dfrac{x + y}{b}$

40. $\dfrac{\dfrac{a - b}{2a}}{a - b}$

Written

Multiply and divide as indicated:

Example: $\dfrac{x^2 - 4}{x^2 - 4x + 4} \cdot \dfrac{x + 3}{x + 2} \div \dfrac{2x + 6}{x - 1}$

Factor as much as possible.

$$\frac{(x - 2)(x + 2)}{(x - 2)^2} \cdot \frac{x + 3}{x + 2} \div \frac{2(x + 3)}{x - 1} =$$

To divide by a fraction, invert it and multiply.

$$\frac{(x - 2)(x + 2)(x + 3)}{(x - 2)^2(x + 2)} \cdot \frac{x - 1}{2(x + 3)} = \frac{x - 1}{2(x - 2)}$$

1. $\frac{26}{9} \cdot \frac{27}{39} \cdot \frac{7}{16}$

2. $\dfrac{28a^2}{19x} \cdot \dfrac{35x^2}{16} \cdot \dfrac{57}{49a}$

3. $\dfrac{-12m^2n}{13x} \cdot \dfrac{-52}{mn^2} \cdot \dfrac{x^3}{24}$

4. $\dfrac{a^2 + ab}{2b} \cdot \dfrac{12a - 12b}{a^2 - b^2} \cdot \dfrac{a}{b}$

5. $\dfrac{x^3 + 2ax^2 + a^2x}{a - x} \cdot \dfrac{x - a}{(a + x)^2}$

6. $\dfrac{x^2 - y^2}{x^2 + y^2} \cdot \dfrac{x^2 + xy}{y^2 - x^2} \cdot \dfrac{1}{x}$

7. $\dfrac{2a + 6}{a^2 - 2a} \cdot \dfrac{a^3 - 4a}{a^2 - 9} \cdot 4a$

8. $\dfrac{x^2 + 3x + 2}{x^2 - 3x} \cdot \dfrac{3 - x}{x^2 + 7x + 6}$

9. $\dfrac{a^2 + 2ab + b^2}{b^2 - a^2} \cdot \dfrac{a}{b^2 + ab} \cdot \dfrac{b^3 - ab^2}{2}$

10. $\dfrac{2a^2 - 3a - 2}{a^2 - 4} \cdot \dfrac{a^2 + 4a + 4}{4a^2 - 1}$

11. $(4x^2 - 9y^2) \div \dfrac{3xy + 2x^2}{2}$

12. $\dfrac{4x^2 + 4x + 1}{x^2} \div \dfrac{8x^2 - 2}{3x^3}$

13. $\dfrac{36a^2 - 81b^2}{8a + 12b} \div \dfrac{4a^2 - 12ab + 9b^2}{16a^2}$

14. $\dfrac{2x^2 - 13x + 15}{x^2 - 2x} \div \dfrac{x^2 - 7x + 10}{4 - 4x + x^2}$

15. $\dfrac{9x^2 - 6x + 1}{2x + 3} \div (6x^2 + 7x - 3)$

16. $\dfrac{3a - 3b - a^2 + ab}{2a^2} \div \dfrac{a - b}{4a}$

17. $\dfrac{x^2}{x^2 - 1} \cdot \dfrac{x^2 + 3x + 2}{x^2 - x} \div \dfrac{x}{1 - 2x + x^2}$

18. $\dfrac{3n^2 - 12m^2}{m + n} \cdot \dfrac{m}{2m - n} \div \dfrac{m^2 + mn}{n + 2m}$

19. $\dfrac{1}{2ax} \cdot \dfrac{x^2 - ax}{a^2x^2 + ax} \cdot \dfrac{4x^2}{a + x} \div \dfrac{a^2 - x^2}{1 + ax}$

20. $\dfrac{2x + 2y}{3x - 27y} \cdot \dfrac{7x + 7y}{x - y} \div \dfrac{28x^2 - 28y^2}{27y - 3x}$

21. $\dfrac{m^4 - n^4}{m^2 + mn} \cdot \dfrac{n^2}{m^2 + n^2} \quad \dfrac{mn}{3m - 3n}$

22. $\dfrac{a^2 - 2a + 15}{a^2 - 5a} \cdot \dfrac{4a}{2a^2 - 4a + 30}$

23. $\dfrac{x^2 + x - 2}{3x^2} \cdot \dfrac{x^2 - x - 2}{7x} \div \dfrac{x^4 - 5x^2 + 4}{63x^4}$

24. $\dfrac{3x}{2x - 2} \div \left(\dfrac{x^2}{x^2 - 1} \cdot \dfrac{x^2 + 5x + 4}{10} \right)$

25. $\left(\dfrac{a + b}{2ab - 2b^2} \div \dfrac{a^2 + 2ab + b^2}{ab} \right) \cdot \dfrac{2a + 2b}{a}$

26. $\dfrac{m - mn}{n} \cdot \dfrac{mn^2 + mn}{2} \div \left(\dfrac{1 - n^2}{m^2} \cdot \dfrac{2m}{n} \right)$

27. $\dfrac{a^2 - 3a + 2}{b^2 + b - 2} \cdot \dfrac{b^2 - 3b - 10}{a^2 + 5a - 6}$

28. $\dfrac{4x^2 - 4a^2}{3x^2 + 18x + 27} \cdot \dfrac{9 + 3x}{6a + 6x} \cdot \dfrac{12}{ax - a^2}$

Example: $\left(x - \dfrac{y^2}{x}\right) \cdot \left(\dfrac{x}{y} + \dfrac{y}{x}\right) \cdot \dfrac{xy}{x^4 - y^4}$

Add as necessary to get each factor in simplest fraction form.

$$\frac{x^2 - y^2}{x} \cdot \frac{x^2 + y^2}{xy} \cdot \frac{xy}{x^4 - y^4} =$$

Multiply numerators and denominators and factor.

$$\frac{(x + y)(x - y)(x^2 + y^2)x \cdot y}{x \cdot x \cdot y(x^2 + y^2)(x + y)(x - y)} =$$

Divide out common factors.

$$\frac{1}{x}$$

Example: $\left(3x + 5 - \dfrac{2}{x}\right) \div \left(x - \dfrac{4}{x}\right)$

Add as necessary to get dividend and divisor in simple fraction form.

$$\frac{3x^2 + 5x - 2}{x} \div \frac{x^2 - 4}{x} =$$

Now invert the divisor and multiply the fractions.

$$\frac{3x^2 + 5x - 2}{x} \cdot \frac{x}{x^2 - 4} =$$

$$\frac{(3x - 1)(x + 2)}{x} \cdot \frac{x}{(x + 2)(x - 2)} = \frac{3x - 1}{x - 2}$$

29. $\left(1 - \dfrac{b^2}{a^2}\right)\left(\dfrac{a}{a + b}\right)\left(1 - \dfrac{b}{a}\right)$

30. $\left[1 + \dfrac{2}{a(a - 3)}\right]\left[1 - \dfrac{1}{a - 2}\right]$

31. $\left(a + \dfrac{1}{b}\right) \div \left(b + \dfrac{1}{a}\right)$

32. $\left(x - 2 + \dfrac{1}{x}\right) \div \left(\dfrac{1 - x^2}{3x^2 + 3x}\right)$

33. $\dfrac{4a^4 - 4x^4}{a} \cdot \dfrac{a - x}{a^4 - 2a^2x^2 + x^4} \cdot \dfrac{a^2 + ax}{x^2 + a^2}$

34. $\left(\dfrac{a^2}{a - b} - a - b\right)\left(\dfrac{b - a}{a^2b^2}\right)\left(b - \dfrac{b^2}{b - a} + a\right)$

35. $\left(a + \dfrac{1}{a+1} - 1\right)\left(a + \dfrac{1}{a} + 2\right) \div \left(a - \dfrac{1}{a}\right)$

36. $\left(m - n - \dfrac{3n^2}{2m - n}\right)\left(\dfrac{n^2 - 4m^2}{2n - m}\right) \div \left(1 + \dfrac{2n}{2m - n}\right)$

37. $\left(\dfrac{x^4 - 1}{x} \cdot \dfrac{1}{1 - 2x}\right) \div \left(\dfrac{1 + x^2}{2x^2 + x} \cdot \dfrac{1 + 2x + x^2}{2x - 1}\right)$

38. $\dfrac{2x^2 - xy - 6y^2}{4x^2 - 4y^2} \cdot \dfrac{x^2 + xy - 2y^2}{x^2 - 4y^2} \cdot \dfrac{x}{x + y}$

39. $\left(\dfrac{m + n}{m - n} - \dfrac{m - n}{m + n}\right)\left(\dfrac{m + n}{n} - \dfrac{m + n}{m}\right)\left(\dfrac{m - n}{m + n} + 1\right)$

40. $\left(\dfrac{a - 3}{a - 2} - \dfrac{a - 1}{a - 3}\right)\left(\dfrac{1}{2 - a} + 1\right)\left(\dfrac{a^2 - 4a + 4}{3a - 7}\right)$

Exercise 29. Complex Fractions

In each problem assume that the domain of the variables excludes division by zero.

Oral

Simplify:

1. $\dfrac{1}{\frac{3}{2}}$ 2. $\dfrac{\frac{1}{3}}{\frac{1}{4}}$ 3. $\dfrac{\frac{2}{5}}{\frac{1}{3}}$ 4. $\dfrac{\frac{3}{7}}{\frac{3}{4}}$

5. $\dfrac{\frac{1}{x}}{\frac{a}{x}}$ 6. $\dfrac{\frac{2}{a}}{\frac{3}{a}}$ 7. $\dfrac{\frac{2a}{3}}{\frac{1}{5}}$

8. $\dfrac{1 + \frac{1}{a}}{\frac{1}{a}}$ 9. $\dfrac{3}{\frac{1}{a} + \frac{1}{2}}$ 10. $\dfrac{2 - \frac{3}{x}}{\frac{2}{x}}$

Written

Simplify:

Example: $\dfrac{\dfrac{a}{b} - \dfrac{b}{a}}{\dfrac{1}{b} - \dfrac{1}{a}}$

Multiply numerator and denominator of the complex fraction by the least common denominator of all the fractions that appear.

$$\frac{\dfrac{a}{b} - \dfrac{b}{a}}{\dfrac{1}{b} - \dfrac{1}{a}} = \frac{a^2 - b^2}{a - b} = a + b$$

Alternatively, treat it as a division problem. Follow the pattern of the example in Exercise 28.

$$\frac{\dfrac{a}{b} - \dfrac{b}{a}}{\dfrac{1}{b} - \dfrac{1}{a}} = \left(\frac{a}{b} - \frac{b}{a}\right) \div \left(\frac{1}{b} - \frac{1}{a}\right) =$$

$$\frac{a^2 - b^2}{ab} \div \frac{a - b}{ab} = \frac{(a + b)(a - b)}{ab} \cdot \frac{ab}{a - b} = a + b$$

1. $\dfrac{\dfrac{1}{a}}{\dfrac{2}{3a}}$ **2.** $\dfrac{\dfrac{1}{a + 1}}{\dfrac{1}{a}}$ **3.** $\dfrac{\dfrac{1}{2} + \dfrac{1}{a}}{\dfrac{1}{2a}}$

4. $\dfrac{\dfrac{1}{a} - \dfrac{1}{b}}{\dfrac{1}{ab}}$ **5.** $\dfrac{\dfrac{x}{2} - \dfrac{y}{3}}{\dfrac{1}{4}}$ **6.** $\dfrac{x}{\dfrac{1}{a} + \dfrac{2}{x}}$

7. $\dfrac{\frac{1}{2}}{\frac{1}{2} + \frac{1}{3}}$ **8.** $\dfrac{\frac{1}{3} + \frac{1}{4}}{\frac{1}{2} + \frac{1}{6}}$ **9.** $\dfrac{\dfrac{1}{x} + \dfrac{1}{a}}{\dfrac{1}{a} + \dfrac{2}{x}}$

10. $\dfrac{\dfrac{1}{x} - \dfrac{1}{a}}{\dfrac{1}{x} + \dfrac{1}{a}}$ **11.** $\dfrac{a + \dfrac{a}{b}}{-b + \dfrac{1}{b}}$ **12.** $\dfrac{\dfrac{x}{y} - \dfrac{y}{x}}{\dfrac{1}{x} - \dfrac{1}{y}}$

$$13.\ \dfrac{\dfrac{a+b}{a-b}-\dfrac{a-b}{a+b}}{\dfrac{b}{a-b}-\dfrac{a}{a+b}}$$

$$14.\ 1+\dfrac{x}{1+x+\dfrac{2x^2}{1-x}}$$

$$15.\ 1-\dfrac{1}{1-\dfrac{1}{1-x}}$$

$$16.\ \dfrac{\left(x-2-\dfrac{3}{x}\right)\left(2-\dfrac{x+2}{x+1}\right)}{\dfrac{x^2-8x+15}{3x-2}}$$

Exercise 30. Review Exercises on Fractions

Written

All variables have domains which exclude division by zero.
Simplify:

1. $\dfrac{a+b}{a^2-b^2}$

2. $\dfrac{a^2-b^2}{ab}-\dfrac{a-b}{a}-\dfrac{a+b}{b}$

3. $\dfrac{c}{c-d}+\dfrac{2cd}{d^2-c^2}-\dfrac{2c}{c+d}$

4. $\dfrac{c-1-\dfrac{5}{c+3}}{3-\dfrac{2c+2}{c+2}}$

5. $\dfrac{y^2-y-1}{y-1}\cdot\dfrac{y^2-1}{y}\div\left(y-\dfrac{1}{y-1}\right)$

6. $\dfrac{3a+1}{3a-1}+\dfrac{a-4}{5-2a}-\dfrac{3a^2+3a-10}{6a^2-17a+5}$

7. $\dfrac{2m}{3+2m}-\dfrac{1-m}{2-m}+\dfrac{7}{2m^2-m-6}$

8. $\dfrac{\dfrac{m^2+n^2}{n}-2m}{\dfrac{1}{m}-\dfrac{1}{n}}$

9. $\dfrac{9x^2+12ax+4a^2}{x^4-a^4}\cdot\dfrac{x^2+ax}{3x+2a}\div\left(4-\dfrac{x-6a}{x-a}\right)$

10. $\dfrac{2x-1}{x^2-7x+12}-\dfrac{3x+2}{2x+x^2-15}+\dfrac{x+1}{x^2+x-20}$

11. $\dfrac{\dfrac{x+y}{x-y}-\dfrac{x-y}{x+y}}{1-\dfrac{x^2+y^2}{(x+y)^2}}$

12. $\dfrac{2x+\dfrac{x}{x-2}}{2x-\dfrac{x}{x-2}}$

69

13. $\dfrac{-\dfrac{a-b}{a+b} + \dfrac{a+b}{a-b}}{\dfrac{b}{a-b} - \dfrac{a}{a+b}}$

14. $\dfrac{\dfrac{a+x}{a} \cdot \dfrac{x}{a-x}}{\dfrac{ax+a^2}{x-a}}$

15. $\dfrac{\dfrac{x^2-3x-10}{x^2+x}}{\dfrac{x^2+2x}{1+x} \cdot \dfrac{x-5}{x^3}}$

16. $\dfrac{\dfrac{2m+n}{m+n} - 1}{1 - \dfrac{n}{m+n}}$

17. $\dfrac{\dfrac{a+b}{a} - \dfrac{a-b}{b} - \dfrac{2a}{b}}{-\dfrac{b}{a} + \dfrac{2a-b}{b}}$

18. $\dfrac{\dfrac{2x^2-8y^2}{3x-9y} \cdot \dfrac{3y-x}{4}}{\dfrac{2y-x}{6x} \cdot \dfrac{2x+4y}{y}}$

19. $\dfrac{\dfrac{m+2n}{m^2-n^2}}{\dfrac{m+n}{m-n}} \cdot \dfrac{m^2+2mn+n^2}{2n^2+mn}$

20. $\dfrac{\dfrac{a^2-4b^2}{a^2}}{\dfrac{2b+a}{a}} + \dfrac{\dfrac{b^2-9a^2}{b^2}}{\dfrac{3a-b}{b}}$

LINEAR EQUATIONS

Exercise 31. One Variable
For simpler equations in one variable see Exercise 12, page 26.

Written

Solve each of the following on the domain of rational numbers.

Example: $\dfrac{x+3}{4} - \dfrac{x+4}{6} = \dfrac{x}{2} - 2$

Multiply both sides by the L.C.D. 12 and indicate the multiplications.

$$3(x+3) - 2(x+4) = 6x - 24$$

$$3x + 9 - 2x - 8 = 6x - 24$$

$$-5x = -25$$

Ans. $x = 5$

1. $\dfrac{x}{5} + \dfrac{x}{2} = 7$

2. $\dfrac{a}{3} - 2a = -10$

3. $\dfrac{m}{6} = \dfrac{m}{2} - \dfrac{1}{3}$

4. $\dfrac{x}{4} - x = \dfrac{x}{3} + \dfrac{1}{2}$

5. $\dfrac{x}{7} - \dfrac{x}{3} = \dfrac{2}{3}$

6. $\dfrac{b}{15} - \dfrac{2b}{5} + 3 = 0$

7. $\dfrac{a}{11} + \dfrac{3a}{2} = \dfrac{7}{4}$

8. $\dfrac{x+1}{6} - \dfrac{x}{8} = -\dfrac{3}{4}$

9. $\dfrac{x+2}{12} = \dfrac{x-1}{9}$

10. $\dfrac{2m-1}{3} - \dfrac{m}{2} = \dfrac{m-2}{5}$

11. $2a + 3 - \dfrac{a-1}{6} - \dfrac{a}{4} = 0$

12. $\dfrac{7x-4}{3} - x + \dfrac{x}{5} = 4 - \dfrac{x}{3}$

13. $\dfrac{4x}{9} - 3\tfrac{1}{3} = \dfrac{x-7}{6}$

14. $\dfrac{2p-7}{13} - \dfrac{p}{2} - 1\tfrac{3}{13} = 0$

15. $\dfrac{9a-3}{2} = -\dfrac{3a-6}{9} - \dfrac{13}{6}$

Determine the solution set in problems 16–31, if the domain of the variables is the set $D = \{-\frac{1}{2}, -2, \frac{1}{10}, \frac{5}{8}, 2, 4.1, 6, 14, 46.5\}$

Example: $\frac{3}{4}(x - 1) = \frac{1}{3}(x - 2)$

Remove the parentheses. $\qquad \frac{3x}{4} - \frac{3}{4} = \frac{x}{3} - \frac{2}{3}$

Clear of fractions. $\qquad\qquad 9x - 9 = 4x - 8$

$$5x = 1$$

$$x = \frac{1}{5}$$

Ans. Since $\frac{1}{5} \notin D$, the solution set is empty.

16. $\dfrac{2}{x} - \dfrac{5}{3x} = \dfrac{1}{3}$

17. $\dfrac{5}{3x - 2} - \dfrac{1}{8} = 0$

18. $\dfrac{2}{x - 1} - \dfrac{3}{x} = \dfrac{7}{2x}$

19. $\dfrac{2x + 3}{5x} - \dfrac{7}{x} + 4 = \dfrac{2}{3x}$

20. $\dfrac{2}{3x - 1} - \dfrac{5}{x - 4} = 0$

21. $2(x - 3) = \dfrac{x}{2} - 3(x - 1)$

22. $\dfrac{1}{3}(2x - 1) + \dfrac{x + 1}{2} = \dfrac{1}{6}(x - 2)$

23. $\dfrac{2}{7}(2a - 4) = \dfrac{3}{2}(a - 1) - \dfrac{a}{2}$

24. $2\frac{1}{3}(m - 7) - \dfrac{3}{2}(2m - 1) = \dfrac{5}{6}(3m + 2)$

25. $\dfrac{4(x - 1)}{5} + \dfrac{3(x + 2)}{10} = 2 - \dfrac{x - 2}{2}$

26. $\dfrac{-2(a + 1)}{4} + \dfrac{3}{2}(a - 5) = \dfrac{1}{5} - a$

27. $3 - \left(\dfrac{x}{6} - \dfrac{x + 1}{4} + x\right) = 1 - \left(2x - \dfrac{1}{12}\right)$

28. $\dfrac{x + 2}{\frac{2}{3}} + \dfrac{3(x - 1)}{5} = \dfrac{x}{\frac{2}{5}}$

29. $\dfrac{2\frac{1}{4}(x + 1)}{3} - \dfrac{3x - 6}{4} - \dfrac{x - 6}{18} = 0$

30. $2\left[\dfrac{1}{x} + \dfrac{5}{4x} - \left(3 - \dfrac{1}{3x}\right)\right] = \dfrac{1}{2}$

31. $\dfrac{1}{2}[x - \dfrac{1}{3}(4 - x)] = \dfrac{3}{4}(2x - 1)$

The domain of the variables in problems 32–60 consists of all the real numbers except those which would produce division by zero.

Specify the restriction, if any, and solve:

Example: $\dfrac{5}{x + 2} - \dfrac{2}{x^2 - 4} - \dfrac{2}{x - 2} = 0$

L.C.D. $= (x + 2)(x - 2)$ and $x \neq 2, -2$.

$$5(x - 2) - 2 - 2(x + 2) = 0$$
$$5x - 10 - 2 - 2x - 4 = 0$$
$$3x = 6$$
$$x = 2$$

Ans. Since 2 is not in the domain, there is no solution.

32. $\dfrac{\frac{3}{4}(2a - 1)}{2} + \dfrac{\frac{1}{2}(1 - 3a)}{3} = \dfrac{7}{12}$

33. $(x - \frac{1}{2})(x - \frac{3}{2}) = x(x - \frac{2}{3})$

34. $\dfrac{3x + 2}{x - 1} = \dfrac{3x + 4}{x + 1}$

35. $\dfrac{x^2 - 9}{x + 3} = 2 - x$

36. $\dfrac{x^2 + 2x + 1}{2(x + 1)} = \dfrac{x^2 - 1}{3(x - 1)}$

37. $\dfrac{3}{x} = \dfrac{2x + 3}{x - 1} - 2$

38. $\dfrac{3a - 2}{a - 2} - 2 = 1 + \dfrac{4}{a - 2}$

39. $\dfrac{x + 1}{x} - \dfrac{x - 2}{x - 1} = \dfrac{3x}{x^2 - x}$

40. $\dfrac{2}{a + 2} - \dfrac{5}{a - 2} = \dfrac{1}{a^2 - 4}$

41. $\dfrac{4}{x^2 - x - 6} + \dfrac{3}{x^2 - 9} = \dfrac{1}{x^2 + 5x + 6}$

42. $\dfrac{x - 2}{2x - 1} - \dfrac{x}{2x + 1} = \dfrac{x + 6}{8x^2 - 2}$

43. $\dfrac{a^2}{1 - a^2} + \dfrac{a}{a - 1} + \dfrac{3}{a + 1} = 0$

44. $\dfrac{1}{1 - m} - \dfrac{m}{m^2 - 2m + 1} = -\dfrac{2}{m + 1}$

45. $\dfrac{2x + 3}{3x - 2} - \dfrac{x - 3}{x - 1} = \dfrac{9 - x^2}{3x^2 - 5x + 2}$

46. $\dfrac{x}{4} - \left(\dfrac{3x}{2x - 2} + \dfrac{x}{6(x - 1)} + \dfrac{x}{4} \right) = \dfrac{1}{1 - x}$

47. $\dfrac{3}{1 - 3x} + \dfrac{5}{2 - x} = -\dfrac{18x + 11}{3x^2 - 7x + 2}$

48. $\dfrac{x + 2}{x^2 - 3x} + \dfrac{2}{9 - x^2} - \dfrac{x - 3}{x^2 + 3x} = 0$

73

49. $\dfrac{x}{x^2 + 2x - 3} - \dfrac{3}{x^2 - 2x + 1} = \dfrac{1}{x - 1}$

50. $\dfrac{6a}{9a^2 - 1} + \dfrac{2}{1 - 3a} - \dfrac{1}{3a^2 - 10a + 3} = 0$

51. $\dfrac{2x}{2x + 1} - \dfrac{1}{x - 2} = \dfrac{x - 1}{x + 2} + \dfrac{1}{2 - x}$

52. $\dfrac{a - 3}{a - 2} - \dfrac{a - 4}{a - 1} = \dfrac{a - 1}{a - 4} - \dfrac{a - 2}{a - 3}$

53. $\dfrac{2(x + 1)}{x^2 - x} + \dfrac{x - 2}{x^2 + x} + \dfrac{3x}{1 - x} = -3$

54. $\dfrac{3x + 1}{15} + \dfrac{2x}{9 - 3x} = \dfrac{2x - 3}{5} - \dfrac{x}{5}$

55. $\dfrac{x - 2}{2(x - 2)^3} - \dfrac{x}{4(x - 2)^2} + \dfrac{2}{8(x - 2)} = 0$

56. $\dfrac{x + 1}{6x^2 - 5x - 4} - \dfrac{x - 1}{8 - 2x - 3x^2} = \dfrac{x}{2x^2 + 5x + 2}$

57. $\dfrac{3x}{x + 2} + \dfrac{6}{2x - x^2} + \dfrac{6}{x} = 3$

58. $\dfrac{\dfrac{3}{2}}{3x - 12} + \dfrac{\dfrac{2x}{3}}{4(x + 4)} + \dfrac{2}{9(4 - x)} = \dfrac{1}{6}$

59. $\dfrac{1}{x} - \left[\dfrac{x}{x - 1} - \left(\dfrac{3}{2x} - \dfrac{2}{x} \right) + \dfrac{x}{1 - x} \right] = 2$

60. $\dfrac{\dfrac{x}{2}}{x(x - 2)} + \dfrac{\dfrac{x}{3}}{x(x + 2)} - \dfrac{\dfrac{1}{4 - x^2}}{2} = 0$

In each of the following problems the variable is x and the other letters represent positive real number constants. The domain of the variable in each case consists of all the real numbers except those which lead to division by zero.

Solve for x:

Example: $\dfrac{x + a}{x - b} = \dfrac{x + c}{x - d}, \quad a - b + c - d \neq 0$

L.C.D. $= (x - b)(x - d)$ and $x \neq b, d$.

$$(x + a)(x - d) = (x - b)(x + c)$$

$$x^2 + ax - dx - ad = x^2 - bx + cx - bc$$

Collect all the terms with the unknown on one side.

$$ax - bx + cx - dx = ad - bc$$

Factor out the unknown.

$$(a - b + c - d)x = ad - bc$$

$$x = \frac{ad - bc}{a - b + c - d}$$

61. $5x - 14a = 26a - 3x$ **62.** $3(x + m) = 4x - 3m$

63. $7x - a = 2x + 2a - b$ **64.** $a - 3b = 3a - 2x + b$

65. $2px - 3p = 9p - px$ **66.** $2(3x - b) = b + 2(b + x)$

67. $4b - 2a - bx = 2(a + b) - 2bx$ **68.** $a(1 + bx) = 3a + b$

69. $a(x + b) = a(2x - b) - 3ax$ **70.** $2x(a + b) = 2(a + b) + 3(a + b)$

71. $3m(x + n) = m^2 + 2mn$

72. $2ax - bx - 4a^2 + 4ab - b^2 = 0,\ b \neq 2a$

73. $m^2x - mnx = m^2 - n^2,\ m \neq n$

74. $ax - a - b = bx + 1,\ a \neq b$

75. $2m(a + nx) = mnx - 2a(m + n)$

76. $(a + x)(a - x) + (x - a)^2 = 3a^2$

77. $(x - a)(x - b) = (x - a)^2 + b(a - b),\ a \neq b$

78. $a(b + x) + b(a - x) - 2b^2 = 0,\ a \neq b$

79. $(ax - b)^2 + (bx - a)^2 = x^2(a^2 + b^2)$

80. $(2m + 3x)^2 - (2n + 3x)^2 = 0,\ m \neq n$

81. $\dfrac{1}{ax + m} = \dfrac{2}{ax - m}$ **82.** $\dfrac{1}{b} - \dfrac{3}{a} = \dfrac{3}{ax} - \dfrac{1}{bx},\ a \neq 3b$

83. $\dfrac{b}{x(a + b)} + \dfrac{b}{x(a - b)} = \dfrac{a}{a^2 - b^2},\ a \neq b,\ a \neq -b$

84. $\dfrac{x + m}{m} - \dfrac{x + n}{n} = 2m^2 - 2n^2,\ m \neq n$

85. $2a - \dfrac{2ax - bx}{b + 2a} - b = 0,\ b \neq 2a$

86. $\dfrac{x + p}{x + q} = \dfrac{p + q}{p - q},\ p \neq q$

87. $\dfrac{x}{x + a} + \dfrac{2}{b - x} = \dfrac{x^2 - 2a}{(x - b)(x + a)},\ b \neq -2$

88. $\dfrac{x}{(x+m)^2} - \dfrac{1}{m^2-x^2} - \dfrac{1}{x+m} = 0,\ m \neq 1$

89. $\dfrac{x+a}{x-b} - \dfrac{x-a}{x+b} = \dfrac{a^2-b^2}{b^2-x^2},\ a \neq -b$

90. $\dfrac{m+n}{m-n+x} = \dfrac{m-n}{m+n+x}$

91. $\dfrac{1}{x+a} - \dfrac{2}{x-a} + \dfrac{1}{x+n} = 0,\ n \neq -3a$

92. $\dfrac{a-x}{a-3x} - 1 = \dfrac{-2x}{a+3x}$

93. $\dfrac{a+b+x}{a-x} + \dfrac{a+b}{x-a} = \dfrac{a+x}{a+b-x},\ a \neq -b$

94. $\dfrac{1}{b(a-x)} + \dfrac{1}{a(b-x)} = \dfrac{1}{b(x-a)},\ b \neq -2a$

95. $\dfrac{x}{2m+n} - \dfrac{2x}{n-2m} - 1 = \dfrac{4mx}{4m^2-n^2},\ n \neq 2m,\ n \neq -2m$

96. $\dfrac{x+3a}{x^2-2ax-3a^2} + \dfrac{2a}{x^2-9a^2} = \dfrac{1}{x-3a}$

97. $\dfrac{x}{mn} - \dfrac{1}{n(m+n)} = \dfrac{1}{m(m-n)}$

98. $\dfrac{x+2a}{x-2a} - \dfrac{x+a}{x-a} = \dfrac{x-a}{x+a} - \dfrac{x-2a}{x+2a}$

99. $\dfrac{\dfrac{mx}{m+n}}{n} - \dfrac{\dfrac{nx}{m+n}}{m} = \dfrac{\dfrac{m-n}{n}}{m},\ m \neq \pm n$

100. $\dfrac{1}{b}\left(\dfrac{a}{x} - \dfrac{b}{a}\right) - \dfrac{1}{a}\left(\dfrac{b}{x} - \dfrac{a}{b}\right) = \dfrac{\dfrac{b^2-a^2}{ax}}{b},\ a \neq b$

Exercise 32. Two Variables

Oral

Make the coefficients of x the same in each of the following pairs of equations. Then make the coefficients of y the same:

1. $x + 2y = 3$
$2x + y = 1$

2. $\dfrac{x}{2} + y = 7$
$x - \dfrac{y}{3} = -4$

3. $2x + 5y = 2$
$3x + y = 3$

76

4. $\dfrac{2}{x} + \dfrac{4}{y} = 3$

$\dfrac{3}{x} + \dfrac{2}{y} = 5$

5. $-x + y = -3$

$-2x - y = -2$

6. $ax + by = c$

$bx - ay = d$

7. $(a - b)x + cy = 2$

$ax + (c - d)y = 3$

8. $\dfrac{a}{x} + \dfrac{b}{y} = m$

$\dfrac{b}{x} + \dfrac{a}{y} = n$

9. $\dfrac{2ax}{3} - \dfrac{by}{3} = 1$

$ax - 2by = 2$

Solve the following for x by addition or subtraction:

10. $x + y = 4$

$-x + y = 2$

11. $2x + y = 6$

$x - y = 3$

12. $x - y = 0$

$2x + y = 6$

13. $x - 2y = 0$

$2x - 2y = 1$

14. $2x + 3y = 5$

$-3x + 3y = 10$

15. $\dfrac{1}{x} + \dfrac{1}{y} = 3$

$\dfrac{1}{x} - \dfrac{1}{y} = 2$

16. $\dfrac{1}{x} - \dfrac{1}{y} = 2$

$\dfrac{2}{x} + \dfrac{1}{y} = 1$

17. $ax + ay = 2$

$bx - ay = 1$

18. $\dfrac{x}{3} + y = 1$

$x - y = 2$

19. $2x - 3y = -1$

$x + 3y = 1$

Graphs of equations in two variables may be found in Exercises 66–70, pages 162-174.

Written

Solve for x and for y:

Examples: (a) $3x - 2y = 5$

$4x + 5y = -1$

Addition and Subtraction Method

Multiply the first equation by 5 and the second by 2.

$$15x - 10y = 25$$
$$8x + 10y = -2$$

Add

$$23x \qquad = 23$$
$$x = 1$$

Substitute in either equation to find y.

$$3 \cdot 1 - 2y = 5$$
$$-2y = 2$$
$$y = -1 \qquad \textbf{Ans.} \ (1, -1)$$

(b) $3x - 2y = 5$
   $x + y = 5$

Substitution Method.

Solve one equation for y (or x if it looks easier) and substitute in the other.

$$3x - 2y = 5$$
$$\underline{y = 5 - x}$$
$$3x - 2(5 - x) = 5$$
$$3x - 10 + 2x = 5$$
$$5x = 15$$
$$x = 3$$
$$\text{then } y = 5 - 3$$
$$y = 2 \qquad \textbf{Ans.} \ (3, 2)$$

Use whichever method is easier in the particular problem you are working on.

1. $x + 3y = 6$
    $2x - y = 5$

2. $5x - 3y = 14$
    $2x - y = 6$

3. $-x + 4y = 7$
    $3x - 2y = 9$

4. $2x - 7y = 3$
    $-5x + 3y = 13$

5. $-6x - 7y = -3$
    $4x - 3y = 25$

6. $7x - 3y = -1$
    $6x + 4y = 9$

7. $12x - 6y = -2$
    $-9x - 7y = -10$

8. $-6x + 10y = 3$
    $18x - 10y = 1$

9. $8x = 3y$
    $5x - 2y = -1$

10. $3x - 5y = -33$
    $y = 13 - 9x$

11. $x - 2y = 4$
    $-3x + 5y = 9$

12. $10x + y - 6 = 0$
    $15x - 2y + 5 = 0$

13. $2y - 3x = -19$
    $4x - 11y = 17$

14. $8x = 6y - 3$
    $y = 3x - 2$

15. $3x - 6 = 4y$
    $12y - 15x = -32$

16. $x = 2y - 2$
    $6x = 9y - 11$

17. $12 = 2x - 3y$
    $7x = 5y - 2$

18. $2x = 35$
    $4x - 15y = -5$

19. $7x - 9y = 0$
    $-4x - 71 = 5y$

20. $-3y = 13$
    $5y + 12x = -15$

21. $2x - 4y + 9 = -13$
    $3y - 5x = 3 + x$

22. $3y - 11 + 9x = 4y + 10$
    $5x + 2y = 16x + 21$

23. $2x - 15 - 3y = 11y - 5$
    $21y - x = -3$

24. $2x = 4(2y + 2)$
$3(x - 3y) + 2 = 17$

25. $4(x - y) = 3(1 - 2x) - y$
$1 = -3(5x + 4y)$

26. $5(3x - y) = 2 - (y - x)$
$9(2x - 1) = y - 3x$

27. $2(2x - y - 11) = 1 - y$
$3(3x + y) - 17 = 2(4x + y)$

28. $\dfrac{x}{6} + \dfrac{y}{2} = -\dfrac{1}{2}$

$\dfrac{x}{3} - 3y = 7$

Solve for x and y:

29. $\dfrac{3x}{2} - \dfrac{y}{8} = -1$

$4x + \dfrac{3y}{4} = -7$

30. $\dfrac{x}{6} + \dfrac{y}{3} = 3$

$\dfrac{2x}{3} - \dfrac{y}{2} = 1$

31. $\dfrac{x}{5} - \dfrac{y}{5} = \dfrac{1}{30}$

$\dfrac{x}{2} - \dfrac{2y}{3} = \dfrac{1}{36}$

32. $\dfrac{x}{2} = \dfrac{y}{14}$

$\dfrac{x}{3} = \dfrac{7}{3} - \dfrac{2y}{7}$

33. $\dfrac{x}{6} - \dfrac{y}{4} = 4 - \dfrac{x}{3} - \dfrac{y}{2}$

$x - \dfrac{x}{6} = \dfrac{11}{2} - \dfrac{y}{8}$

34. $-\dfrac{1}{2}\left(x + \dfrac{y}{2}\right) = \dfrac{y}{3} + 2(x + 2)$

$\tfrac{2}{15}(x + y) = -\tfrac{1}{5}(y - 2) + 1 - \dfrac{x}{15}$

Solve for x and y noting any restrictions on the domains.

35. $\dfrac{2x + 5y}{6} + \dfrac{3x - 8y}{5} = 5$

$\dfrac{3y - x}{3} + \dfrac{x + 4y}{5} = 2\tfrac{2}{3}$

36. $\dfrac{2x + 5y + 11}{4} + 3 = \dfrac{y + 6x + 7}{7}$

$\tfrac{1}{5}(7x + 6y) - \tfrac{1}{15}(2y - x) = \tfrac{8}{3}$

37. $\dfrac{3x + y}{3x - 2y} = 2$

$(x - 2)(y + 2) = xy$

38. $\dfrac{y}{x} + \dfrac{x}{2} = \dfrac{x - 4}{2}$

$y(x - 5) = (x - 6)(y + 1)$

Example: $\dfrac{6}{x} - \dfrac{3}{y} = 5$

$$\dfrac{5}{x} + \dfrac{2}{3y} = 1$$

Solve for $1/x$ and $1/y$ first

$$6\left(\dfrac{1}{x}\right) - 3\left(\dfrac{1}{y}\right) = 5$$

$$15\left(\dfrac{1}{x}\right) + 2\left(\dfrac{1}{y}\right) = 3$$

$$\overline{\phantom{15\left(\dfrac{1}{x}\right) + 2\left(\dfrac{1}{y}\right) = 3}}$$

$$30\left(\dfrac{1}{x}\right) - 15\left(\dfrac{1}{y}\right) = 25$$

$$30\left(\dfrac{1}{x}\right) + 4\left(\dfrac{1}{y}\right) = 6$$

$$\overline{\phantom{30\left(\dfrac{1}{x}\right) + 4\left(\dfrac{1}{y}\right) = 6}}$$

$$-19\left(\dfrac{1}{y}\right) = 19$$

$$\dfrac{1}{y} = -1$$

$$y = -1$$

$$6\left(\dfrac{1}{x}\right) + 3 = 5$$

$$6\left(\dfrac{1}{x}\right) = 2$$

$$\dfrac{1}{x} = \dfrac{1}{3}$$

$$x = 3 \qquad \textbf{Ans.} \ (3, -1)$$

39. $\dfrac{2}{x} + \dfrac{1}{y} = 7$

$\dfrac{3}{x} + \dfrac{2}{y} = 12$

41. $\dfrac{6}{x} = -\dfrac{1}{y}$

$\dfrac{8}{x} + \dfrac{3}{y} = 5$

40. $\dfrac{5}{x} - \dfrac{10}{y} = 3$

$\dfrac{3}{x} - \dfrac{25}{y} = -2$

42. $\dfrac{5}{x} - \dfrac{3}{y} = \dfrac{1}{12}$

$\dfrac{3}{x} + \dfrac{2}{y} = 1$

43. $\dfrac{3}{x} - \dfrac{4}{y} - 2 = 0$

$-\dfrac{1}{x} + \dfrac{3}{y} + 9 = 0$

44. $\dfrac{2}{x} - 1 = -\dfrac{7}{y}$

$\dfrac{1}{x} + \dfrac{8}{y} + \dfrac{2}{x} = 9$

45. $\dfrac{1}{3x} + \dfrac{1}{2y} = 3$

$\dfrac{1}{2x} + \dfrac{1}{4y} = 2\tfrac{1}{2}$

46. $\dfrac{2}{x} - \dfrac{5}{6y} = \dfrac{19}{6}$

$\dfrac{3}{2x} + \dfrac{4}{y} = 7$

47. $\dfrac{3}{5x} + \dfrac{1}{4y} = \dfrac{13}{4}$

$\dfrac{2}{10x} - \dfrac{5}{2y} = -\dfrac{3}{2}$

48. $\dfrac{7}{x} - \dfrac{18}{y} = \dfrac{1}{3}$

$\dfrac{14}{x} + \dfrac{9}{y} = \dfrac{7}{3}$

49. $\dfrac{3}{x} - \dfrac{10}{y} = 1$

$\dfrac{4}{x} + \dfrac{5}{y} = 5$

50. $\dfrac{7}{x} - \dfrac{12}{y} = 4$

$\dfrac{6}{x} - \dfrac{10}{y} = \dfrac{7}{2}$

In the following problems the variables are x and y. All other letters represent positive real number constants.

Solve for x and for y:

Example: $x + y = 3a$

$bx + ay = 2a^2 + b^2,\ a \neq b$

Use the method of addition and subtraction. Multiply the first equation by a and subtract to find x.

$$ax + ay = 3a^2$$
$$bx + ay = 2a^2 + b^2$$
$$\overline{ax - bx = a^2 - b^2}$$

$$(a - b)x = (a + b)(a - b)$$
$$x = a + b \quad \text{since } a - b \neq 0$$
$$y = 3a - x = 3a - (a + b)$$
$$= 2a - b$$

Ans. $x = a + b$

$y = 2a - b$

51. $2x - y = 5m$

$-4x - 3y = 5m$

52. $5x + 3y = 7a$

$3x - 2y = -\dfrac{3a}{2}$

53. $x - y = a - 2b$
    $3x + 2y = 4b + 3a$

54. $x - \dfrac{y}{2} = \dfrac{m + n}{2}$
    $6x + 2y = 3m - 2n$

55. $x + y = 2a$
    $5x - 3y = 2(a + 4b)$

56. $bx = ay, a \neq b$
    $2x - 2y = 3(a - b)$

57. $ax - 2by = -1$
    $3ax + 4by = 7$

58. $mx + 4ny = -a$
    $3mx - 2ny = 4a$

59. $bx + ay = 1, a^2 \neq b^2,$
    $ax + by = -1$

60. $mx - y = a, m \neq n$
    $nx + y = 2a$

61. $ax + by = b, a^2 \neq b^2$
    $bx + ay = -a$

62. $ax - y = 3, a \neq \dfrac{1}{b}$
    $x - by = 2$

63. $mx + ny = 2, m^2 \neq n^2$
    $nx + my = -2$

64. $2ax + by = 1, b^2 \neq 4a^2$
    $bx + 2ay = 1$

65. $ax + by = c, an \neq bm$
    $mx + ny = d$

66. $x = 2a - y, a \neq -1$
    $ay = x + a + 3$

67. $2(x - 3m) = 3(n + 1) - y$
    $x - 3(m - n) = y$

68. $ax = 2b(y + 1), a \neq b$
    $2(y + b) = x + 2(a - 1)$

69. $x(m + n) - y(m - n) = 0$
    $x = y - 2n$

70. $x(a + b) + yb = a + b$
    $xb - y(a + b) = b$

71. $\dfrac{3m}{x} - \dfrac{2n}{y} = 0, 3m \neq 2n$
    $(2n + 1)x - (3m - 1)y = 3m + 2n$

72. $ax = by$
    $bx + ay = 1$

The following problems are to be done using a hand-held electronic calculator. The coefficients of equations coming from practical application usually are only approximate and expressed to a certain number of decimals. Thus all intermediate calculations in such problems should be rounded to the same accuracy as the numbers given in the problem. Because of this rounding, the answers will be only approximate.

Example: $3.42x - 2.65y = 7.32$
$4.13x + 1.73y = -6.42$

$14.12x - 10.94y = 30.23$
$14.12x + 5.92y = -25.38$

$-5.02y = 4.85$
$y = -0.97$

$3.42x - 2.57 = 7.32$
$3.42x = 9.89$
$x = 2.89$ **Ans.** $(2.89, -0.97)$

73. $1.6x + 3.7y = 4.5$
$-3.6x + 4.3y = 8.6$

74. $6.72x - 4.53y = 6.10$
$2.35x + 1.63y = 7.83$

75. $56x - 35y = 64$
$27x + 19y = 103$

76. $19.3x - 14.7y = 63$
$26.4x + 13.2y = 75$

77. $0.17x - 0.25y = 0.36$
$0.81x + 0.89y = 2.04$

Exercise 33. Three Variables

Written

Solve:

Example: $4x - 2y + z = -2$ $\quad$ (1)

$3x - y - 2z = 11$ $\quad$ (2)

$6x - y + 3z = -3$ $\quad$ (3)

To eliminate z, multiply (1) by 2 and add to (2), then multiply (1) by -3 and add to (3).

$8x - 4y + 2z = -4$ $\qquad\qquad$ $-12x + 6y - 3z = 6$

$3x - y - 2z = 11$ $\qquad\qquad$ $6x - y + 3z = -3$

$11x - 5y \quad = 7$ $\quad$ (4) $\qquad$ $-6x + 5y \quad = 3$ $\quad$ (5)

Solving (4) and (5) as in Exercise **32**, we obtain $x = 2$ and $y = 3$.

Substituting these values into (1) we obtain $z = -4$.

Ans. $x = 2$, $y = 3$, $z = 4$

1. $\quad x + y + z = 2$
$2x - y + z = 5$
$x + 2y + 3z = 5$

2. $\quad 6x - 4y - 7z = 17$
$9x - 7y - 16z = 29$
$10x - 5y - 3z = 23$

3. $4x - 5y - 6z = 22$
$x - y + z = -6$
$9x \quad\quad + z = 22$

4. $4x - 3y = 1$
$4y - 3z = -15$
$4z - 3x = 10$

5. $3x + y - z = 14$
$x + 3y - z = 16$
$x + y - 3z = -10$

6. $\quad x + 2y + z = 7$
$2x + y + 3z = 14$
$x + 3y - z = 2$

7. $\quad 2x + 4y - z + 2 = 0$
$18x - 8y + 4z + 25 = 0$
$10x + 4y - 9z + 30 = 0$

8. $y = 3z - 2x$
$z = 1 + 2x - 2y$
$x = 3 + 2y - 4z$

9. $4x - 5y + 3z = 18$
$5x - 3y - 4z = 2$
$3x + 4y - 5z = 32$

10. $\quad x + 3y = 4 - 2z$
$3x + 4z = 10 - 6y$
$9y + 8z = 15 - 4x$

Exercise 34. Ratio, Proportion and Variation

Oral

Express the following in simplest reduced form:

1. $6 : 10$

2. $14 : -7$

3. $3a : 15a$

4. $\frac{3}{5} : \frac{4}{5}$

5. $\frac{7}{10} : \frac{2}{3}$

6. $5x : 7x$

Express the following proportions as equations without fractions.

7. $\dfrac{a}{b} = \dfrac{d}{c}$

8. $3 : a = 5 : b$

9. $x : y = a : b$

10. $5 : 3 = 2 : x$

11. $\dfrac{2}{x} = \dfrac{9}{y}$

Solve the following proportions for x:

12. $x : 3 = 1 : 3$

13. $x : 5 = 2 : 10$

14. $2x : 4 = 16 : 8$

15. $3x : 7 = 1 : 2$

16. $x : 2 = 3 : 9$

17. $5 : x = 4 : 3$

18. $\dfrac{3}{5} = \dfrac{x}{10}$

19. $\dfrac{2}{15} = \dfrac{1}{x}$

20. $\dfrac{4}{3x} = \dfrac{9}{2}$

Written

Determine the numbers necessary to make the following true proportions.

1. $\dfrac{6}{9} = \dfrac{2}{x}$

2. $\dfrac{5}{7} = \dfrac{x}{3}$

3. $\dfrac{2x}{3} = \dfrac{3}{4}$

4. $\dfrac{x-1}{3} = \dfrac{5}{6}$

5. $6 : 5 = x : 15$

6. $\dfrac{a}{9} = \dfrac{4}{a}$

7. Find a if 4 is the mean proportion between 8 and a.

8. The sum of the two numbers $4x$ and $5x$ is 36. Find the numbers.

Example: Three numbers whose sum is 80 are in the ratio $2 : 3 : 5$. Find the numbers.

Since $2x : 3x = 2 : 3$ and $3x : 5x = 3 : 5$, we let $2x$, $3x$ and $5x$ stand for the numbers.

$$2x + 3x + 5x = 80$$

$$10x = 80$$

$$x = 8 \quad \text{But this is not the answer.}$$

Ans. The three numbers are $2 \cdot 8 = 16$, $3 \cdot 8 = 24$, and $5 \cdot 8 = 40$

9. If two numbers are in the ratio of 3 : 4 and their sum is 21, find the numbers.

10. Two numbers are in the ratio of 5 : 2. The difference of the numbers is 36. Find the numbers.

11. The measures of the angles of a triangle are in the ratio of 1 : 2 : 3. The sum of the measures is 180. Find the measure of each angle.

12. Repeat problem 11 if the measures are in the ratio of 2 : 3 : 5.

13. Repeat problem 11 if the measures are in the ratio of 4 : 7 : 9.

14. If $3x = 5y$, write a proportion which will determine the ratio $x : y$.

15. If $5x = 7y$, determine the ratio $2x : y$.

16. Write the proportion which says that the ratio of the circumferences of two circles is the same as the ratio of their diameters. If the circumferences of the circles are 100 feet and 40 feet, write the ratio of their diameters in reduced form.

17. Mr. Williams, Mr. Thompson, and Mr. Mandeville furnished amounts of capital in the ratio 7 : 3 : 4. If the profits from the enterprise were $2800, how much should each man receive?

18. Two men share their wages according to the time they spend on a piece of work. If the first man works $\frac{2}{3}$ as long as the second, how should they divide wages of $68?

19. A profit of d dollars is divided between two men so that they receive amounts in the ratio $m : n$. How much does each man receive?

20. One number is 96 more than another and their ratio is 5 : 17. Find the numbers.

21. The ratio of two numbers is 9 : 16. Find the numbers if the larger number is 14 less than twice the smaller number.

22. The ratio of the sum of two numbers to their difference is 8 : 1. If twice the larger is 3 less than 3 times the smaller, find the numbers.

23. Find a number such that if 16 is added to it, the result is to the original number as 4 is to 3.

24. Find a number such that if 9 is added to it and subtracted from it, the results are in the ratio 3 : 2.

25. If 8 is added to and subtracted from a certain number, the results are in the ratio $5 : 7$. Find the number.

26. What number must be added to each of the numbers 3, 11, 37, and 79 to give four numbers which will be in proportion in that order?

27. Divide \$72 into two parts such that the less increased by \$8 is to the greater decreased by \$10 as 2 is to 5.

28. Two boys had sums of money in the ratio $3 : 2$. After each boy had spent \$4, the amounts that they had left were in the ratio $5 : 3$. How much money did each boy have at first?

Problems in direct and inverse variation can be set up either as equations involving a constant factor or in the form of a proportion.

Example: The distance a plane flies varies directly with the weight of fuel it carries. If it can fly 225 kilometers on 600 kilograms of fuel, how far can it fly on 800 kilograms?

(a) Let D be the number of kilometers the plane flies and f be the number of kilograms of fuel it carries.

Then $D = kf$ and $D = 225$ when $f = 600$

$$225 = k \cdot 600$$

$$k = \frac{225}{600} = \frac{3}{8}$$

So

$$D = \frac{3}{8} f \text{ and if } f = 800$$

$$D = \frac{3}{8} \cdot 800 = 300.$$

Ans. 300 kilometers.

(b) Let D_1 and D_2 be the number of kilometers in the two flights and f_1 and f_2 be the number of kilograms of fuel.

Then $\dfrac{D_1}{D_2} = \dfrac{f_1}{f_2}$ and $D_1 = 225$, D_2 is unknown

$$f_1 = 600 \qquad f_2 = 800$$

$$\frac{225}{D_2} = \frac{600}{800} = \frac{3}{4}$$

$$D_2 = \frac{4}{3} \cdot 225 = 300. \qquad\qquad \textbf{Ans.} \text{ 300 kilometers.}$$

86

Write equations and porportions to express the variations as stated in problems **29–41**.

29. (a) *y* varies directly as *x*

(b) *y* varies inversely with *x*

(c) *y* varies directly with x^2

(d) *y* varies inversely with $\sqrt{x}$

30. Pressure per square unit varies directly as the depth below the surface.

31. The volume of a sphere varies directly as the cube of the radius of the sphere.

32. The distance travelled varies directly with time.

33. The perimeter of an equilateral triangle is directly proportional to the altitude.

34. The time required to do homework varies directly with the number of problems assigned.

35. The area of a circle varies as the square of the radius.

36. The time it takes to go from Boston to New York varies inversely with the speed you travel.

37. The illumination provided by a lamp varies inversely with the square of the distance from the lamp.

38. The force of gravitation between the earth and a body on the surface varies directly with the mass of the body.

39. The force of gravitation between the sun and the earth varies inversely with the square of the distance between them.

40. The number of liters of gas a motor boat uses per hour varies as the square of the speed of the boat.

41. The length of a steel bar varies directly with the absolute temperature.

42. *y* varies directly with *x* and *y* is 14 when *x* is 4. Find *y* when *x* is 7.

43. The cost of oil varies directly with the price per liter. If 75 liters cost $11.25, how many liters may be bought for $20.00?

44. A car travelling at 60 km per hour takes 6 hours to go from Boston to New York. How long should it take if you travel at 80 km an hour?

45. A boy is sitting 3 meters from a lamp. How close to the lamp should he get to receive twice as much light on his book as he receives where he is sitting? (Hint: see **37**.)

46. A drive shaft supplies power to several machines by means of belts which run to pulleys on the machines. The drive shaft turns at constant speed, but the pulleys are of varying diameters which provide for different speeds for each machine. The speed of each machine varies inversely as the diameter of its pulley. If a machine with a 60 cm pulley turns at 1000 rpm, what is the speed of a machine whose pulley is 90 cm in diameter? How large a pulley would you need if you want to run a machine at 5000 rpm?

47. Boyle's Law says that if the temperature of a gas is kept constant, the volume of the gas varies inversely with the pressure. If, however, the pressure is kept constant, the volume varies directly with the temperature. If 2 cu. meters of gas exerts a pressure of 2.5 kilograms per square cm at 80°, what pressure will result if the gas is confined to 1 cu. meter and the temperature is still 80°? If the pressure remains at 2.5 kilograms but the gas is heated to 100° what will be the volume?

48. If A varies directly with B and inversely with C, write a formula for A in terms of B and C. Write a proportion.

49. Boyle's Law can be stated as the volume of a gas varies directly with the temperature and inversely with the pressure. Write a formula for V in terms of P and T. If 500 cc of gas has a pressure of 2 kg per sq. cm at 60°, what will be the temperature of the gas when the volume is 300cc and the pressure 4 kg/sq cm?

50. The pitch of a piano string varies directly with the tension on the string and inversely with the length of the string. If a tension of 60 kg on a string 1 meter long produces a pitch of 256 vibrations per second, find the tension required to produce a pitch of 512 vibrations per second on a string 80 cm long.

Exercise 35. Linear Inequalities
See Exercises 15. and 16. for simpler problems on inequalities.

Oral

Solve:

1. $x - 4 > 0$
2. $x + 2 < 0$
3. $4x > 7$
4. $3x \leq 24$
5. $2x - 3 > 3$
6. $6x < x - 20$
7. $5y - 21 < 2y$
8. $4x + 8 \geq 0$
9. $7 - y < 5$
10. $5h + 1 > h + 1$
11. $3z - 17 \geq 7$
12. $10m + 7 < -3$
13. $6 - 5y > 21$
14. $4x + 5 < 3x + 7$
15. $4x - 5 \leq x + 7$
16. $9 - 8n > 5n + 22$
17. $2x + 3 + 6x - 19 < 0$
18. $5z + 8 - z + 4 > 0$
19. $6m - 10 \leq 2m - 22$
20. $11y + 10 > 14y + 31$

Describe each solution set without using absolute value symbols.

21. $|x| > 0$ **22.** $|x| < 0$ **23.** $|x| \geq 2$

24. $|x| \leq 3$ **25.** $|x| > -1$ **26.** $|x| < -1$

27. $|x| > 10$ **28.** $|x| < 10$ **29.** $|x + 1| > 0$

30. $|x + 1| < 0$

In each of the following, a and b are any real numbers. Determine if the statement is always true (T), never true (F), or sometimes true (S).

31. $a > a$ **32.** $a \geq b$ **33.** $b \leq b$

34. $a - b = b - a$ **35.** $|a| \geq 0$ **36.** $a + b \geq b + a$

37. $a + 4 \geq a - 4$ **38.** $a > -a$ **39.** $a + b > b$

40. $a - 2 > a - 4$ **41.** $5 - a < 2 - a$ **42.** $2a - 3 > 2a - 1$

43. If $a > b > 0$, then $ab > b^2$.   **44.** If $a > b$, then $a + b > 2b$.

45. If $a > b$, then $a - 2 > b - 2$.   **46.** If $a < b < 0$, then $\dfrac{a}{b} < 0$.

47. If $a < b < 0$, then $\dfrac{a}{b} < 1$.   **48.** If $a > 0$ and $b < 0$, then $ab > 0$.

49. If $a > 0$ and $b < 0$, then $a - b > 0$.

50. If $a < b$, then $a^2 < b^2$.

51. If $a > b$, then $a - b > 0$.   **52.** If $a > b$, then $ab > b^2$.

Written

Determine the solution set for each of the following:

1. $5(5 - x) \leq x - 13$ **2.** $8(5 - 2y) > 4(y - 5)$

3. $2x + 26 - 3(10 - x) > 0$ **4.** $80 - 6(4x + 3) \leq 4x - 3(5x + 1)$

5. $(x - 5)(x - 3) \geq (x + 3)(x - 5) - 30$

6. $(x + 2)^2 - (x - 2)^2 < 4$

7. $(2x + 5)^2 - 4(x - 3)^2 < -55$

8. $(4x + 1)(3x + 7) - (3x - 5)(4x + 3) \geq 80$

9. $\dfrac{x}{2} + \dfrac{x}{3} \geq 10$ **10.** $\dfrac{2x}{3} - \dfrac{x}{2} \leq 5$

11. $\dfrac{3x}{5} - \dfrac{5x}{2} < 38$ **12.** $\dfrac{x}{4} + \dfrac{x - 3}{3} > 6$

13. $\dfrac{5x-3}{8} - \dfrac{3x-6}{5} \le 1$

14. $\dfrac{3x+2}{3} \ge 2 - \dfrac{2-3x}{5}$

15. $1 - \dfrac{2x-6}{4} > \dfrac{4x+13}{3}$

16. $\dfrac{x}{2} - \dfrac{5x}{6} < 2 - \dfrac{x-2}{9}$

17. $-3 < x + 2 < 3$

18. $2x - 1 > 3$ or $2x - 1 < -3$

19. $3x + \frac{1}{3} \ge 4$ or $3x + \frac{1}{3} \le -4$

20. $3 < 2x - 1 < 7$

21. $5 \ge 2x - 3 \ge 0$

22. $4 > 2 - 3x > -2$

Example: $5|2x - 1| < 4$

First divide by 5 to obtain $|2x - 1| < \frac{4}{5}$.
But $|2x - 1| = |2(x - \frac{1}{2})| = |2| \cdot |x - \frac{1}{2}| = 2|x - \frac{1}{2}|$.
Then divide by 2 to obtain $|x - \frac{1}{2}| < \frac{2}{5}$.
Now solve on the number line.

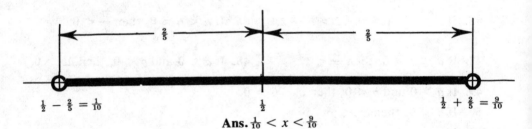

$\frac{1}{2} - \frac{2}{5} = \frac{1}{10}$ $\frac{1}{2}$ $\frac{1}{2} + \frac{2}{5} = \frac{9}{10}$

Ans. $\frac{1}{10} < x < \frac{9}{10}$

23. $|x + 2| > -1$

24. $4|2x - 1| > 3$

25. $|3x + \frac{1}{2}| \ge 4$

26. $2|3x - 1| \le 7$

27. $|2x + 1| < -2$

28. $2|3 - 2x| > 4$

29. $|x + 4| \ge 3$

30. $|x + 2| \ge 2$

In problems **31–35**, solve for x in the domain of positive real numbers.

31. $4 + \dfrac{1}{x} > \dfrac{x-1}{x}$

32. $\dfrac{x-1}{2} - \dfrac{1-x^2}{2x} > \dfrac{2x}{2} - \dfrac{1}{x}$

33. $\dfrac{2}{x+3} > \dfrac{3}{x+2}$

34. $\dfrac{x-1}{x} + \dfrac{x}{x+1} \ge 2$

35. $\dfrac{27x+11}{7} - \dfrac{33x-3}{9x} < \dfrac{27(2x-1)}{14}$

In problems **36–40** solve for x in the domain of negative real numbers.

Example: $\dfrac{1}{x} + 5 > \dfrac{8}{3x} + 4$

Since $x < 0$, the inequality will change when we multiply by the L.C.D. of $3x$.

$$3 + 15x < 8 + 12x$$

$$3x < 5$$

$$x < \tfrac{5}{3}$$

But since the domain is $x < 0$ the answer is the intersection of these two sets.

Ans. $x < 0$.

36. $\dfrac{1}{x} - 2 < \dfrac{4}{x} - \dfrac{1}{2}$

37. $\dfrac{x-1}{x} < 4 + \dfrac{1}{x}$

38. $\dfrac{x+1}{x} - 1 > \dfrac{3}{2x}$

39. $\dfrac{1-x}{3x} + 1 < \dfrac{7}{5x}$

40. $\dfrac{x-1}{2} - \dfrac{4-x^2}{2x} > \dfrac{2x}{2} - \dfrac{1}{x}$

WORD PROBLEMS

Exercise 36. Whole Numbers and Fractions

Oral

1. If two numbers are represented by x and y, express the sum of $\frac{1}{3}$ of the first number and $\frac{3}{5}$ of the second. Express as an equation the fact that $\frac{1}{2}$ of the second number exceeds 3 times the first number by 4.

2. Express a number that is 4 more than $\frac{1}{2}$ of $(x + 3)$.

3. If a number, n, is divided into two parts the smaller of which is m, express the other part. What is the difference between the parts? Express as an equation the fact that $\frac{1}{2}$ of the smaller part is 17 less than the larger part.

4. If the difference between two numbers is 6 and if the large number is x, express the smaller number. Express their sum.

5. Express a fraction whose numerator is x and whose denominator is 3 more than the numerator. Express the fraction if 5 is added to both the numerator and the demoninator.

6. $x + 3$ divided by x gives 1 for a quotient and 3 for a remainder, or $\dfrac{x + 3}{x} = 1 + \dfrac{3}{x}$. In the same manner express as an equation the fact

    that a divided by b gives 7 for a quotient and 2 for a remainder.

7. Express as an equation the fact that the sum of two numbers, a and b, divided by their difference gives 8 for a quotient and 5 for a remainder.

8. Express three consecutive numbers, the first of which is x. Express their sum. Express three consecutive numbers, the second of which is x. Express their sum.

9. Express three consecutive even numbers, the first of which is $2x$. Express three consecutive odd numbers, the first of which is $2x + 1$.

Written

Use either one variable or two variables to set up the equations you need.

Example: Find two numbers whose sum is 36 and whose ratio is $7:5$.

92

(a) Let $7x$ and $5x$ be the two numbers.

$$7x + 5x = 36$$
$$12x = 36$$
$$x = 3$$
$$7x = 21$$
$$5x = 15$$

Ans. The numbers are 21 and 15.

(b) Let x = the larger number
y = the smaller number

$$x + y = 36$$
$$\frac{x}{y} = \frac{7}{5}$$

$$y = 36 - x$$
$$5x = 7y$$

$$5x = 7(36 - x)$$
$$5x = 252 - 7x$$
$$12x = 252$$
$$x = 21$$
$$y = 15$$

Ans. The numbers are 21 and 15.

1. Separate 136 into two parts so that one part will be 24 more than the other part.

2. Separate 180 into two parts so that one part will be $3\frac{1}{2}$ times the other part.

3. Two men share a profit of $1200 so that one receives $800 less than 3 times as much as the other receives. How much does each man receive?

4. Divide 72 into three parts so that the first part is 3 less than the second part and the third part is $\frac{1}{2}$ of the second part.

5. A shipment of 930 bushels of potatoes is divided into three lots so that the second lot contains 20 bushels more than the first and the third lot contains $\frac{1}{2}$ as many bushels as the first two lots together. How many bushels are there in each lot?

6. Find two consecutive numbers whose sum is 47.

7. Find the fraction whose numerator is 35 less than its denominator and which, when reduced, will equal $\frac{2}{9}$.

8. Find two numbers whose difference is 8 and $\frac{1}{4}$ of whose sum is 16.

9. If a sum of money is increased by \$14 and the result is multiplied by $\frac{2}{3}$, the answer is \$60. Find the original sum.

10. Find two consecutive numbers whose sum is a.

11. What number divided by 13 gives 60 for a quotient and 6 for a remainder?

12. Find a number such that the difference between $\frac{1}{3}$ of it and $\frac{1}{8}$ of it is 14 less than $\frac{1}{2}$ of it.

13. Find three consecutive odd numbers whose sum is 45.

14. The difference between two numbers is 14. If $\frac{1}{3}$ of the larger number is subtracted from the smaller number, the result is equal to $\frac{1}{10}$ of their sum. Find the numbers.

15. The numerator of a fraction is 21 less than its denominator. If 6 is subtracted from both the numerator and the denominator, the resulting fraction equals $\frac{1}{2}$. Find the original fraction.

16. One fourth of the sum of two numbers is 2 less than the smaller, and the difference between the two numbers exceeds the smaller number by 6. Find the numbers.

Exercise 37. Distribution and Cost

Oral

1. What is the cost of 7 meters of cloth at c cents a meter? of 7 meters at c cents a centimeter? of 27 centimeters at 20 cents a meter? of y centimeters at c cents a meter?

2. If 5 oranges cost c cents, what is the cost of each orange? What is the cost of a dozen oranges? How much will m oranges cost?

3. Express in cents the sum of 5 quarters, 3 dimes, and 4 nickels. Express in cents the sum of q quarters, d dimes, and n nickels. Express as an equation the fact that the value of x quarters, $2x$ dimes, and $3x$ nickels is \$67.35.

4. Express in cents the value of 5 kilograms of sugar at c cents a kilogram; of 7 kilograms of coffee at d cents a kilogram. Express as an equation the fact that the sum of the above amounts is \$3.35.

5. If five 2-ton trucks and two 3-ton trucks take 4 loads of gravel each, how many tons have they moved?

6. If a apples are divided among b boys, how many apples will each boy receive?

7. If a man sells t tickets for a show at c cents each and spends d dollars for advertising and m dollars for other expenses, what profit does he make?

8. If 18 families contribute x dollars each for charity, how much is given in all? If 5 families had not contributed and if the others had given $5 more apiece, how much would have been given? Express as an equation the fact that the two amounts are equal.

9. In running a car, expenses for gas and oil are c cents a kilometer; for tires, t cents a kilometer; and for repairs, m cents every 100 kilometers. What is the cost of a 500 kilometer trip?

Written

Example: In Las Vegas, Nevada, a purse contains $10.50 in silver dollars and quarters. If there are 21 coins in all, how many of each are there?

Let x = number of dollars
y = number of quarters
$100x$ = value of dollars in cents
$25y$ = value of quarters in cents

$$x + y = 21$$
$$100x + 25y = 1050$$

$$5x + 5y = 105$$
$$20x + 5y = 210$$

$$15x = 105$$
$$x = 7$$
$$y = 14$$

Ans. There are 7 dollars and 14 quarters.

1. A farmer bought three cows for $270. If the first cow cost twice as much as the second and the second cost $\frac{2}{3}$ as much as the third, find the cost of each cow.

2. There is $2.25 in a cash register. There are $\frac{1}{2}$ as many dimes as quarters and 3 times as many nickels as dimes. How many coins of each kind are there?

3. Three trucks, one holding $2\frac{1}{2}$ tons more than each of the other two, take 8 loads apiece to move 92 tons of coal. What is the capacity of each truck?

4. A boy has $2.50 in quarters and nickels. If he has 22 coins in all, how many are quarters and how many are nickels?

5. A baseball club buys 70 balls for $120. The balls used for practice cost $1.50 apiece, and the balls used in games cost $2.25 each. How many balls of each kind were bought?

6. Two boys have together $2.80. If the first boy gives the second boy $.35, they then have equal amounts. How much money did each boy have to start with?

7. At a concert 650 tickets were sold for $4375. If orchestra seats were $7.50 and balcony seats were $3.50, how many of each kind were sold?

8. A boy has $1.60 in nickels and dimes. If he has 5 less than $\frac{2}{3}$ as many dimes as nickels, how many coins of each kind has he?

9. In 7 small tanks and 3 large tanks there were stored 7250 liters of gasoline. If each large tank held $2\frac{1}{2}$ times as much as each small tank, what was the capacity of each size tank?

10. If 7 kilos of sugar and 2 kilos of coffee cost $8.50, and if, at the same price per kilo, 5 kilos of sugar and 3 kilos of coffee cost $10, find the cost of 1 kilo of each.

11. An art dealer bought 12 etchings for $375. He sold part of them at $35 each and the rest at $40 each, gaining $80 on the whole transaction. How many etchings did he sell at each price?

Exercise 38. Averages

Oral

1. If a boy's grades in 3 subjects are 65, 80, and 95, what is his average grade? What is his average if his grades are a, b, and c?

2. If a boy's grades in 3 tests in a course are 60, 60, and 75, what is his average in that course? What is his average if his marks are x, x, and y?

3. If the sales in a store amounted to $450 on Wednesday, $450 on Saturday, and $300 on each of the other 4 days of the week, what was the average sale per day for that week?

4. If the average weight of the first 3 truckloads of gravel is x kilograms per load, and the next 5 loads is y kilograms per load, express as an equation the fact that the average for all 8 loads is 2700 kilograms.

5. If a student gets 70%, 60%, and 80% on three short tests, and then gets x% on an hour examination that counts as much as the three short tests together, express as an equation the fact that his average grade is 75%.

6. A baseball player's batting average is computed by dividing his number of hits by the number of times that he is at bat and multiplying the result by 1000. What is the batting average of a player who gets 5 hits out of 20 times at bat? What is the average of a player who gets x hits out of y times at bat?

7. If a team's standing is computed by dividing the number of games won by the number of games played and multiplying the result by 1000, what is the average of a team that has won 4 games out of 20 games? If this team plays 4 more games and wins all of them, what is its standing? If it had lost 2 of the 4 games, what would have been its standing?

8. What is the standing of a team that has lost 5 games out of 10 and then plays x more games, winning them all? What would be its standing if it had played x more games and lost them all? If it had played x more games and won 2 of them?

Written

Example: Nancy made 68, 73 and 85 on three tests. The final exam counted as much as two tests. If she made 82 on the exam, what was her final grade?

Let x = the Final grade

$$x = \frac{68 + 73 + 85 + 2(82)}{5}$$

$x = 390/5 = 78$ **Ans.** Final grade = 78.

1. A boy's grades in three tests are 85%, 63%, and 82%. What must be his grade in a fourth test to give him an average of 80%?

2. Passing mark in a certain course is 60%. A boy has received grades of 72%, 65%, and 83% on three tests. What is the lowest mark that he can get on the fourth test and still pass the course?

3. The average temperature for three days was 15°C. What must it be on the fourth day to make the average for the four days 18°C?

4. For two years a store's average profit was $3400. The third year it was $3600. What must the profit be the fourth year to make the average for the four years $3537.50?

5. If the average weight of three truckloads was 2500 kilograms, what would have to be the average weight of the next two loads to make the average for all five loads 2380 kilograms?

6. A boy receives grades of 78%, 83%, and 58% on three tests. What would he have to get on his final examination, which counts as much as the three tests together, to receive a grade of 71% in the course?

7. A basketball team has won 10 games out of 13 games. How many games can it lose in succession and still have its average 625?

8. A baseball club has won 17 games out of 24 games. How many games must it win in succession to make its average 750?

9. A team has lost 4 games out of 16 games. If it wins $\frac{1}{2}$ of its remaining games, its average will be $666\frac{2}{3}$. How many games are there left to play?

10. A crew has entered 15 sailing races. If it enters 9 more races and wins 8 of them, its average will be 750. How many races has it won so far?

11. A team had won 4 of the games it had played. It then won as many games in succession as it had previously played, making its average 625. How many games had it previously played?

12. A baseball player has made 10 hits out of 28 times at bat. How many more times must he be at bat to have an average of 400 if he gets hits half of the times he is at bat?

Exercise 39. Per Cent and Investment

Oral

1. What fractional part of 15 is 5? 5 is what per cent of 15? What per cent of 24 is 6? a is what per cent of b?

2. What fractional part of 1 yard is 1 foot? What per cent?

3. A ball player gets 17 hits out of x times at bat. What percent of his times at bat are the hits?

4. There are m boys and n girls in a class. What fractional part of the class are the boys? What per cent? What fractional part of the class are the girls? What per cent?

5. If 12 is increased by 50% of itself, what is the result? If 18 is decreased by 50% of itself, what is the result?

6. Express a number that is 10% more than x. Express a number that is 10% less than x.

7. If a man has $100 invested and gains 10%, how much does he then have? If later he loses 10% of his new amount, how much has he left?

8. What is the interest on p dollars for t years at 5%? at r%?

9. If $\frac{1}{2}$ of x dollars is invested at 5%, $\frac{1}{3}$ at 6%, and the rest at 4%, express the annual income. Express as an equation the fact that the annual income is $20 less than 6% of the amount invested.

Written

Example: A man invested $8000, part at $5\frac{1}{2}\%$ and the rest at 6%. If the total income for the first year was $459, find the amount invested at each rate.

Let $x =$ number of dollars at $5\frac{1}{2}\%$

$8000 - x =$ number of dollars at 6%

$$.055x + .06(8000 - x) = 459$$

$$55x + 60(8000 - x) = 459000$$

$$55x + 480000 - 60x = 459000$$

$$-5x = -21000$$

$$x = 4200$$

Ans. $4200 at $5\frac{1}{2}\%$ and $3800 at 6%.

1. The sum of 2 numbers is 99. If one number is 20% more than the other, find the numbers.

2. What number increased by 6% of itself equals 2544?

3. A man invested $1158, part at 5% and part at 6%. If his yearly income is $65.62, how much did he invest at each rate?

4. What number increased by 5% of itself and 25 equals 109?

5. One partner receives 12% more than the other in sharing a profit of $9540. How much does each receive?

6. One number is 1000 more than $66\frac{2}{3}\%$ of another number. If their sum is 10,000, find the numbers.

7. A man invests $18,600, part at 5% and part at $3\frac{1}{2}\%$. If his income is $4\frac{1}{2}\%$ of the total investment, how much does he invest at each rate?

8. Mr. Williams invests $\frac{1}{2}$ his money at 5%, $\frac{1}{3}$ at 4%, and the rest at $3\frac{1}{2}\%$. If his total income is $530, how much money does he invest?

9. Two boys share m marbles so that one receives 20% more than the other. How many marbles does each boy receive?

10. A speculator bought stocks and later sold them for $4815, making a gain of 7%. How much did the stocks cost him?

11. A man invested $17,000, part at 4% and the rest at 5%. If he got $193.45 income every three months, how much did he invest at each rate?

12. After setting aside 10% of a profit of m dollars, two partners share the rest so that one partner receives 25% more than the other. How much does each receive?

Exercise 40. Measures of Length and Area

Oral

1. If l is the length and w the width of a rectangle, express the perimeter and the area. If 2 is added to the length and 3 is added to the width, express the new length, width, perimeter, and area.

2. Express as an equation the fact that the area of the second rectangle in problem 1 is 36 more than the area of the first rectangle.

3. If the base of a triangle is x and the altitude is y, express the area. Express as an equation the fact that the area of the triangle equals the area of a square whose side equals the base of the triangle.

4. The dimensions of a rectangle are l and $l - 2$. What must be added to the width to make the figure a square? If the dimensions are l and w, what must be added to the width to make the figure a square?

5. If a strip x centimeters wide is cut off all the way around a rectangle whose dimensions are l and w, express the new length, width, perimeter, and area.

6. Express 2 meters 42 centimeters 8 millimeters in millimeters. Express the same quantity in centimeters, in meters.

7. A lot is $l \times w$ meters. If 10% is added to the length and to the width, what are the new dimensions?

8. The area of a square is 25 square meters. What is its perimeter?

9. The perimeter of a rectangular lot is 980 meters. If its length is x meters express its width.

10. The side of a square is 6 meters. The length of a rectangle having the same area as the square is 9 meters. What is its width?

Written

Example: The length of a rectangle is 7 cm longer than the side of a square, and the width is 2 cm longer. The area of the rectangle is 68 sq cm greater than that of the square. Find the dimensions of the rectangle.

There are times when it is easier to let x represent something else than the number we are asked to find. This is one such case. Let x = number of cm in the side of the square instead of the length or width of the rectangle.

$x + 2$ = width of rectangle
$x + 7$ = length of rectangle
x^2 = area of the square
$(x + 2)(x + 7)$ = area of the rectangle

The equation to express the given relationship between the two areas is

$$(x + 7)(x + 2) = x^2 + 68$$

$$x^2 + 9x + 14 = x^2 + 68$$

$$9x = 54$$

$$x = 6$$

Ans. The rectangle is 8 cm wide by 13 cm long.

1. The length of a rectangle is 11 m more than its width. If the perimeter is 82 m, find the dimensions.

2. The length of a polo field is 50 m more than twice the width. If the perimeter is 700 m find the dimensions.

3. The length of a rectangle is twice the width, and the perimeter is 10 m more than 5 times the width. Find the dimensions.

4. If one side of a square is increased by 8 cm, a rectangle is formed whose area is 184 sq cm greater than that of the square. Find the side of the square.

5. The length of a rectangle is 6 more than the side of a square, and its width is 4 less. If the areas are equal, find the dimensions of the rectangle.

6. A rectangular platform is 3 m longer than it is wide. If 5 m is added to the width and 2 m to the length, the area is increased by 95 square m. Find the original dimensions.

7. A rectangle is twice as long as it is wide. If 8 m is added to the width and 3 m to the length, the figure will be a square. Find the dimensions of the rectangle.

8. The part of a diving board over the water is 1 m longer than the part over the floor, and the total length is 2 m less than 3 times the part over the floor. Find the total length of the board.

9. If a 4 cm strip is added to the width of a square, a rectangle with a perimeter $\frac{9}{8}$ that of the square will be formed. Find the dimensions of the rectangle.

10. A rectangular piece of cardboard is 13 cm longer than it is wide. A strip 2 cm wide is cut off all around. If the area is decreased by 124 sq cm, what were the original dimensions?

Exercise 41. Digits

1. Express the number whose tens' digit is t and whose units' digit is u.

2. Express the number whose tens' digit is 3 and whose units' digit is x.

3. Express the number whose tens' digit is x and whose units' digit is y. Express the sum of the digits of the number. Express the number if the order of its digits is reversed.

4. Express the number whose digits from left to right are l, m, and n. Express the sum of the digits. Express the number if the order of its digits is reversed.

5. The digits of a number from left to right are t and u. Express as an equation the fact that the number is 12 more than the sum of its digits.

Written

Example: The units' digit of a two digit number is twice as large as the tens' digit. If the digits are reversed, the new number is 9 less than twice the original number. Find the number.

A number whose tens' digits is t and units' digit is u is expressed as $10t + u$.

Let x = the tens' digit, then
$2x$ = the units' digit.

$$10(x) + (2x) = \text{the number.}$$

$$10(2x) + x = \text{the number with its digits reversed.}$$

$$10(2x) + x = 2[10(x) + 2x] - 9$$

$$20x + x = 24x - 9$$

$$3x = 9$$

$$x = 3 \qquad \textbf{Ans.}\ 10(3) + 6 = 36$$

1. The units' digit of a number is 5 more than the tens' digit. The number is 3 times the sum of its digits. Find the number.

2. The units' digit of a number is 2 less than its tens' digit. The number is 4 more than 10 times its tens' digit. Find the number.

3. The tens' digit of a number is 1 more than 3 times the units' digit, and the number is 6 more than 7 times the sum of its digits. Find the number.

4. Find a number whose tens' digit is 3 less than its units' digit, and which, when the order of its digits is reversed, is 2 more than twice as large as it was originally.

5. The sum of the digits of a number is 12. If the order of the digits is reversed, the new number exceeds the old number by 54. Find the original number.

6. Find a number of three digits if the units' digit is $\frac{1}{2}$ the tens' digit, the hundreds' digit is 3 times the tens' digit, and the number is 27 more than 66 times the sum of its digits.

Exercise 42. Distance, Rate, and Time

Oral

1. An automobile goes at the rate of 90 kilometers an hour. How far will it go in 3 hours? How far will it go in 20 minutes?

2. A man walks 16 kilometers. If he walks 3 kilometers an hour, how long will he take? If he makes the trip in 5 hours, what is his average rate?

3. A boy walks at a rate of r kilometers an hour. How long will he take to go m kilometers? How long will he take if he rests twice, once for 20 minutes and once for 10 minutes?

4. One train starts from a station at 60 kilometers an hour. A second train, starting from the same station 3 hours later and going 85 kilometers an hour, overtakes the first train after traveling x hours. How many hours has the first train traveled? Express the distance that each train has gone. Give an equation expressing the fact that these distances are equal.

5. Two men, one walking at 3 kilometers an hour and the other at 4 kilometers an hour, start in opposite directions from the same place. How far has each man walked after x hours? Express as an equation the fact that they are 35 kilometers apart after x hours.

6. Two trains start toward each other at the same time from cities 330 kilometers apart and meet after x hours. If the first train travels 75 kilometers an hour and the second travels 90 kilometers an hour, express as an equation the fact that the sum of the distances they travel is 330 kilometers.

7. A man can row x kilometers an hour in still water. If he should row downstream where the current is y kilometers an hour, what would be his rate? What would be his rate rowing upstream at the same place? How much farther could he go downstream than upstream in an hour?

Written

Example: A train running at 60 kilometers per hour left a station 45 minutes before a train running at 90 kilometers per hour. How many hours did it take the second train to overtake the first?

Let $x =$ number of hours the second train travels at 90 kph.

$x + \frac{3}{4} =$ number of hours the first train travels at 60 kph.

Since the distances traveled are the same for both trains,

$$60(x + \tfrac{3}{4}) = 90x$$

$$60x + 45 = 90x$$

$$-30x = -45$$

$$x = \tfrac{3}{2}$$

Ans. The second train travels $1\frac{1}{2}$ hours to overtake the first.

1. At what rate must a man walk to go 21 kilometers in 4 hours if he rests for 30 minutes on the way?

2. A boy walking 6 kilometers an hour starts from a place 2 hours before a boy riding a bicycle at 15 kilometers an hour. How long does it take the boy on the bicycle to catch the boy walking?

3. Two cars start in opposite directions from a crossroad—one at 85 kilometers an hour and the other at 95 kilometers an hour. How long will it be before they are 480 kilometers apart?

4. Two trains start toward each other at the same time from cities 600 kilometers apart. One train travels 70 kilometers an hour and the other travels 80 kilometers an hour. How long will it be before they meet? How far will each train have traveled?

5. Walking 6 kilometers an hour along trails and 8 kilometers an hour along the road, a boy goes 34 kilometers in 5 hours. How much of his trip is over trails?

6. A boy rides to a town on his bicycle at 20 kilometers an hour and returns at 18 kilometers an hour. How far away is the town if the whole trip takes him $9\frac{1}{2}$ hours?

7. A man starts from a crossroad at 65 kilometers an hour. Three hours later a second man passes the same crossroad, driving at 90 kilometers an hour. How long after the first man started will the second man overtake him?

8. One man starts from A toward B, 315 kilometers distant. At the same time a second man, traveling twice as fast as the first, starts from B toward A. If they meet after 5 hours, what is the rate of each man?

9. A boat takes 3 hours to go 25 kilometers downstream, but it takes 5 hours to come back. Find the rate of the current and the rate of the boat in still water.

10. An airplane, whose normal rate is 900 kilometers an hour, goes 5500 kilometers with the wind in a certain time, and returns to within 1000 kilometers of its starting point against the wind in the same time. What is the rate of the wind?

11. A man driving to a town m kilometers away goes at the rate of a kilometers an hour on paved roads and b kilometers an hour on dirt roads. If the trip takes h hours, how many kilometers of the road are paved?

Exercise 43. Mixtures

Oral

1. There are 24 pieces of fruit in a basket. One fourth of them are apples and the rest are pears. How many of each are there? If 6 pears are taken out, how many apples are left? What fractional part of the number of pieces left are the apples?

2. If 3 kilos of water are evaporated from a salt solution weighing 27 kilos that is $\frac{1}{3}$ salt, how many kilos of salt are left? How many kilos were there in the original solution? How much water is left? How much water was there originally?

3. To 5 liters of a solution that is 60% alcohol, x liters of water are added; 30% of the solution is now alcohol. Express the number of liters of alcohol in the original solution and in the resulting solution and form an equation between these amounts. Express the number of liters of water in the original solution and in the resulting solution and form an equation between these amounts.

4. One mixture of corn and oats is $\frac{1}{2}$ corn. A second mixture is $\frac{1}{3}$ corn. If x bushels taken from the first mixture were added to y bushels taken from the second mixture, how many bushels of corn would be taken from each mixture? How many bushels of corn would there be in the resulting mixture?

5. Five liters of a solution that is 40% acid and x liters of a solution that is 30% acid are mixed. The resulting solution is 37% acid. Express the number of liters of acid in each of the three solutions. Form an equation between these amounts.

Example: A druggist has one rubbing compound which is 20% alcohol and another with the same ingredients that is 30% alcohol. How much of each compound should he use to fill a 500 cubic centimeter bottle with rubbing compound that is 22% alcohol?

Let x = number of cc at 20%
500 − x = number of cc at 30%

$$.20(x) + .30(500 - x) = .22(500)$$
$$20x + 30(500 - x) = 22(500)$$
$$20x + 15000 - 30x = 11000$$
$$-10x = -4000$$
$$x = 400$$

Ans. He should use 400 cc of 20% alcohol and 100 cc of 30% alcohol.

1. A 24 liter solution is $\frac{1}{4}$ alcohol. How much water must be added to make it 20% alcohol?

2. A 90 kilogram solution is 10% salt. How much water must be evaporated to leave a solution that will be 20% salt?

3. A mixture of corn and oats is $\frac{1}{5}$ corn. If 14 bushels of oats are added to it, it will be $\frac{1}{7}$ corn. How many bushels in all are there in the original mixture?

4. A solution of p liters of brine is $\frac{1}{10}$ salt. How much water must be evaporated to get a solution that is 15% salt?

5. How much tin must be added to an alloy of tin and copper that weighs 42 kilos and is $\frac{1}{7}$ tin to make an alloy that will be $\frac{1}{5}$ tin?

6. In an alloy weighing a kilos, b kilos are copper and the rest zinc. How much copper must be added to get an alloy that is 10% zinc?

7. How much of a solution 60% acid must be added to 24 liters of a solution 75% acid to get a solution that will be $\frac{5}{8}$ acid?

8. How many bushels from a mixture that is $\frac{1}{3}$ oats must be added to 480 bushels of a mixture that is 75% corn to get a mixture that will be 70% corn?

9. How many liters must be taken from a 10% solution of acid, and how many from a 5% solution, to get a solution of 64 liters that will contain 4.6 liters of acid?

10. A 12-liter pail is $\frac{1}{3}$ full of water. How much of a 95% solution of alcohol must be added to make the resulting solution $\frac{9}{10}$ water?

Exercise 44. Work

Oral

1. If a man takes 5 days to do a job, what fractional part of the job can he do in 1 day? in 2 days? in x days?

2. If one man takes 4 days to do a job and a second man takes 5 days to do the same job, how much of it can each man do alone in 1 day? How much of it can they do together in 1 day?

3. If a pipe fills a hot-water tank in x minutes, how much of it can it fill in 1 minute? in 3 minutes? in m minutes?

4. A can do a job in 13 days. B can do it in 17 days. Working together they take x days.

    Give the meaning of $\frac{1}{13} + \frac{1}{17}$; of $\frac{1}{x}$; of $\frac{x}{13}$; of $\frac{x}{17}$; of $\frac{x}{13} + \frac{x}{17}$.

    Complete the following equations:

    $$\frac{1}{13} + \frac{1}{17} = \qquad\qquad \frac{x}{13} + \frac{x}{17} =$$

5. One pipe can fill a tank in 14 hours. A second pipe can fill it in 18 hours. If the first pipe is open alone for x hours and then the pipes are both open for 6 hours, they completely fill the tank. Give the meaning of

    $\frac{x}{14} + \frac{6}{14}$. Complete the following equation: $\frac{x}{14} + \frac{6}{14} + \frac{6}{18} =$

Written

Example: Tom could paint a barn in 10 hours while Sam would take 15 hours. If they work together and work as hard as if they were working alone, how many hours would it take them to paint the barn?

In such problems it is usually best to determine the fractional part of the total work that each individual does. The sum of these fractions equals 1 since, if one does 2/3 of the job and the other does 1/3, then the total is 2/3 + 1/3 = 1.

107

Let x = number of hours to do the job together. Since Tom does the job in 10 hours, he does 1/10 each hour and in x hours does x times 1/10. Similarly, Sam does 1/15 each hour or in x hours does x times 1/15.

$$x\left(\frac{1}{10}\right) + x\left(\frac{1}{15}\right) = 1$$

$$\frac{x}{10} + \frac{x}{15} = 1$$

$$3x + 2x = 30$$

$$5x = 30$$

$$x = 6 \qquad \textbf{Ans.} \ \ 6 \text{ hours}$$

1. A boy can do a job in 6 hours. A man can do it in 4 hours. How long would it take them to do it together?

2. One pipe empties a pool in $1\frac{1}{2}$ hours. A second pipe empties it in 1 hour 45 minutes. How long will it take to empty the pool if both pipes are open?

3. Two men together can mow a field in $5\frac{5}{11}$ hours. One man alone can do it in 12 hours. How long would it take the other man alone?

4. One workman can load a truck in 25 minutes. A second workman can do it in 20 minutes. After the first man has worked 16 minutes alone, how long will it take them to finish it together?

5. Two boys together can shovel a walk in $1\frac{3}{7}$ hours. One boy alone can do it in $2\frac{1}{2}$ hours. How long would it take the other boy alone?

6. One pipe alone will fill a tank in 20 hours. A second pipe alone will fill it in 15 hours. If the first pipe were open for 16 hours and then closed, how long would it take the second pipe to finish filling the tank?

7. Two men together can do a job in 12 days. After one man has worked alone 26 days, the second man finishes the job alone in 5 days. How long would the whole job take each man alone?

8. Two stenographers together can do a typing job in d hours. If the first stenographer worked alone for a hours, it would then take the second b hours to finish. In how many hours could each stenographer do the work alone?

Exercise 45. Miscellaneous

Written

1. Separate 46 into four parts such that the second part is 1 more than twice the first, the third is twice the fourth, and the fourth is 3 more than the first.

2. Find two consecutive numbers such that $\frac{1}{4}$ of the larger added to $\frac{1}{2}$ of the smaller will equal $\frac{1}{5}$ of their sum.

3. A man is now 30 years older than his son. Fifteen years from now he will be twice as old as his son. What is the present age of each?

4. A man pays $9.50 a month for telephoning service, which allows him 10 calls a month to a neighboring town. All calls above 10 cost him 25 cents apiece. How many calls has he made to that town in a month when his bill is $14.40?

5. A post 10 meters long is anchored at one end at the bottom of the ocean. At high tide the part above the surface is $\frac{1}{3}$ of the part below it. If the tide changes 2 meters at this place, how deep is the water at low tide?

6. A 12 liter solution is $33\frac{1}{3}\%$ acid. How much water must be added to get a solution that will be 20% acid?

7. The denominator of a fraction is 5 more than twice as large as its numerator. If 11 is added to both numerator and denominator, the resulting fraction is equal to $\frac{2}{3}$. Find the original fraction.

8. A boy's father agreed to add $1.25 to every $.50 that the boy earned and put in the bank during one year. At the end of the year the boy had $29.75 in the bank. How much money had he earned during the year?

9. A boy shoveling snow earned 50 cents more on Wednesday than on Tuesday, 40 cents less on Thursday than on Tuesday, and $\frac{1}{2}$ as much on Friday as on Tuesday and Thursday together. If, in all, he earned $9.10, how much did he earn each day?

10. Find two numbers whose sum is a and $\frac{1}{2}$ of whose difference is b.

11. A newsboy sells 20 papers the first hour and 18 papers the second hour. How many papers must he average per hour for the next 3 hours to make his average 37 papers per hour for the 5 hours?

12. A girl is now 4 years older than her brother. Nine years ago she was twice as old. What is the present age of each?

13. Eight years ago a certain sum was invested at $3\frac{1}{2}\%$ simple interest. The amount is now $1824. What was the sum invested?

14. If I invest $\frac{1}{2}$ of my property at $4\frac{1}{2}\%$, $\frac{1}{3}$ of it at 5%, and the rest at 4%, my annual income will be $357.50. How much money have I to invest?

15. A man averages 45 kilometers an hour for the first 60 kilometers of a 100 kilometer trip. What will he have to average on the rest of the trip to make the total trip in $3\frac{1}{8}$ hours?

16. Ann and Babs together can do a piece of work in 4 days; but Ann alone would take 12 days. How many days would it take Babs alone?

17. A man invests d dollars, part at 6% and part at 5%. If his total income is m dollars, how much does he invest at each rate?

18. If the sum of two consecutive numbers is divided by $\frac{1}{3}$ of the smaller number, the quotient is 6 and the remainder is 1. Show by an equation that this is true for any two consecutive numbers.

19. A boy is now 13 years younger than his uncle, and m years ago he was half as old. How old is he now?

20. In 8 hours a man walks 12 kilometers more than a boy walks in 7 hours, and in 13 hours the boy walks 7 kilometers more than the man walks in 9 hours. What is the rate of each per hour?

21. A man paid a cents for 6 loaves of bread and 2 dozen eggs. If he had bought 4 loaves of bread and 4 dozen eggs, the cost would have been b cents. Find in terms of a and b, the cost of 1 loaf of bread and of 1 dozen eggs.

22. If 5 times the difference between a certain number and 5 is 9 less than 3 times the number, find the number.

23. Find three consecutive numbers whose sum divided by the difference between the third number and the first number will be 3 more than the middle number.

24. A man swimming with the current goes 7 kilometers an hour. Swimming against a current that is twice as strong, he goes only 1 kilometer an hour. Find his rate of swimming in still water.

25. A boy will be twice as old as his sister 3 years from now; 3 years ago he was 4 times as old as his sister. How old is each one now?

26. In a shooting match, hitting the bull's-eye counts 3 more than just hitting the target. One boy who made 6 bull's-eyes and 9 hits scored 15 more points than another boy who made 5 bull's-eyes and 7 hits. How much does a bull's-eye count?

27. The cost of 1 dozen fresh eggs and 1 dozen storage eggs together is $1.44, and 4 dozen storage eggs can be bought for $1.35 less than 5 dozen fresh eggs. What is the cost per dozen of each?

28. A bird flying against the wind goes twice as far the second hour as it did the first hour, 4 kilometers less the third hour than it did the second hour, and 4 kilometers more the fourth hour than it did the third hour. If it flies at an average of 13 kilometers an hour for the 4 hours, how far does it fly each hour?

29. A rectangular strip of cardboard is 13 centimeters longer than it is wide. A strip 2 centimeters wide is cut off all the way around. If the area is decreased by 124 sq cm, what were the original dimensions?

30. A man invests $3600, part in $3\frac{1}{2}\%$ bonds and part in $4\frac{1}{2}\%$ bonds. The income from the $3\frac{1}{2}\%$ bonds exceeds the income from the $4\frac{1}{2}\%$ bonds by $6. How much does this man invest in each kind of bond?

31. If the report of an explosion traveled 320 meters per second against the wind and 350 meters per second with the wind, what is the rate of sound in still air?

32. The numerator of a fraction is equal to twice the difference between two consecutive numbers, and the denominator is equal to their sum. If the value of the fraction is $\frac{2}{7}$, what are the numbers?

33. A light car goes 32 kilometers on a liter of gasoline. A heavy car goes 20 kilometers on a liter. On a trip of 224 kilometers the cost for gas for the light car was $2.31 less than that for the heavy car. What was the price per liter of the gasoline?

34. A train going 33 kilometers an hour passes a station 20 minutes before another train going 36 kilometers an hour. How far from the station will the two trains be when the second train overtakes the first?

35. If 4 boys and 3 men together can do a job in 2 days, but 2 boys and 4 men would take $2\frac{2}{11}$ days, how long would it take 1 man or 1 boy alone to do it?

36. A man sets aside 25% of the money he takes in on his business for upkeep and repairs on his plant. He pays $16\frac{2}{3}\%$ of the remainder for taxes and interest and finds that he has $2000 left. What was the amount of money that he took in?

37. Seven trucks, 3 of them with trailers, carry 60 tons of wool. If all the trucks together carry 7 times as much as all the trailers, how many tons are carried by each truck and each trailer?

38. A number is twice as large as the sum of its digits. If the order of the digits were reversed, the resulting number would be 9 less than 5 times the original number. Find the original number.

39. A man puts 1.6 liters of a solution that is 60% alcohol in his car radiator. He then fills the radiator with water, making the solution in the radiator 8% alcohol. How many liters does the radiator hold?

40. A train running 24 kilometers an hour starts from a station at 8:15. Another train, running 48 kilometers an hour, starts from the same station at 9:45. At what time will the second train overtake the first?

41. A man bought some antique furniture at an auction and turned it over to a dealer, who sold it at a profit of 8%. The dealer kept 12% of this profit

as his commission and made $24 on the transaction. How much did the furniture cost?

42. At one time 3 kilos of tea and 4 kilos of coffee cost $43.05; but the price of tea went up 20% and the price of coffee went up 10%, making the above amounts worth $48.78. What was the original cost per kilo of each?

43. A train going by the shore route between two cities averages 36 kilometers an hour. Another train going by the inland route, which is 28 kilometers shorter, averages only 25 kilometers an hour and consequently takes $\frac{1}{5}$ of an hour longer. How long is each route?

44. A boy ran to a fire at the rate of $7\frac{1}{2}$ kilometers an hour. He stayed twice as long as the time it took him to get there, and then walked back at $2\frac{1}{2}$ kilometers an hour. In all he was gone 1 hour 36 minutes. How far away was the fire?

45. In a mixture of sand and cement, the cement was $\frac{1}{3}$ of the mixture. If 13 bags of cement were added, the cement was then $\frac{5}{12}$ of the mixture. How many bags in all were there in the original mixture?

46. If 3 carts and 3 trucks could move a certain amount of coal in 15 days and if 4 carts and 2 trucks could move it in 20 days, how long would it take 1 cart to move the coal? How long would it take 8 carts?

47. An investor purchased two kinds of securities, one paying 2% and the other 4%, and got an annual income of $900. If he had reversed the amounts invested in the two securities, his income would have been only $600. How much did he invest at each rate?

48. A dump cart can haul enough gravel to fill a hollow in 6 days. A motor truck can do it in 2 days. How long would it take 2 dump carts and 1 truck, working together, to fill the follow?

49. A fruit dealer bought apples at $1.80 a dozen. He sold $\frac{1}{5}$ of them at the rate of 3 for 50¢; then he had to sell the rest at the rate of 4 for 25¢ thereby losing $1 on the whole transaction. How many dozen apples did he buy?

50. In a brine solution, the amount of salt is $\frac{1}{5}$ of the amount of water. How much water must be evaporated to leave 60 liters of the solution that will be $\frac{1}{3}$ salt?

Exercise 46. Review Exercises on Linear Equations

(A)

1. If $P = A + Akt$, find A if $P = 28$, $t = 0.2$, and $k = 2$.

2. Find the solution set for $\dfrac{x}{2} - \dfrac{3}{4} < 2x$.

3. If t is an odd integer, find the sum of the next two consecutive even integers.

4. Solve for x: $(3x + 1)^2 - 3(x + 1)(3x - 2) = 4$.

5. If John goes x kilometers at 3 kilometers per hour and y kilometers at 5 kilometers per hour, how many hours does the entire trip take him?

6. The sum of two numbers is 48. If twice the larger is subtracted from three times the smaller, the result is 14. Find the numbers.

7. Solve for y: $\dfrac{2y - 3}{3} - \dfrac{7 - y}{4} = y$.

8. How many kilos of corn worth 50 cents a kilo must be mixed with 60 kilos of beans worth 40 cents a kilo in order to make a mixture worth 44 cents a kilo?

9. Solve for x: $(5x - 1)(x + 1) - (x + 5)(x - 6) \geq (2x - 1)^2 - 3(x - 5) + 1$.

10. Supply the missing reasons for the proof of the following theorem. If $a + b = c$, then $a = c - b$.

statements	*reasons*
(1) $a + b = c$	(1) Given
(2) $(a + b) + (-b) = c + (-b)$	(2) If equals are added to equals, then the sums are equal.
(3) $a + \{b + (-b)\} = c + (-b)$	(3) ?
(4) $a + 0 = c + (-b)$	(4) ?
(5) $a = c + (-b)$	(5) ?
(6) $a = c - b$	(6) ?

(B)

Multiple Choice: Select the correct answer for each of the following.

1. If $2 - 3x = -1$, then $x =$

   (a) $-\dfrac{1}{3}$ (b) -1 (c) 0 (d) $\dfrac{1}{3}$ (e) 1

2. The solutions of $2x + y = 1$
$$x - 2y = 3 \quad \text{are}$$

   (a) $(1, 0)$ (b) $(1, 1)$ (c) $(1, -1)$ (d) $(0, 1)$ (e) $(-1, 1)$

3. $\left(1 - \dfrac{a}{b}\right) \div \left(1 - \dfrac{b}{a}\right) =$

   (a) $\dfrac{a}{b}$ (b) $\dfrac{b}{a}$ (c) 1 (d) $-\dfrac{a}{b}$ (e) $\dfrac{-b}{a}$

4. If x is an integer, the solutions of $|x - 2| < 3$ are

(a) $\{- 1, 0, 1, 2, 3\}$ (b) $\{0, 1, 2, 3, 4\}$ (c) $\{1, 2, 3, 4, 5\}$

(d) $\{1, 2, 3\}$ (e) $\{0, 1, 2\}$

5. If a number is 18 more than the sum of its digits, the number is

(a) 19   (b) 29   (c) 39   (d) 49   (e) 59

6. The average weight of a group of five byos is 58 kilos. Three of the boys weigh 55, 59 and 64 kilos respectively. If the weights of the remaining two boys are identical, they are each equal to

(a) 56   (b) 57   (c) 58   (d) 60   (e) 62

7. The prime factors of $x^5 - xy^4$ are

(a) $x(x^4 - y^4)$ (b) $x(x^2 + y^2)(x^2 - y^2)$ (c) $x(x - y)^4$
(d) $x(x^2 + y^2)(x + y)$ (e) $x(x^2 + y^2)(x + y)(x - y)$

8. The difference between the sum of the numbers m and n and their difference is

(a) $2m$ (b) $-2m$ (c) 0 (d) $2n$ (e) $-2n$

9. The solution of the inequality $2(3 - x) < 9 + x$ is

(a) $x < 3$ (b) $x < - 1$ (c) $x > 1$ (d) $x < -3$ (e) $x > - 1$

10. $\dfrac{b}{a - b} + \dfrac{a}{b - a} =$

(a) $\dfrac{a + b}{a - b}$ (b) 0 (c) 1 (d) -1 (e) $\dfrac{a - b}{a - b}$

EXPONENTS AND RADICALS

Exercise 47. Positive Integral Exponents

Oral

All letters represent positive integers.
Multiply:

1. $a \cdot a^2$
2. $x^3 \cdot x^2$
3. $m^2 \cdot m^4$
4. $a \cdot b \cdot a^3$
5. $x^2 \cdot y^2 \cdot x \cdot y^3$
6. $3x \cdot 2x^2$
7. $3a^2 \cdot 2b \cdot 5ab^2$
8. $a^5b \cdot 4a^2b^3$
9. $(-2x^2y)(3x^3y^4)$
10. $(-5mn)(-3n^2)$
11. $x^n \cdot x^2$
12. $a^{n+1} \cdot a^3$
13. $b^{2n} \cdot b^4$
14. $x^n \cdot x^{n+1}$
15. $2a^{x+1} \cdot a^{x+2}$
16. $x^ny^n \cdot x^2y^3$
17. $2^2 \cdot 2^3 \cdot 2$
18. $3^2 \cdot a^2 \cdot 3 \cdot a^4$
19. $2^2 + 2^2$
20. $3^3 + 3^3 + 3^3$
21. $(x^3 + x^2 - x)x^2$
22. $(a^2b - ab^2)a^2$
23. $(xy + x^2y + xy^2)x^2y^2$

Divide:

24. $\dfrac{a^5}{a^3}$
25. $\dfrac{a^7}{a^2}$
26. $\dfrac{m^2n^3}{mn}$
27. $\dfrac{27x^8y^4}{9x^2y^3}$
28. $\dfrac{5a^7b^6}{10a^5b^2}$
29. $m^5n^2 \div m^3$
30. $x^{n+2} \div x^3$
31. $a^{2+x} \div a^x$
32. $y^{n+4} \div y^{n+1}$
33. $(a^3b^x) \div (a^xb)$
34. $2^{n+1} \div 2^4$
35. $(x^{n+1}y^{n+1}) \div (xy)$
36. $(x^2 - x^3) \div x$
37. $(a^{2n} - a^{3n}) \div a^n$
38. $(x^n - x^{n+2}) \div x^2$
39. $\dfrac{b^x}{b}$
40. $\dfrac{(-1)^7}{(-1)^5}$

Perform the indicated operations:

41. $(a^2)^3$
42. $(x^3)^2$
43. $(-a)^2$
44. $-(a)^2$
45. $-(-a)^2$
46. $(-x)^3$
47. $(-m)^{12}$
48. $(-n)^7$
49. $(ab)^3$
50. $(x^2y)^2$
51. $(ab^2c)^3$
52. $(x^3y^2)^2$
53. $(5ax)^2$
54. $(-3m^2n)^2$
55. $(4a^2m^3x)^3$
56. $(2^2x^5)^2$
57. $(2^3x^2y)^2$
58. $(-5ax^3y^5)^3$
59. $\left(\dfrac{a}{b}\right)^3$
60. $\left(\dfrac{m}{2}\right)^4$

61. $\left(-\dfrac{a}{x}\right)^3$ **62.** $-\left(\dfrac{ab}{c}\right)^2$ **63.** $\left(\dfrac{3ax}{m^2}\right)^4$ **64.** $\left(\dfrac{-a^2b^3}{x^3y}\right)^4$

65. $\left(\dfrac{m^5n}{-a^2b^3}\right)^2$ **66.** $\left(\dfrac{3ay^2}{2bx}\right)^2$ **67.** $-\left(\dfrac{-3a}{5b}\right)^2$ **68.** $(x^m)^2$

69. $(a^x)^3$ **70.** $(m^x n^x)^4$ **71.** $(a^{2x}b^x)^3$ **72.** $(x^a)^b$

73. $(a^m b^m)^n$ **74.** $(a^2 \cdot a)^3$ **75.** $(a^2 \cdot b \cdot ab)^2$ **76.** $\left(\dfrac{a^3b}{ab^2}\right)^3$

Written

Perform the indicated operations:

Example: $\left[2a\left(\dfrac{m^2n^2}{mn^4}\right)^2\right]^3$

Begin inside by reducing the fraction and then raise to powers.

$$\left[2a\left(\dfrac{m}{n^2}\right)^2\right]^3 = \left[\dfrac{2am^2}{n^4}\right]^3 = \dfrac{8a^3m^6}{n^{12}}$$

1. $\left(\dfrac{4xy^2}{2ax}\right)^2$ **2.** $2 \cdot 2^4 \cdot 2^3$ **3.** $(-1)^3(-1)^2(-1)^7$

4. $(a_1)^2(a_2)^3(a_1a_2)$ **5.** $(-m)^3(-m)^2(-m)$ **6.** $[(x^2)^2]^2$

7. $a(x^2)^3$ **8.** $-m(n^3)^2$ **9.** $[x(y^2)^2]^2$

10. $2(a^3b^2)^2$ **11.** $(x^a \cdot x^a)^2$ **12.** $\left(\dfrac{x^{2+m}}{x^2}\right)^3$

13. $(x^m \cdot x^n)^3$ **14.** $\left(\dfrac{2b^2}{a}\right)^4$ **15.** 1^{3k+1}

16. $\left(\dfrac{-mn}{a}\right)^3$ **17.** $[(x)^4]^5$ **18.** $[(-m)^5]^2$

19. $(a^n - b^2)(a^n + b^2)$ **20.** $(a^{n+1} - b^2)^2$

21. $(a^{2n} + a^n - 1)(a^n - 1)$ **22.** $(3a^x - b^2)(5a^x - 3b^2)$

23. $\left(\dfrac{-3x^2y^5}{4a^3}\right)^3$ **24.** $\left(\dfrac{3a^2 \cdot 3ab^4}{2a^3b}\right)^2$ **25.** $\left(\dfrac{2^3 \cdot 2^4}{2^5}\right)^2$

26. $(2^2 \cdot 3a \quad 3b^4)^2$ **27.** $\left(\dfrac{x^a y^a}{2m}\right)^3$ **28.** $\dfrac{(2x^3y^2)^3}{(4xy^3)^2}$

29. $(4x)^2 \cdot (2y^2)^3$ **30.** $[(x^2)^3x]^2$ **31.** $[(2x^2)^2]^3$

32. $\dfrac{(4a^2b)(ab^3)^4}{(2a^2b)^2}$ **33.** $[2(a^3)^2]^5$ **34.** $\{a[a(a)^2]^2\}^2$

116

Exercise 48. Integral Exponents

Oral

All letters represent *positive* integers.
Perform the indicated operations leaving the answer in simplest form with positive exponents.

1. $2^2 \cdot 3^0$

2. $(2^2 \cdot 3)^0$

3. 3^{-2}

4. $\left(\dfrac{9}{4}\right)^{-2}$

5. $b^{-2}c$

6. $2a^{-2}b^{-3}$

7. $x^{n-3} \cdot x^3$

8. $7b^{x-1} \cdot 2b^3$

9. $x^5 \cdot x^{-3}$

10. $(x^{-2})^{-3}$

11. $(x^2)^{-1}$

12. $(a^{-3}b^{-2})^{-2}$

13. $\left(\dfrac{a^{-1}}{b^{-2}}\right)^{-4}$

14. $a^{n-2} \cdot 2a^2 \cdot a^3$

15. $x^5 \cdot y^4 \cdot x^{-1} \cdot y^{-3}$

16. $(a + b)^{-1}$

17. $\dfrac{1}{(a - b)^{-1}}$

18. $\dfrac{ma^{-3}}{n^{-2}a}$

19. $\dfrac{x^2}{3y^{-3}}$

20. $3^{10} \cdot 3^{-6}$

21. $\dfrac{x^2}{3y^{-1}}$

22. $\dfrac{a^0b^2}{b^{-2}c}$

23. $3x^0 \div (3x)^0$

24. $(x^2)^{-3}$

25. $(a - b)^{-1}$

26. $\left(\dfrac{x}{y}\right)^{-1}$

27. $(x^0)^{-2}$

28. $\dfrac{5y^3}{5^{-1}y^{-2}}$

29. $(-\tfrac{1}{8})^0$

30. $a^{-1} + b^{-1}$

31. $\left(\dfrac{x}{y}\right)^{-2}$

32. $(-x^2)^{-3}$

33. $(-x)^{-2}$

34. $\dfrac{abc}{(abc)^{-1}}$

35. $3a^{-3} \cdot 3a^{-2}$

36. $a^{-2} + x^{-2}$

37. $x^{-5}x^2$

38. $\dfrac{a^{-2}}{a^{-5}}$

39. $-5a^{-2}b$

40. $a^{-1} - b^{-1}$

41. $2a^{-2} \cdot 2a^2$

42. $(x^ny^n + x^{n-1}y^2) \cdot xy^{n+1}$

43. $(2^4 \cdot a^3) \div (2^3a^{-2})$

44. $x^{n+1} \div x^{n-1}$

45. $a^{3n+4} \div a^{2n-3}$

46. $(a^{-2}b^{-2})^{-1}$

47. $(4a^{x+y}) \div (2a^{x-y})$

48. $(a^nb^3 - a^{n+1}b^2) \div ab$

49. $(a^{n+3} - a^{n+2}) \div a^2$

50. $(xy - x^2y^2) \div x^{-1}y^{-1}$

All letters represent positive integers. Perform the indicated operations leaving your answer with positive exponents

1. $\dfrac{a^6 \cdot a^2}{a^3}$

2. $\dfrac{2x^3 \cdot 3x^2 y}{6xy}$

3. $\dfrac{x^{n-1} \cdot x^3}{x^2}$

4. $\dfrac{2^5 \cdot 2^{-2}}{2^2}$

5. $\dfrac{5^2 a^3 b^n}{5a^2 b^2}$

6. $\dfrac{x^{m+n} \cdot x^{m-n}}{x^m}$

7. $\dfrac{a^{n+1} b^{n+1}}{ab^{-1}}$

8. $(x + y) \div (x^{-1} y^{-1})$

Example: $(a^{-1} + b^{-1})(a^{-1} - b^{-1})$

$$\left(\frac{1}{a} + \frac{1}{b}\right)\left(\frac{1}{a} - \frac{1}{b}\right) = \left(\frac{1}{a}\right)^2 - \left(\frac{1}{b}\right)^2$$

$$= \frac{1}{a^2} - \frac{1}{b^2} = \frac{b^2 - a^2}{a^2 b^2}$$

9. $(a^{-1} + b)(a^{-1} - b)$

10. $(x^{-1} + y^{-1})^2$

11. $6a^{2n-5} b^{n-1} \cdot 12a^{4+3n} b^{3n-2}$

12. $(x^n y + x^{n-1} y^2 + x^{n-2} y^3)(x^2 y^n)$

13. $a^{n+1} \cdot a^{n-2} \cdot a^{3-3n} \cdot a^n$

14. $(a^{-2} + b^{-1})(a^{-2} - b^{-1})$

15. $(a^{n-1} + b^{n-1})(a^{n-1} - b^{n-1})$

16. $(x^3 + x^2 + x)(x^{-1} - 1)$

17. $(m^{n-2} + m^{n-1} + m^n)(m^2 + m)$

18. $(8x^5 y^8 z^{-3}) \div (4xy^5 z^6)$

19. $(3^{m+1} x^{m-1} a^m) \div (3^{m-1} x^3 a^2)$

20. $(7x^{-2} y^{-3} - 14xy^{-1} + 21x^3 y) \div (7x^{-3} y^2)$

21. $(a^{2n-4} - 7a^{n-2} - 30) \div (a^{n-2} + 3)$
22. $(a^5 b \cdot a^{-2} b^4 \cdot ab^{-3})^5$

23. $(a^{x+1} \cdot a^{x-1} \cdot a^{2x+1})^3$

24. $(2m^{-2} \div n^{-2})^{-5}$

25. $(a^{m-n})^{m+n} \cdot a^{m^2} \cdot a^{n^2}$

26. $\left(\dfrac{m^{x-1} \cdot m^{x-2}}{m^{2x-5}}\right)^3$

27. $\left(\dfrac{x^{m+n} \cdot x^{m-n}}{x^m}\right)^n$

28. $\left(\dfrac{-x^n y^{n+1}}{x^{-1} y}\right)^2$

29. $\dfrac{(x^{a+b})^{a-b} \cdot (x^b)^{a+b}}{x^{a^2}}$

Example: $\dfrac{x^{-1} + y^{-1}}{x^{-1} \cdot y^{-1}} = \dfrac{\dfrac{1}{x} + \dfrac{1}{y}}{\dfrac{1}{x} \cdot \dfrac{1}{y}} = y + x$

30. $\dfrac{c^{-2} - d^{-2}}{c^{-1} + d^{-1}}$

31. $\dfrac{a^{-1}b^{-1}}{a^{-1} + b^{-1}}$

32. $\dfrac{r^{-2} + r^{-1}}{r}$

33. $\dfrac{1^x + b^0}{2^{-3}}$

34. $\dfrac{p - e}{p^{-1} - e^{-1}}$

35. $\dfrac{1}{m^{-1} + n^{-1}}$

36. $\dfrac{6^{-1}}{2^{-1} + 3^{-1}}$

37. $\dfrac{2^{-2} - 3^{-2}}{6^{-2}a^0}$

38. $\dfrac{2}{2^{-1} + 2^{-2}}$

39. $\dfrac{3^{-1} + 2^{-1}}{3^{-1} - 2^{-1}}$

40. $\dfrac{a^{-2} + b^{-2}}{a^{-1}b + ab^{-1}}$

Exercise 49. Rational Exponents

Oral

All letters represent *positive* integers.

Perform the indicated operations, leaving your answer in simplest form with positive exponents.

1. $4^{1/2}$

2. $9^{1/2}$

3. $8^{1/3}$

4. $64^{1/3}$

5. $32^{1/5}$

6. $81^{1/4}$

7. $4^{3/2}$

8. $8^{2/3}$

9. $16^{3/4}$

10. $25^{3/2}$

11. $64^{2/3}$

12. $81^{3/4}$

13. $2 \cdot 27^{1/3}$

14. $5 \cdot 16^{1/2}$

15. $(4 \cdot 9)^{1/2}$

16. $a^{1/2}b^2 \div a^{1/2}$

17. $m^{3/4} \cdot m^{1/2}$

18. $x^{4/3} \div x^{1/3}y^{1/2}$

19. $b^{2/3} \div b^{1/2}$

20. $a^{1/2} \div a^{1/3}$

21. $(n^{1/2})^{2/5}$

22. $27^{-2/3}$

23. $(\tfrac{4}{9})^{1/2}$

24. $(\tfrac{1}{81})^{-3/4}$

25. $(\tfrac{25}{9})^{-1/2}$

26. $(25a^2)^{1/2}$

27. $(x^{mn})^{1/n}$

28. $(a^3)^{1/3}$

29. $(x^{1/2})^4$

30. $(m^{1/3})^2$

31. $(a^2b^4)^{1/2}$

32. $(x^3y^3)^{1/4}$

33. $\left(\dfrac{m^2}{n^4}\right)^{1/2}$

34. $\left(\dfrac{a}{b}\right)^{1/3}$

35. $(x^{1/3}y^{1/6})^{12}$

36. $\left(\dfrac{a^{1/2}b^{1/3}}{c^{1/6}}\right)^6$

37. $(mn)^{2/3}$ **38.** $(x^{1/2})^{1/3}$ **39.** $(a^2b^{1/3})^{1/2}$

40. $\left(\dfrac{xy^4}{z^2}\right)^{1/3}$ **41.** $(a^m b^n)^{1/mn}$ **42.** $(x^{1/2} \cdot y \cdot x^{3/2})^2$

43. $(m^{-1/2})^2$ **44.** $\left(\dfrac{x^{-3}}{y^{-1}}\right)^{-1/3}$ **45.** $\dfrac{5x^{-1/3}}{x^{2/3}}$

46. $\dfrac{2y^{3/2}}{4y^{5/2}}$ **47.** $[(m-n)^{1/3}]^{3/4}$ **48.** $(m^6 y^4 z^2)^{1/2}$

49. $(m^{-4} y^{-6} z^{-2})^{-1/2}$ **50.** $m^{3/2} \cdot m^{-2/3}$ **51.** $2^{-5/6} \cdot 2^{-2/3}$

Written

All letters represent positive integers.

Perform the indicated operations. Leave your answer in simplest form with positive exponents.

Example: $[\frac{9}{4}(x^{m/2}y^{-2n})^2]^{3/2}$

Simplify inside first. Do the negative exponents last.

$$[\tfrac{9}{4}x^m y^{-4n}]^{3/2} = \frac{27x^{(3m)/2}}{8}y^{-6n} = \frac{27x^{(3m)/2}}{8y^{6n}}$$

1. $(5a^{1/2}b^{1/2} + 3ab - 4a^{3/2}b^{3/2})(a^{1/2}b^{1/2})$ **2.** $(-5m^x np^{1/2})(-2m^3 n^{-1}p^{1/3})$

3. $(x^{1/2} - y^{1/2})(x^{1/2} + y^{1/2})$ **4.** $(-8a^{3/4}b^n c^{2/3}) \div (2a^{1/4}bc^{1/2})$

5. $(x^{2/5} + x^{1/5} + 1)(x^{1/5} + 1)$ **6.** $(4a^{1/2}b^y c^{m-2})(-2a^{1/3}bc^{2-m})$

7. $(x^{3/5} - y^{3/5}) \div (x^{1/5} - y^{1/5})$ **8.** $(8a^3 n^{1/2}p^{-3/4})^{2/3}$

9. $\left(\dfrac{-2a^{1/3}}{b^{2/3}c^{1/2}}\right)^6$ **10.** $\{(m^{-3}n^2)^{1/2}\}^{-2/3}$

11. $[(a+b)^{1/2}]^6$ **12.** $\left(\dfrac{a^2b}{64a^{-3}b^{1/3}}\right)^{-1/3}$

13. $-(-2a^{4/3}b^{1/3})^3$ **14.** $M^{(m+n)/2} \cdot M^{(m-n)/2}$

15. $(a^x b^{xy})^{2/x}$ **16.** $(a^{-2/3}b^{1/2})^6$

17. $(b^{m/2} \cdot b^{(3m)/2})^{3/m}$ **18.** $\dfrac{x^{7/2}y^{4/3} \cdot x^{3/2}y^{1/3}}{xy^{2/3}}$

19. $(x^{(mn)/2}y^{n/4})^{4/n}$ **20.** $\dfrac{x \cdot y^2 \cdot x^{1/2} \cdot y^{3/2}}{x^{3/2}y^{5/2}}$

21. $\dfrac{(a+b)^{1/2}(a+b)^{3/2}}{a+b}$ **22.** $\dfrac{x^{1/2} \cdot x^{1/3}y^4}{y^{1/2}y^{3/2}}$

23. $\dfrac{(a^{1/2} + b^{1/2})(a^{1/2} - b^{1/2})}{a^2 - b^2}$, $(a \neq b)$ **24.** $\dfrac{(x + y)(x + y)^5}{(x + y)^{1/2}(x + y)^{3/2}}$

25. $\dfrac{x^{2/3} \cdot x^{4/9} \cdot x^{1/3}}{x^{4/3}}$ **26.** $\dfrac{2^{1/2} a^{1/6} \cdot 2^{3/2}\, a^{1/4}}{2 a^{1/12}}$

27. $\left(\dfrac{x^{-2}y^{-3}}{a^{-1/2}}\right)^{-2/3}$ **28.** $\left(\dfrac{2^x a^{2x}}{b^{x/2}}\right)^{2/x}$

29. $[(x^{3/2})^{2/3}]^2$ **30.** $\dfrac{(a^{3/2})^{1/3} \cdot (b^{2/3})^{3/4}}{a^{1/2}b^{1/2}}$

31. $\dfrac{(x^{1/m})^{mn} \cdot (y^{1/n})^{mn}}{xy}$ **32.** $\dfrac{m^{1/3}n^{1/3}(m^2 n^2)^{2/3}}{(mn)^{2/3}}$

33. $12^0 + 4^{1/2} - \left(\tfrac{1}{27}\right)^{-1/3}$ **34.** $5x^0 + 8^{2/3} - 2^{-2}$

35. $25^{1/2} - 3^{-1} + 2m^0 - 1^{-x}$ **36.** $\dfrac{1}{8^{-2/3}} - 3a^0 + 27^{1/3} - 1^{2/3}$

37. $(6\tfrac{1}{2})^0 + 2^3 \cdot 4^{-3/2} + 2y^0$ **38.** $8^{-2/3} - (2x)^0 \cdot 2^{-1} - \dfrac{1}{3^{-2}}$

Exercise 50. Simple Roots

Oral

All letters represent positive integers.
Find the roots indicated:

1. $\sqrt{4}$ **2.** $\sqrt[3]{27}$ **3.** $\sqrt{81}$

4. $\sqrt[4]{16}$ **5.** $\sqrt[3]{-8}$ **6.** $\sqrt{a^2 b^2}$

7. $\sqrt[3]{a^6 b^3}$ **8.** $\sqrt{36x^2 y^4}$ **9.** $\sqrt[3]{-a^9 n^{12}}$

10. $\sqrt[5]{m^{10} n^{15} p^5}$ **11.** $\sqrt{\dfrac{a^4}{b^2}}$ **12.** $\sqrt[3]{\dfrac{a^{15} b^6}{27 c^3}}$

13. $\sqrt[5]{\dfrac{-a^5}{32}}$ **14.** $\sqrt{144a^2 \cdot 4b^2}$ **15.** $\sqrt[3]{-64x^6 y^9}$

16. $\sqrt[4]{\dfrac{81a^4 x^{8n}}{b^8}}$ **17.** $\sqrt{a^2 b^6}$ **18.** $\sqrt[v]{a^n b^{2n}}$

19. $\sqrt{4a^{2n} x^{2n}}$ **20.** $3\sqrt{25a^4 b^6}$ **21.** $2x^2 y^3 \sqrt{x^3 y^6}$

22. $\sqrt{9x^{2n+2}}$ **23.** $\sqrt[2n]{\dfrac{a^{4n} b^{6n}}{x^{2n}}}$ **24.** $\sqrt{(a + b)^2 x^2}$

25. $\sqrt[3]{27(x + y)^6}$ **26.** $\sqrt{\dfrac{4(a + b)^2}{9(m + n)^2}}$ **27.** $\sqrt{\dfrac{400(a + b)^4}{(x - y)^2}}$

28. $\sqrt{27a^3 \cdot 3ab^2}$ **29.** $\sqrt{35a^5 \cdot 35a^3}$ **30.** $\sqrt[3]{\dfrac{81a^5b^4}{3a^2b^7}}$

31. $\sqrt{(-3)^2}$ **32.** $\sqrt[3]{(-8)^2}$ **33.** $\sqrt[3]{-8^2}$

Exercise 51. Numerical Square Root

Written

Example: 720

If you don't have a hand calculator, here is an easy way to approximate the square root by guessing, using common sense and long division. The square root of 720 is between 20 and 30; first guess 25. Divide 720 by 25 and see if the quotient is more or less than 25.

$$\frac{720}{25} = 28.8$$

Since 25 is too small, we average 25 and 28.8, getting 26.9, and use this for the second guess.

$$\frac{720}{26.9} = 26.7$$

The square root is somewhere between 26.9 and 26.7, so 27 is the value of $\sqrt{720}$ to the nearest integer. Depending on the accuracy desired, only three or fewer guesses are needed.

Find the square root of each of the following to the nearest integer.

1. 116   **2.** 250   **3.** 840

4. 8,000   **5.** 9,600   **6.** 12,472

Find, to the nearest tenth, the square root of:

7. 46   **8.** 50   **9.** 75

10. 120   **11.** 230   **12.** 473

Exercise 52. Reduction of Radicals

Oral

All letters represent positive integers.
Reduce the following radicals completely:

1. $\sqrt{4a}$ **2.** $\sqrt{2a^2b^2}$ **3.** $\sqrt{4 \cdot 7}$

4. $\sqrt{8a^2}$ **5.** $\sqrt[3]{a^3b}$ **6.** $\sqrt{27a^3}$

7. $\sqrt[3]{a^4b^4}$ **8.** $\sqrt[3]{24}$ **9.** $\sqrt{48a^2b^3}$

10. $4\sqrt{4m}$ **11.** $2a\sqrt{8a^3}$ **12.** $-3\sqrt[3]{81}$

13. $\sqrt[5]{-32a}$ **14.** $\sqrt{a^4b^2}$ **15.** $\frac{1}{2}\sqrt[3]{8a^4}$

16. $\dfrac{a}{3}\sqrt{\dfrac{28}{a^2}}$ **17.** $3x\sqrt{\dfrac{5}{9x^2}}$ **18.** $\sqrt[5]{a^{11}b^6c}$

19. $\sqrt[4]{81a^7b^3}$ **20.** $\sqrt{2(a+b)^2}$ **21.** $\sqrt{48(x-y)^2}$

22. $\sqrt{(a-b)^3}$ **23.** $\sqrt{(a^2-b^2)(a-b)}$ **24.** $\sqrt{8(x^2-2xy+y^2)}$

25. $\sqrt{\frac{1}{2}}$ **26.** $\sqrt{\frac{1}{3}}$ **27.** $\sqrt{\dfrac{1}{a}}$

28. $\sqrt{\frac{2}{3}}$ **29.** $\sqrt{\dfrac{a^2}{2}}$ **30.** $\sqrt{\frac{1}{8}}$

31. $\sqrt[3]{\dfrac{1}{a^2}}$ **32.** $\sqrt{\dfrac{1}{a^2b}}$ **33.** $\sqrt{\frac{1}{12}}$

34. $\frac{1}{2}\sqrt[3]{\frac{1}{4}}$ **35.** $\sqrt[5]{\dfrac{1}{a^4}}$ **36.** $\sqrt{\dfrac{1}{2a^3}}$

37. $\sqrt[3]{\dfrac{2}{9a^3}}$ **38.** $-\sqrt{\dfrac{1}{11x}}$ **39.** $\sqrt{\dfrac{a}{b}}$

40. $\sqrt{\dfrac{a^2b}{c}}$ **41.** $\sqrt[3]{\frac{9}{16}}$ **42.** $\sqrt[6]{\dfrac{1}{a^{11}}}$

Reduce to similar radicals:

43. $\sqrt{8}, \sqrt{50}, \sqrt{72}$ **44.** $\sqrt{\frac{1}{2}}, \sqrt{200}, \sqrt{\frac{9}{2}}$

45. $\sqrt{18}, \sqrt{2}, \sqrt{32}$ **46.** $\sqrt{\frac{1}{3}}, \sqrt{12}, \sqrt{\frac{3}{16}}$

47. $\sqrt[3]{a^5}, \sqrt[3]{8a^2}, \sqrt[3]{27a^8}$ **48.** $\sqrt{4x^3}, \sqrt{x^3}, \sqrt{25x^3}$

49. $\sqrt{8x^3}, \sqrt{\dfrac{2}{x}}, \sqrt{\dfrac{1}{8x^3}}$ **50.** $\sqrt{\dfrac{a}{b}}, \sqrt{\dfrac{b}{a}}, \sqrt{ab}$

51. $\sqrt[4]{\dfrac{1}{a^3}}, \sqrt[4]{a^5b^8}, \sqrt[4]{16a}$ **52.** $\sqrt{32ab^3c}, \sqrt{98a^3bc}, \sqrt{72abc^3}$

Express as radicals:

53. $2^{1/2}$ **54.** $3^{2/3}$ **55.** $a^{3/4}$ **56.** $(ab)^{1/2}$ **57.** $2 \cdot 5^{1/3}$

58. $x^{2/3}y^{1/3}$ **59.** $2^{1/2}a^{1/2}$ **60.** $3^{1/3}a^{2/3}x^{1/3}$ **61.** $(25a^2)^{1/2}$ **62.** $4(ab)^{1/2}$

Express with fractional exponents:

63. $\sqrt{2}$ **64.** $\sqrt[3]{5^2}$ **65.** $\sqrt[5]{a^3}$ **66.** $\sqrt{xy}$ **67.** $a\sqrt{b}$

68. $\sqrt[3]{a^2b}$ **69.** $\sqrt{5m}$ **70.** $3\sqrt{ax}$ **71.** $\sqrt[3]{10a^2x}$

72. $\sqrt[4]{5^2 a^3 x^2 y}$ **73.** $\sqrt[4]{a^2}$ **74.** $\sqrt[6]{a^3 b^3}$

75. $\sqrt[4]{9}$ **76.** $\sqrt[10]{32}$ **77.** $\sqrt[4]{36a^2 b^2}$

78. $\sqrt[9]{8a^3 b^6}$ **79.** $\sqrt[4]{9a^2 b^2 c^2}$ **80.** $\sqrt[8]{49a^2 b^4 c^6}$

81. $\sqrt[4]{a^4 b^2 c^4}$ **82.** $\sqrt[6]{27a^9 b^6 c^3}$ **83.** $\sqrt[4]{\dfrac{a^2}{b^2}}$

84. $\sqrt[6]{\dfrac{64a^8 c^2}{b^4}}$

Written

$\sqrt{2} \approx 1.414; \quad \sqrt{3} \approx 1.732; \quad \sqrt{5} \approx 2.236$

Approximate each of the following to the nearest tenth.

The simplest method is to use a hand calculator, rounding off its result to the required number of places. If you do not have a calculator, simplify the radical and use the approximations supplied.

Example: $\sqrt{27}$

$\qquad 3\sqrt{3} \approx 3(1.732) = 5.196$

Ans. $\qquad \sqrt{27} \approx 5.2$

1. $\sqrt{8}$ **2.** $\sqrt{12}$ **3.** $\sqrt{18}$ **4.** $\sqrt{20}$ **5.** $\sqrt{50}$

6. $\sqrt{75}$ **7.** $\sqrt{98}$ **8.** $\sqrt{108}$ **9.** $\sqrt{147}$ **10.** $\sqrt{288}$

Approximate each of the following to the nearest hundredth.

11. $\sqrt{200}$ **12.** $\sqrt{300}$ **13.** $\sqrt{27}$

14. $\sqrt{125}$ **15.** $\sqrt{500}$ **16.** $\sqrt{507}$

All letters represent positive real numbers.
Simplify:

Example: $(4^{3/2})(8^{2/3})(2^{-1})$

Try to express each number as a power of the lowest possible base and them simplify.

$$(2^2)^{3/2}(2^3)^{2/3}(2^{-1}) =$$

$$2^3 \cdot 2^2 \cdot 2^{-1} = 2^4 = 16$$

17. $\sqrt[3]{(216)^2}$ **18.** $2^{2/3} \cdot \sqrt[3]{2}$ **19.** $\frac{3}{4}\sqrt[3]{\left(\frac{8}{27}\right)^2}$

20. $\left(\frac{81}{16}\right)^{3/4}$ **21.** $2^3 \cdot 4^{3/2} \cdot 8^{1/3}$ **22.** $5 \cdot 9^{1/2} \cdot 8^{2/3}$

23. $\dfrac{27^{2/3} \cdot 81^{1/4}}{9^2}$ **24.** $\dfrac{a^{1/3} \sqrt[3]{a^2}}{a^{1/2}\sqrt{a}}$ **25.** $\dfrac{9^{1/3} \cdot 3^{1/3}}{6}$

26. $(\frac{1}{64})^{3/2}$

27. $(\frac{1}{8})^{1/3} (\frac{1}{16})^{1/4} (\frac{1}{4})^{1/2}$

28. $(27a^6c^3)^{2/3}$

29. $(-8x^9y^{12})^{1/3}$

30. $(-243a^5b^{10})^{2/5}$

31. $[(8a^3c)^{1/3}]^2$

32. $5(-125)^{2/3}$

33. $\sqrt[3]{(a-b)^2} \cdot (a-b)^{1/3}$

34. $(\frac{1}{27})^{4/3} (\frac{9}{4})^{3/2} (8)^{2/3}$

35. $(-125)^{4/3} \cdot (\frac{1}{25})^{3/2}$

36. $(3 \cdot 9)^{2/3}(3 \cdot 12)^{1/2}$

37. $9 \cdot (4^{1/2} \div 4) \cdot 9^{1/2}$

38. $(\frac{1}{27})^{2/3} + (\frac{1}{3})^2 - (\frac{16}{81})^{1/2}$

39. $32^{2/5} - (\frac{1}{4})^{5/2} + (\frac{1}{16})^{5/4}$

40. $625^{3/4} - (\frac{49}{4})^{1/2} - (\frac{216}{8})^{1/3}$

41. $(2\frac{1}{4})^{3/2} - (5\frac{4}{9})^{1/2} + (3\frac{1}{16})^{1/2}$

42. $3\sqrt{\frac{1}{27}}$

43. $\frac{1}{2}\sqrt{\frac{2}{3}}$

44. $\frac{2}{3}\sqrt{\frac{9}{2}}$

45. $\sqrt{\dfrac{a^2}{a+b}}$

46. $\sqrt{\dfrac{a+b}{a-b}}$

47. $\sqrt{\dfrac{a}{(a-b)^3}}$

48. $\sqrt{\frac{4}{3}}$

49. $\sqrt{\dfrac{3}{x}}$

50. $\sqrt[3]{\frac{3}{8}}$

51. $\sqrt{\dfrac{a^3}{b^3}}$

52. $\sqrt{a^3 - a^2b}$

53. $\sqrt{a(a-b)^2}$

54. $\sqrt[3]{-\frac{1}{4}}$

55. $\sqrt{\dfrac{a-b}{a+b}}$

56. $\sqrt{\dfrac{a}{(a-b)^2}}$

57. $\sqrt{\dfrac{a}{a+b}}$

58. $\sqrt[3]{\frac{16}{27}}$

59. $\sqrt[3]{\frac{27}{16}}$

60. $\sqrt{\frac{3}{8}}$

Exercise 53. Addition and Subtraction of Radicals

Oral

All letters represent positive real numbers.
Collect:

1. $\sqrt{2} - 2\sqrt{2} + 3\sqrt{2}$

2. $\sqrt{3} + 4\sqrt{3} - 2\sqrt{3}$

3. $a\sqrt{b} + 2a\sqrt{b}$

4. $\sqrt{2a} + 2\sqrt{2a} - 3\sqrt{2a}$

5. $2\sqrt{5} - 3\sqrt{5} + 4\sqrt{5}$

6. $4\sqrt{7} + 3\sqrt{7} - 5\sqrt{7}$

7. $\sqrt{3} - \sqrt{12}$

8. $\sqrt{18} - \sqrt{2}$

9. $\sqrt{8} + 3\sqrt{2}$

10. $\sqrt{27} - 3\sqrt{3}$

11. $\sqrt{32} - 5\sqrt{2}$

12. $\sqrt{9} - \sqrt{8}$

13. $\sqrt[3]{16} - \sqrt[3]{2}$

14. $\sqrt[3]{3} - \sqrt[3]{81}$

15. $\sqrt[4]{16x} - 3\sqrt[4]{x}$

16. $\sqrt{9} - \sqrt[4]{81}$

125

All letters represent positive real numbers.
Collect:

Example: $\sqrt{120} + \sqrt{\tfrac{6}{5}} - \dfrac{\sqrt{10}}{\sqrt{3}}$

Write each radical in reduced form with rational denominators.

$$\sqrt{4 \cdot 30} + \sqrt{\tfrac{6}{5} \cdot \tfrac{5}{5}} - \dfrac{\sqrt{10}}{\sqrt{3}} \cdot \dfrac{\sqrt{3}}{\sqrt{3}}$$

$$2\sqrt{30} + \dfrac{\sqrt{30}}{5} - \dfrac{\sqrt{30}}{3}$$

$$\dfrac{30\sqrt{30} + 3\sqrt{30} - 5\sqrt{30}}{15} = \dfrac{28\sqrt{30}}{15}$$

1. $\sqrt{18} - 3\sqrt{2} + \sqrt{32}$

2. $2\sqrt{12} - \sqrt{27} - \sqrt{75}$

3. $\tfrac{1}{2}\sqrt{72} + 5\sqrt{8} - \tfrac{1}{3}\sqrt{18}$

4. $\sqrt{18} + \sqrt{12} + \sqrt{2}$

5. $\sqrt{8a} + 3\sqrt{2a} - \sqrt{50a}$

6. $\sqrt{4x^3} - 2\sqrt{x^3} + \sqrt{25x^3}$

7. $\sqrt{27} - 2\sqrt{32} + \tfrac{1}{2}\sqrt{12} - \sqrt{98}$

8. $\sqrt{16a^5} - \sqrt{20a^3} - 4a\sqrt{a^3}$

9. $4\sqrt{\tfrac{1}{2}} - 2\sqrt{200} + 2\sqrt{\tfrac{9}{2}}$

10. $9\sqrt{\tfrac{2}{3}} + \sqrt{24} - 12\sqrt{\tfrac{1}{6}}$

11. $\sqrt{\tfrac{1}{8}} - \tfrac{1}{2}\sqrt{\tfrac{1}{2}} + 3\sqrt{\tfrac{1}{18}}$

12. $\sqrt{a^3} + \sqrt{ab^2} - \sqrt{9a^3}$

13. $\sqrt{\dfrac{m}{25}} - \sqrt{64m} + 3\sqrt{16m}$

14. $\sqrt{\dfrac{b}{a}} + \sqrt{\dfrac{a}{b}} - \sqrt{\dfrac{ab}{c^2}}$

15. $14\sqrt{\tfrac{2}{7}} - 8\sqrt{\tfrac{7}{2}} + 2\sqrt{56}$

16. $\sqrt{40a^3} + \sqrt{\dfrac{a}{5}} - \sqrt{1000a}$

17. $\sqrt{(a + b)^2 a} + \sqrt{a(a - b)^2}, \; a > b$

18. $\sqrt{(a + b)^3} + \sqrt{a^3 + a^2b} - \sqrt{(a - b)^3}, \; a > b$

19. $\sqrt[3]{16a^5} - a^2\sqrt[3]{\dfrac{2}{a}} + \sqrt[3]{25a^2}$

20. $\sqrt[3]{16a} - \sqrt{18a} + \sqrt{8a} - \sqrt[3]{81a}$

21. $\sqrt[3]{64} + \sqrt[3]{40} - 5\sqrt[3]{\tfrac{8}{25}}$

22. $\sqrt{\dfrac{8}{a}} + \dfrac{1}{a}\sqrt{72a} + 2a\sqrt{\dfrac{1}{2a^3}}$

Exercise 54. Multiplication and Division of Radicals

Oral

All letters represent positive real numbers.
Multiply and divide as indicated:

1. $\sqrt{2} \cdot \sqrt{5}$

2. $\sqrt{3} \cdot \sqrt{7}$

3. $\sqrt{2} \cdot 2\sqrt{3}$

4. $\frac{1}{2}\sqrt{6} \cdot 4\sqrt{5}$

5. $\frac{1}{2}\sqrt{2} \cdot \frac{1}{3}\sqrt{7}$

6. $\sqrt{3} \cdot \sqrt{3}$

7. $\sqrt{a} \cdot \sqrt{ab}$

8. $\sqrt{4} \cdot \sqrt{2}$

9. $\sqrt{6} \cdot \sqrt{3}$

10. $\sqrt{2a} \cdot \sqrt{10a}$

11. $\sqrt{10} \cdot \sqrt{15}$

12. $\sqrt{3a^3} \cdot \sqrt{6a}$

13. $\sqrt[3]{2} \cdot \sqrt[3]{4}$

14. $\sqrt[3]{9} \cdot \sqrt[3]{9}$

15. $\frac{1}{2}\sqrt{2a} \cdot \sqrt{2a^2}$

16. $\sqrt{8} \div \sqrt{2}$

17. $\sqrt{12} \div \sqrt{6}$

18. $6\sqrt{24} \div 3\sqrt{8}$

19. $\sqrt{x^2 y} \div \sqrt{y}$

20. $\sqrt{16} \div \sqrt{2}$

21. $\sqrt[3]{18} \div \sqrt[3]{3}$

22. $\sqrt[3]{81} \div \sqrt[3]{3}$

23. $a\sqrt{9a^2 x^3} \div b\sqrt{x^2 a^2}$

24. $3\sqrt{10a} \div \frac{1}{2}\sqrt{2a}$

25. $2\sqrt{3} \div \sqrt{27}$

26. $3\sqrt{2} \div \sqrt{8}$

27. $\frac{1}{2}\sqrt{12} \div \frac{1}{3}\sqrt{4}$

28. $\sqrt{\frac{1}{3}} \div \sqrt{\frac{1}{6}}$

29. $\sqrt{\frac{4}{5}} \div \sqrt{\frac{1}{5}}$

30. $(\sqrt{12} - \sqrt{6} + \sqrt{3}) \div \sqrt{3}$

31. $\sqrt[4]{2} \cdot \sqrt[4]{8}$

32. $\sqrt{12} \cdot \sqrt{3}$

33. $\sqrt{18} \cdot \sqrt{4}$

34. $\sqrt{\frac{1}{2}} \cdot \sqrt{2}$

35. $\sqrt{\frac{2}{3}} \cdot \sqrt{\frac{1}{3}}$

36. $\sqrt{xy^3} \cdot \sqrt{x^2 y}$

37. $\sqrt[4]{2} \cdot \sqrt[4]{2}$

38. $\sqrt{2} \cdot \sqrt{3} \cdot \sqrt{5}$

39. $\sqrt{6} \cdot \sqrt{15} \cdot \sqrt{2}$

40. $\sqrt{ab} \cdot \sqrt{ab^2} \cdot \sqrt{a^2 b}$

41. $\sqrt{\frac{2}{7}} \cdot \sqrt{14} \cdot \sqrt{\frac{1}{2}}$

42. $(\sqrt{2} + \sqrt{3})\sqrt{2}$

43. $(3 - 2\sqrt{5})\sqrt{5}$

44. $(2 - \sqrt{3})^2$

45. $(\sqrt{5} + \sqrt{3})(\sqrt{5} - \sqrt{3})$

46. $(2\sqrt{18} - 3\sqrt{8} + 2\sqrt{12}) \div 2\sqrt{2}$

47. $(\sqrt{ab} + \sqrt{a^2 b} - \sqrt{ab^3}) \div \sqrt{ab}$

48. $(\frac{1}{2}\sqrt[3]{2} - \frac{1}{3}\sqrt[3]{4} - \frac{1}{5}\sqrt[3]{6}) \div \sqrt[3]{2}$

All letters represent positive real numbers.
Multiply and divide as indicated:
There are two methods of doing these problems.

First method: Simplify each radical first, then multiply or divide.

Example: $\sqrt{12} \cdot \sqrt{24} \div \sqrt{40}$

$$2\sqrt{3} \cdot 2\sqrt{6} \div 2\sqrt{10} =$$

$$\frac{2 \cdot 2\sqrt{3 \cdot 6}}{2\sqrt{10}} =$$

$$2\sqrt{\frac{3 \cdot 3 \cdot 2}{5 \cdot 2}} =$$

$$6\sqrt{\tfrac{1}{5}} =$$

$$\tfrac{6}{5}\sqrt{5}$$

Second method: Multiply or divide first, then simplify.

Example: $\tfrac{2}{3}\sqrt{75} \div \tfrac{1}{2}\sqrt{125}$

$$\frac{\tfrac{2}{3}\sqrt{75}}{\tfrac{1}{2}\sqrt{125}} =$$

$$\tfrac{2}{3} \cdot \tfrac{2}{1}\sqrt{\tfrac{75}{125}} =$$

$$\tfrac{4}{3}\sqrt{\tfrac{3}{5}} =$$

$$\tfrac{4}{3}\sqrt{\tfrac{15}{25}} = \tfrac{4}{15}\sqrt{15}$$

1. $\sqrt{10} \cdot \sqrt{8} \cdot \sqrt{15}$

2. $\sqrt[3]{18} \cdot \sqrt[3]{6} \cdot \sqrt[3]{6}$

3. $\tfrac{1}{2}\sqrt{14} \cdot 4\sqrt{35}$

4. $\sqrt{100a^3} \cdot \tfrac{1}{5}\sqrt{3a}$

5. $\tfrac{1}{2}\sqrt{27} \cdot \tfrac{1}{3}\sqrt{8} \cdot \tfrac{1}{5}\sqrt{50}$

6. $\sqrt{54ab^3} \cdot \sqrt{12a^2} \cdot \sqrt{ab}$

7. $\sqrt{7a} \cdot \sqrt{\dfrac{21a}{2}} \cdot \sqrt{6a}$

8. $\tfrac{1}{2}\sqrt{\tfrac{3}{4}} \cdot \tfrac{1}{6}\sqrt{\tfrac{32}{3}}$

9. $\sqrt[3]{66ax} \cdot \sqrt[3]{22a^2x} \cdot \sqrt[3]{11ax^2}$

10. $\sqrt{\tfrac{96}{7}} \cdot \sqrt{\tfrac{42}{3}} \cdot \sqrt{\tfrac{1}{3}}$

11. $\sqrt{288} \div \sqrt{18}$

12. $\sqrt[3]{72} \div \sqrt[3]{3}$

13. $\sqrt{48} \div \sqrt{27}$

14. $\sqrt{36} \div \sqrt{8}$

15. $\sqrt[3]{54} \div \sqrt[3]{4}$

16. $\tfrac{1}{2}\sqrt{200} \div 3\sqrt{50}$

17. $6\sqrt[3]{24} \div \tfrac{1}{3}\sqrt[3]{3}$

18. $\tfrac{1}{9}\sqrt{125} \div \tfrac{1}{6}\sqrt{45}$

19. $\tfrac{1}{4}\sqrt{8} \div \tfrac{5}{2}\sqrt{2}$

20. $\sqrt{\tfrac{9}{32}} \div \sqrt{\tfrac{3}{4}}$

21. $\sqrt{\tfrac{1}{2}} \cdot \sqrt{\tfrac{8}{3}} \cdot 3\sqrt{2}$

22. $\sqrt{\tfrac{3}{5}} \cdot \tfrac{1}{3}\sqrt{\tfrac{15}{2}} \cdot \sqrt{\tfrac{1}{4}}$

23. $\sqrt[3]{\tfrac{16}{49}} \cdot \sqrt[3]{\tfrac{4}{21}}$

24. $\tfrac{4}{5}\sqrt{\tfrac{125}{18}} \cdot \tfrac{1}{2}\sqrt{\tfrac{25}{2}}$

25. $(3\sqrt{\tfrac{1}{2}} - \tfrac{1}{3}\sqrt{\tfrac{2}{3}})3\sqrt{6}$

26. $(4\sqrt{6} + 3\sqrt{3} - 2\sqrt{2})\sqrt{6}$

27. $\sqrt{\tfrac{15}{16}} \div \sqrt{\tfrac{3}{2}}$

28. $\sqrt{\tfrac{3}{4}} \cdot \sqrt{\tfrac{2}{9}} \div \sqrt{\tfrac{5}{6}}$

29. $(\sqrt{8} - \sqrt{4} - 7\sqrt{2})\sqrt{\tfrac{1}{2}}$

Example: $\sqrt{x^2 - y^2} \cdot \sqrt{5x + 5y}$

$$\sqrt{(x + y)(x - y) \cdot 5(x + y)} =$$
$$\sqrt{(x + y)^2 \cdot 5(x - y)} =$$
$$(x + y)\sqrt{5(x - y)}$$

30. $3\sqrt{\dfrac{a^2 - b^2}{2}} \div \dfrac{1}{3}\sqrt{\dfrac{a + b}{a - b}}, \ a \neq \pm b$

31. $\sqrt{a^2 - ab - 2b^2} \div \sqrt{\dfrac{a^2 + ab}{a - 2b}}$

32. $(\sqrt{5} - 2\sqrt{3})(\sqrt{5} + 2\sqrt{3})$

33. $(\sqrt{2} - \sqrt{3})^2$

34. $\sqrt{a^2 - b^2} \cdot \sqrt{a + b}$

35. $(\sqrt{(a + b)} + \sqrt{a})^2$

36. $(\sqrt{2} + \sqrt{3})(\sqrt{2} + \sqrt{5})$

37. $(\sqrt{15} - \sqrt{6})(\sqrt{3} + \sqrt{2})$

38. $2\sqrt[3]{16} \cdot \sqrt[3]{\tfrac{1}{9}} \div 4\sqrt[3]{\tfrac{2}{27}}$

39. $(\sqrt{98} - 3\sqrt{242} - \tfrac{1}{2}\sqrt{18}) \div \sqrt{2}$

40. $(\sqrt{ac} + \sqrt{ab} + \sqrt{bc}) \div \sqrt{abc}$

41. $(\sqrt[3]{\tfrac{1}{3}} - \sqrt[3]{\tfrac{1}{2}} + \sqrt[3]{\tfrac{1}{6}}) \div \sqrt[3]{\tfrac{1}{24}}$

42. $\{\sqrt{a^2 - b^2} + \sqrt{a - b} + \sqrt{(a - b)^2}\} \div \sqrt{\dfrac{1}{a - b}}$

43. $(\tfrac{3}{4}\sqrt{\tfrac{28}{3}} - \tfrac{1}{6}\sqrt{\tfrac{49}{3}} - \tfrac{2}{3}\sqrt{\tfrac{98}{6}}) \div \tfrac{1}{12}\sqrt{\tfrac{7}{3}}$

44. $\{\sqrt{x - y} + \sqrt{x^2 - y^2} + \sqrt{(x - y)^2}\}\sqrt{x - y}$

45. $\{\sqrt{x} + \sqrt{x - y} + \sqrt{x(x + y)}\}\sqrt{x(x - y)}$

46. $(\sqrt{m + n} - \sqrt{m - n})(\sqrt{m + n} + \sqrt{m - n})$

47. $(\sqrt{6} + \sqrt{3} - \sqrt{2})(\sqrt{3} + \sqrt{2})$

48. $(\sqrt{a^2 - b^2} + \sqrt{a + b} - \sqrt{a - b})\sqrt{a + b}$

49. $(\sqrt{3} + \sqrt{2} - \sqrt{5})(\sqrt{3} + \sqrt{2} + \sqrt{5})$

50. $(\sqrt{\tfrac{1}{2}} + \sqrt{\tfrac{1}{3}} + \sqrt{\tfrac{1}{6}})\sqrt{\tfrac{2}{3}}$

Exercise 55. Rationalization of Numerators and Denominators

Oral

All letters represent positive real numbers.
Rationalize the denominator in each of the following:

1. $\dfrac{1}{\sqrt{2}}$

2. $\dfrac{1}{\sqrt{3}}$

3. $\dfrac{2}{\sqrt{5}}$

4. $\dfrac{1}{2\sqrt{3}}$

5. $\dfrac{7}{\sqrt{7}}$

6. $\dfrac{1}{\sqrt{a}}$

7. $\dfrac{a}{\sqrt{b}}$

8. $\dfrac{x}{\sqrt{xy}}$

9. $\dfrac{1}{\sqrt{8}}$

10. $\dfrac{1}{\sqrt{12}}$

11. $\dfrac{1}{\sqrt[3]{4}}$

12. $\dfrac{1}{\sqrt[3]{3}}$

13. $\dfrac{1}{1-\sqrt{2}}$

14. $\dfrac{1}{\sqrt{2}+\sqrt{3}}$

15. $\dfrac{1}{2\sqrt{5}-1}$

16. $\dfrac{\sqrt{2}}{3}$

17. $\dfrac{\sqrt{3}}{2}$

18. $\dfrac{\sqrt{5}}{2}$

19. $\dfrac{\sqrt{5}}{5}$

20. $\dfrac{\sqrt{6}}{3}$

21. $\dfrac{\sqrt{a}}{a}$

22. $\dfrac{\sqrt{8}}{2}$

23. $\dfrac{2+\sqrt{2}}{2}$

24. $\dfrac{\sqrt{3}-\sqrt{2}}{2}$

25. $\dfrac{\sqrt{2}-1}{2}$

Written

All letters represent positive real numbers.
Rationalize the denominator in each of the following:

Example: $\dfrac{2a\sqrt{x}}{x\sqrt{8ax}}$

$$\frac{2a\sqrt{x}}{x\sqrt{8ax}} \cdot \frac{\sqrt{2ax}}{\sqrt{2ax}} = \frac{2a\sqrt{2ax^2}}{x\sqrt{16a^2x^2}} = \frac{2ax\sqrt{2a}}{4ax^2} = \frac{\sqrt{2a}}{2x}$$

1. $\dfrac{8}{2\sqrt{32}}$

2. $\dfrac{2\sqrt{x}}{3\sqrt{2a^3}}$

3. $\dfrac{abc}{\sqrt{ab^2c^3}}$

4. $\dfrac{10x^3}{\sqrt{5ab^3x^5}}$

5. $\dfrac{4\sqrt{15}}{2\sqrt{12}}$

6. $\dfrac{a\sqrt{bc}}{b\sqrt{ac}}$

7. $\dfrac{5}{3\sqrt[3]{5}}$

8. $\dfrac{5a}{\sqrt[4]{3a}}$

9. $\dfrac{3axy}{\sqrt[3]{9ax^2y^3}}$

Example: $\dfrac{3}{\sqrt{11}-\sqrt{2}}$

$$\dfrac{3}{\sqrt{11}-\sqrt{2}}\cdot\dfrac{\sqrt{11}+\sqrt{2}}{\sqrt{11}+\sqrt{2}}=\dfrac{3(\sqrt{11}+\sqrt{2})}{11-2}=\dfrac{\sqrt{11}+\sqrt{2}}{3}$$

10. $\dfrac{3}{\sqrt{5}-\sqrt{3}}$

11. $\dfrac{\sqrt{2}}{\sqrt{3}+\sqrt{2}}$

12. $\dfrac{\sqrt{3}-1}{\sqrt{3}+1}$

13. $\dfrac{8}{2\sqrt{7}-5\sqrt{2}}$

14. $\dfrac{3\sqrt{5}-2\sqrt{7}}{\sqrt{5}+\sqrt{7}}$

15. $\dfrac{x-y}{\sqrt{x}+\sqrt{y}},\ x\neq y$

16. $\dfrac{3\sqrt{5}}{\sqrt{10}-\sqrt{5}}$

Rationalize the numerator in each of the following:

Example: $\dfrac{3\sqrt{2}+1}{3\sqrt{2}-1}$

$$\dfrac{3\sqrt{2}+1}{3\sqrt{2}-1}\cdot\dfrac{3\sqrt{2}-1}{3\sqrt{2}-1}=\dfrac{9(2)-1}{9(2)-6\sqrt{2}+1}=\dfrac{17}{19-6\sqrt{2}}$$

17. $\dfrac{3\sqrt{2}}{2\sqrt{3}}$

18. $\dfrac{2\sqrt{6}}{3\sqrt{10}}$

19. $\dfrac{a\sqrt{bc}}{b\sqrt{ac}}$

20. $\dfrac{4\sqrt{15}}{2\sqrt{12}}$

21. $\dfrac{2\sqrt[3]{3}}{3\sqrt[3]{2}}$

22. $\dfrac{\sqrt{a+b}}{\sqrt{a-b}},\ a\neq b$

23. $\dfrac{2\sqrt{6}}{\sqrt{3}-\sqrt{2}}$

24. $\dfrac{a-\sqrt{a}}{a}$

25. $\dfrac{3\sqrt{5}}{\sqrt{10}-\sqrt{5}}$

26. $\dfrac{\sqrt{2+h}-\sqrt{2}}{h}$

27. $\dfrac{\sqrt{x+h}-\sqrt{x}}{h}$

28. $\dfrac{\sqrt{3x+h}-\sqrt{3x}}{h}$

Exercise 56. Review Exercise

(A)

Exponents and Radicals: Perform the indicated operations. All letters represent positive rational numbers.

Written

1. $(-4x^2y^a)(3x^{a-1}y^3)$

2. $(20ab^4c^2) \div (-5a^2b^{-3}c^2)$

3. $5\sqrt{\frac{3}{5}} - 12\sqrt{\frac{5}{3}} + 6\sqrt{60}$

4. $(a^{-1} + 1)^{-1}$

5. $\dfrac{(2m^5r)(-2mn^0r^{-1})}{(2m^{-2})^2}$

6. $1^{2x} + 6x^0 - (2x)^0 + (\frac{1}{2})^{-1}$

7. $\sqrt{12} + 6\sqrt{\frac{1}{3}} - \dfrac{12}{\sqrt{3}} + \sqrt{50}$

8. Evaluate $\dfrac{6x^{-1}}{x^{-2} + y^{-2}}$ when $x = 2$ and $y = -2$.

9. $(-4x^2y^{5/2})\left(\dfrac{x^{-1}y^{-1/2}}{-2}\right)^2$

10. $\left(\dfrac{b^{m+n} \cdot b^{m-n}}{b^{2m}}\right)^{-4}$

11. Rationalize the numerator: $\dfrac{\sqrt{3} + \sqrt{2}}{\sqrt{3} - \sqrt{2}}$.

12. $\dfrac{a^{-2} + a^{-1}}{a}$

13. Find the value of a^7b^7 if $a = x^{2/7}y^{-3/2}$ and $b = \frac{1}{2}x^{-1/7}y^{1/2}$.

14. Rationalize the denominator: $\dfrac{3\sqrt{2} + 5\sqrt{3}}{3\sqrt{2} - \sqrt{3}}$

15. $\dfrac{a^2 - a^{-2}}{(a^{1/2} + a^{-1/2})(a^{1/2} - a^{-1/2})}$

16. If $x = 2$, find the value of $\dfrac{1 + 8^{-x/3}}{(8x)^{1/2} + 10^{x-2}}$.

17. Rationalize the denominator: $\dfrac{\sqrt{20}}{2\sqrt{5} + 1}$.

18. $(\sqrt{x} + \sqrt{y} + \sqrt{2y})(\sqrt{x} - \sqrt{y} - \sqrt{2y})$

19. $\dfrac{2^{-2} - 3^{-2}}{6^{-2} \cdot 5^0} + \dfrac{3}{7 - 4\sqrt{3}} + \dfrac{9}{\sqrt{27}}$

20. $2(8)^{2/3} - \sqrt{3}(12)^{1/2} - 10(3)^0 + \dfrac{1}{16^{-3/4}} + (a^{1/3}b^{-1})^3b^3 - (a^{-1} + b^{-1})^{-1}$

Multiple Choice: Select the correct answers for each of the following.

1. The prime factors of $x^3 - 8$ are

   (a) $(x - 2)^3$ (b) $(x - 2)(x^2 + 4)$
   (c) $(x - 2)(x + 2)(x + 2)$ (d) $(x - 2)(x^2 + 4x + 4)$
   (e) $(x - 2)(x^2 + 2x + 4)$

2. Simplify: $2^{-1} - 4^{-1}$

   (a) 2^{-1} (b) -2^{-1} (c) $-\frac{1}{4}$ (d) $\frac{1}{8}$ (e) $\frac{1}{4}$

3. Add: $\dfrac{a}{a + b} + \dfrac{b}{a - b}$

   (a) $\dfrac{a^2 + b^2}{a^2 - b^2}$ (b) $\dfrac{a^2 - ab + b^2}{a^2 - b^2}$ (c) 1

   (d) $\dfrac{2ab}{a^2 - b^2}$ (e) $\dfrac{1}{a - b}$

4. Simplify: $\sqrt{\frac{3}{4}} + \sqrt{\frac{1}{3}}$

   (a) $\frac{1}{5}\sqrt{3}$ (b) $\frac{5}{6}\sqrt{3}$ (c) $\frac{7}{12}\sqrt{3}$ (d) $\frac{1}{6}\sqrt{3}$
   (e) $5\sqrt{3}$

5. Solve the equations: $2x - y = 1$
$$x + y = 8$$

   (a) $(5,3)$ (b) $(3,5)$ (c) $(4,4)$
   (d) $(2,6)$ (e) $(-3,-5)$

6. John can dig his father's garden in 3 hours while Jim can do it in 6 hours. Working together they could do it in

   (a) 9 hrs   (b) 6 hrs   (c) 3 hrs   (d) 2 hrs   (e) 1 hr

7. If $2x - 3(x + 1) = 4x + 5$ then $x =$

   (a) $\frac{5}{8}$ (b) $\frac{8}{5}$ (c) $-\frac{8}{7}$ (d) $\frac{2}{5}$ (e) $-\frac{8}{5}$

8. Simplify: $\dfrac{2x + 1}{x} \div \left(1 - \dfrac{1}{4x^2}\right)$

   (a) $\dfrac{2x}{2x - 1}$ (b) $\dfrac{4x}{4x^2 - 1}$ (c) $\dfrac{2x}{4x^2 - 1}$ (d) $\dfrac{x}{2x - 1}$ (e) $\dfrac{4x}{2x - 1}$

9. The prime factors of $p^2q - pq^2$ are

   (a) $p(p + q)(p - q)$ (b) $q(p + q)(p - q)$ (c) $pq(p + q)$
   (d) $pq(p - q)$ (e) $pq(p - q)^2$

10. If $a = 2$, $b = -1$, $c = 3$ and $d = 1$, the value of $a^2(bd - bc) =$

    (a) 8   (b) 16   (c) -16 (d) -8 (e) 4

11. Simplify: $\dfrac{3}{\sqrt{2} + \sqrt{5}}$

    (a) $\sqrt{2} - \sqrt{5}$ (b) $\sqrt{2} + \sqrt{5}$ (c) $-\sqrt{2} + \sqrt{5}$

    (d) $\dfrac{\sqrt{2} - \sqrt{5}}{3}$ (e) $\dfrac{\sqrt{5} - \sqrt{2}}{3}$

12. Simplify: $\dfrac{a^{-1} + b^{-1}}{a^{-1}}$

    (a) $\dfrac{a}{a + b}$ (b) $\dfrac{b}{a + b}$ (c) $\dfrac{a + b}{a}$ (d) $\dfrac{a + b}{b}$ (e) $\dfrac{1}{b}$

13. Evaluate: $2 \cdot 2^{-1} + 3x^0 - (5x)^0$

    (a) -1 (b) 0 (c) 1 (d) $2\tfrac{1}{4}$ (e) 3

14. Simplify: $3^{a+3} \cdot 3^{a-3}$

    (a) 3^{a-6} (b) 3^{2a} (c) 9^{2a} (d) 3^{a^2-9} (e) 9^{a^2-9}

15. Two numbers whose ratio is 4:3 have their difference equal to 7. The larger number is

    (a) 4   (b) 7   (c) 21   (d) 28   (e) 49

16. If $\dfrac{1}{r} + \dfrac{1}{s} = \dfrac{1}{x}$, then $x =$

    (a) $r + s$ (b) $\dfrac{rs}{r + s}$ (c) $\dfrac{r + s}{rs}$ (d) rs (e) $\dfrac{1}{r + s}$

17. The sides of a rectangle are 6 and 8 units. If a square has the same area as the reactangle, the length of its side will be

    (a) 7   (b) $4\sqrt{3}$ (c) $3\sqrt{4}$ (d) $3\sqrt{6}$ (e) $4\sqrt{6}$

18. Multiply: $(2x - 3)(3x + 2) =$

    (a) $6x^2 - 6$ (b) $6x^2 - 13x - 6$ (c) $6x^2 + 13x - 6$

    (d) $6x^2 - 5x - 6$ (e) $6x^2 - 5x + 6$

19. Simplify: $\dfrac{\dfrac{1}{x} - \dfrac{1}{a}}{\dfrac{1}{x} + \dfrac{1}{a}}$

    (a) $\dfrac{a - x}{a + x}$ (b) $a - x$ (c) $\dfrac{a - x}{ax}$ (d) $\dfrac{x + a}{x - a}$ (e) $\dfrac{x - a}{x + a}$

20. The solution of $|2 - x| \le 2$ is

    (a) $-2 \le x \le 2$ (b) $-4 \le x \le 0$ (c) $0 \le x \le 4$

    (d) $2 \le x \le 6$ (e) $x \le 4$

QUADRATIC EQUATIONS

Oral

Solve for x. All other letters represent non-zero, real number constants.

1. $x^2 = 9$
2. $x^2 = 64$
3. $2x^2 = 8$

4. $-x^2 = -25$
5. $x^2 - 3 = 13$
6. $3x^2 - 12 = 0$

7. $47 = x^2 - 2$
8. $x^2 = a^2$
9. $x^2 - b^2 = 3b^2$

10. $x^2 = 4a^2b^2$
11. $x^2 = \dfrac{9m^2}{n^2}$
12. $a^2x^2 = b^2$

13. $x^2 = a^2 - 2ab + b^2$
14. $\dfrac{9x^2}{a^2} = 1$
15. $\dfrac{n^2x^2}{4} = m^2$

Written

State restrictions on the domain, if any, and solve for x. All other letters represent real number constants.

Example: $\dfrac{x^2 - 11}{3(x - 2)} = \dfrac{x + 2}{4}$

L.C.D. $= 12(x - 2)$ and $x \neq 2$.

$$4(x^2 - 11) = 3(x + 2)(x - 2)$$
$$4x^2 - 44 = 3(x^2 - 4)$$
$$4x^2 - 44 = 3x^2 - 12$$
$$x^2 = 32$$
$$x = \pm \sqrt{32}$$
$$x = \pm 4\sqrt{2}$$

1. $5x^2 - 116 = 9$
2. $\dfrac{16x^2}{9} - 3 = -\frac{2}{9}$

3. $x(4x - 6) = 81 - 6x$
4. $\dfrac{3x^2}{4} - \dfrac{2x^2}{3} = 3$

5. $4(x^2 - 7) = 3(x^2 + 4)$
6. $(x + 2)^2 + (x - 2)^2 = 8$

7. $x(3x - 7) + 4x = 3(3 - x)$ **8.** $2x(3x - 4) - 4x(2x - 2) = -9$

9. $\dfrac{1}{3x^2} + 2 = \dfrac{1}{x^2} - 1$

10. $(x + 1)(x - 1) - 3(x^2 - 6) - 2 = 0$

11. $a^2x^2 - 2a = a^2 + 1$ **12.** $mx^2 + m = m^2 + m, \; m > 0$

13. $-b^2 + a^2x^2 = 5b^2$ **14.** $mx^2 - n = m - 2n, \; m > n$

15. $(m + n)x^2 = m^2 - 2mn + n^2, \; m > n > 0$

16. $\dfrac{1}{3x - 2} - \dfrac{1}{3x + 2} = 3$

17. $\dfrac{2}{x + a} - 1 - \dfrac{2}{x - a} = \dfrac{-4}{x^2 - a^2}, \; x^2 \ne a^2$

18. $(x + 3m)(x - m) - (2x - m)(2x + m) = x(2m - 5x)$

19. $\dfrac{x}{x + 3} + \dfrac{2x}{2 - x} = 1 - \dfrac{3 + 9x}{x^2 + x - 6}$

20. $\dfrac{a + b}{a + x} - 2 - \dfrac{a - b}{x - a} + \dfrac{2bx - a^2}{a^2 - x^2} = 0$

Exercise 58. Complete Quadratic Equations

Oral

Complete the square in each of the following:

1. $x^2 + 4x$ **2.** $x^2 + 6x$ **3.** $x^2 - 12x$

4. $4x^2 + 12x$ **5.** $9x^2 + 30x$ **6.** $x^2 - 3x$

7. $x^2 - 7x$ **8.** $a^2 - \frac{2}{3}a$ **9.** $m^2 + m$

10. $p^2 - 5p$ **11.** $x^2 - \frac{3}{2}x$ **12.** $x^2 - \frac{4}{7}x$

13. $a^2x^2 + 2abx$ **14.** $x^2 - 3mx$ **15.** $x^2 + \dfrac{bx}{a}$

16. $x^2 - \dfrac{3mx}{n}$

Change to equivalent equations in which the left member is a trinomial square:

17. $x^2 + 2x = 3$ **18.** $x^2 + 8x = 0$ **19.** $x^2 - 4x + 2 = 0$

20. $x^2 - 6x - 1 = 0$ **21.** $x^2 - 3x = \frac{7}{4}$ **22.** $x^2 - \frac{2}{3}x = 2$

23. $4x^2 + 4x - 3 = 0$ **24.** $x^2 - 7x + 6 = 0$ **25.** $x^2 - 2mx = 3m^2$

26. $x^2 + bx = -c$ **27.** $a^2x^2 + 4abx = 0$ **28.** $x^2 + \dfrac{bx}{a} = -\dfrac{c}{a}$

Solve by factoring;

29. $x^2 - x = 0$ **30.** $x^2 - 3x = 0$ **31.** $x^2 + 7x = 0$

32. $4x^2 = 16x$ **33.** $x^2 - 2ax = 0$ **34.** $x^2 - 3x + 2 = 0$

35. $x^2 - 7x + 10 = 0$ **36.** $x^2 + 3x + 2 = 0$ **37.** $x^2 - 4x + 3 = 0$

38. $x^2 + 19x + 90 = 0$ **39.** $x^2 - 5x - 6 = 0$

40. $x^2 - 7x - 18 = 0$ **41.** $x^2 - 3ax + 2a^2 = 0$

42. $x^2 - 2mx - 15m^2 = 0$ **43.** $x^2 + 6x = 7$

Written

In each of the following problems, the domain of the variable x is the set of real numbers. All other letters represent real constants.

Solve by factoring:

Example: $6x^2 - 3x = 2x^2 + 9x$

$4x^2 - 12x = 0$

$4x(x - 3) = 0$

$4x = 0$ or $x - 3 = 0$

Ans. $x = 0$ or $x = 3$

1. $5x^2 + 3x = 2x^2 - 9x$ **2.** $2(x^2 + x) = 6x + 5x^2$

3. $27 + 6x = x^2$ **4.** $x^2 + 42 = 13x$

5. $x^2 - .5x - .24 = 0$ **6.** $3x^2 - 18x - 48 = 0$

7. $92 - 42x = 2x^2$ **8.** $6x^3 + 5x^2 + x = 0$

9. $2x^2 + 3x + 1 = 0$ **10.** $3x^2 + 13x = -4$

11. $8x + 5x^3 = 14x^2$ **12.** $x^2 - ax = 30a^2$

13. $a^2x^2 + 18 = 11ax, a \neq 0$ **14.** $m^2x^2 - 5mnx - 14n^2 = 0, m \neq 0$

15. $x^2 + (a + b)x + ab = 0$ **16.** $x^2 - (2b - 3c)x - 6bc = 0$

17. $x^2 + 3x - ax - 3a = 0$ **18.** $7(x^2 + x) = 24 + 6(x^2 - 6)$

19. $-33 + 3x(2x + 1) = 5(x^2 - 1)$ **20.** $2(x^2 - 7) + 2(2x + 7) = 7(x + 2)$

21. $5(x^2 + mx) - 18(2m^2 + 1) = 2(2x^2 - 9)$

22. $\dfrac{x^2}{x+2} + \dfrac{2x^2}{x-1} = \dfrac{6x}{x^2+x-2}$

23. $\dfrac{1}{3x+2} + \dfrac{1}{2-3x} - \dfrac{1}{2} = \dfrac{-12x}{18x^2-8}$

Solve by completing the square:

Example: $6x^2 - 15x = 9a^2$

Divide by 6, the coefficient of x^2.

$$x^2 - \frac{5x}{2} = \frac{3a^2}{2}$$

Add $(\frac{1}{2} \cdot \frac{5}{2})^2$, the square of half the coefficient of x.

$$x^2 - \frac{5x}{2} + \frac{25}{16} = \frac{3a^2}{2} + \frac{25}{16}$$

$$\left(x - \frac{5}{2}\right)^2 = \frac{24a^2 + 25}{16}$$

$$x - \frac{5}{2} = \pm\frac{\sqrt{24a^2 + 25}}{4}$$

$$\textbf{Ans.} \quad x = \frac{5}{2} \pm \frac{\sqrt{24a^2 + 25}}{4}$$

24. $x^2 + 4x + 3 = 0$

25. $x^2 + 8x + 3 = 12$

26. $x^2 + 6x - 7 = 0$

27. $x^2 - 10x = 11$

28. $4x^2 - 4x - 3 = 0$

29. $x^2 + \dfrac{2x}{3} - \dfrac{8}{9} = 0$

30. $x^2 - 3x = \frac{7}{4}$

31. $x^2 - \dfrac{5x}{2} = \frac{11}{16}$

32. $5x^2 - 20x - 25 = 0$

33. $2x^2 - 3x + \frac{5}{8} = 0$

34. $x^2 + 5x = -4$

35. $x^2 + 3x - 3 = 1$

36. $3x^2 + 2x = -\frac{1}{3}$

37. $x^2 + \dfrac{11x}{3} + \dfrac{10}{9} = 0$

38. $x^2 + 4x + 2 = 0$

39. $7x^2 - 7x + 42 = 56$

40. $x^2 + 6x + 1 = 0$

41. $x^2 + 10x - 2 = 0$

42. $x^2 + 8x = -4$

43. $10x + 3 = x^2 + 4$

44. $2x^2 - x - 3 = 0$

45. $2x^2 - 12x + 17 = 0$

46. $x^2 - x = \frac{1}{4}$

47. $9x^2 - 12x + 1 = 0$

48. $1 - x = x^2$

49. $x^2 + 6ax = 7a^2$

50. $m^2x^2 + 5mx = -4, m \neq 0$

51. $x^2 + \dfrac{3x}{a} + \dfrac{2}{a^2} = \dfrac{3}{4a^2}, a \neq 0$

52. $x^2 - ax - \dfrac{15a^2}{4} = 0$

53. $x^2 - 2x = a - 1$

54. $x^2 - 4x - m = -4$

55. $4x^2 - 6x = a - 36$

56. $x^2 - 2x = \dfrac{b}{4} - 1$

57. $4x^2 - 4ax - b^2 + a^2 = 0$

58. $4x^2 - 4mx - n = -m^2$

59. $x^2 - 4ax + 3 = 0$

60. $x^2 - 8ax - 4b = 0$

61. $x^2 + bx + c = 0$

62. $ax^2 + bx + c = 0, a \neq 0$

63. $ax^2 - 2bx + c = 0, a \neq 0$

Solve by using the quadratic formula:

Example: $3x^2 + 2 = 6x$

$\qquad 3x^2 - 6x + 2 = 0$

$\qquad$ Formula: $\quad x = \dfrac{-b \pm \sqrt{b^2 - 4ac}}{2a}$

$\qquad\qquad a = 3, b = -6, c = 2$

$\qquad\qquad x = \dfrac{6 \pm \sqrt{6^2 - 4(3)(2)}}{6}$

$\qquad\qquad x = \dfrac{6 \pm \sqrt{36 - 24}}{6} = \dfrac{6 \pm \sqrt{12}}{6} = \dfrac{6 \pm 2\sqrt{3}}{6}$

$\qquad\qquad$ Ans. $x = \dfrac{3 \pm \sqrt{3}}{3}$

64. $x^2 + 2x - 1 = 0$

65. $2x^2 + 3x + 1 = 0$

66. $2x^2 - 4x = 3$

67. $x^2 - 4x - 1 = 0$

68. $2x^2 - 2x = 2$

69. $x^2 + 7x = 0$

70. $2x^2 - 5 = 0$

71. $3x^2 = x + 14$

72. $6x + 2 = -3x^2$

73. $19 + 4x^2 = 20x$

74. $2(3x - 4) = x(x - 3)$

75. $(x + 2)(x - 1) = x^2 + (x + 1)^2$

76. $x(3x - 5) - (x + 2)(x - 2) = 7$

77. $\dfrac{x(x + 1)}{3} - \dfrac{x - 1}{2} = x^2 + x$

78. $(x + 5)(x - 1) - (2x + 3)^2 = x - 10$

Example: $x^2 - 4px = q^2 - 4p^2$

$x^2 - 4px + 4p^2 - q^2 = 0$

In the formula $a = 1$, $b = -4p$, $c = 4p^2 - q^2$

$$x = \frac{4p \pm \sqrt{16p^2 - 4(1)(4p^2 - q^2)}}{2}$$

$$= \frac{4p \pm \sqrt{16p^2 - 16p^2 + 4q^2}}{2}$$

$$= \frac{4p \pm \sqrt{4q^2}}{2} = \frac{4p \pm 2q}{2} = 2p \pm q$$

This problem could also be done by factoring.

$$x^2 - 4px + 4p^2 - q^2 = 0$$

$$(x^2 - 4px + 4p^2) - q^2 = 0$$

$$(x - 2p)^2 - q^2 = 0$$

$$[(x - 2p) + q][(x - 2p) - q] = 0$$

$$x - 2p + q = 0 \quad \text{or} \quad x - 2p - q = 0$$

$$x = 2p - q \quad \text{or} \quad x = 2p + q$$

79. $x^2 - 2x + 1 - a^2 = 0$

80. $x^2 - 2ax + a^2 = b^2$

81. $a^2x^2 - 3abx = -2b^2$, $a \neq 0$

82. $m^2x^2 - 2m^2x = n^2 - m^2$, $m \neq 0$

83. $4(x^2 - x) = a - 1$

84. $9x^2 - 6bx + b^2 - a = 0$

85. $m^2x^2 - 2amx + a^2 - b = 0$, $m \neq 0$

86. $a^2x^2 - b^2x^2 - 2ax + 1 = 0$, $a \neq 0$

87. $ax^2 - bx + 2c = 0$, $a \neq 0$

88. $mx^2 - 2nx - p = 0$, $m \neq 0$

Solve by the easiest method. Some equations may not have any solutions in the given domain.

89. $x^2 - 11x = 42$

90. $a^2x^2 + 6ax + 5 = 0$, $a \neq 0$

91. $x^2 - 1.3x + .42 = 0$

92. $3x^2 - 6x + 7 = 0$

93. $8x^2 = 32x$

94. $x^2 + 4m^2 = 1 - 4mx$

95. $5x = 3 + 3x^2$

96. $5x = 2 + 3x^2$

97. $5x = 3 - 3x^2$

98. $3x^2 - 6x - 7 = 0$

99. $x^2 - 4m^2 = 1 - 4m$

100. $x^2 + mx - nx - mn = 0$

101. $6x^2 = 12 - x$

102. $(2x - 3)(x + 1) + x(x + 1) = (x + 1)(x - 1)$

103. $4x + 6(3x^2 + 4x) = 4(11 - x)$

104. $\dfrac{7x^2}{2} + \dfrac{3 - x}{5} = \dfrac{x + 3}{4} + 2x^2$

105. $\dfrac{x}{2x + 5} + \dfrac{3x}{x - 2} = -\dfrac{7}{2 - x}$

106. $\dfrac{x + 1}{x^2 - x} + \dfrac{x - 2}{x^2 + x} + \dfrac{3x}{1 - x} = -3$

107. $\dfrac{1}{x^2 + 2x - 3} - \dfrac{3x}{x^2 - 2x + 1} - \dfrac{1}{x - 1} = 0$

Solve, finding the roots to the nearest hundredth:

Example: $x^2 - 3x - 6 = 0$

$$x = \frac{3 \pm \sqrt{9 - 4(1)(-6)}}{2} = \frac{3 \pm \sqrt{33}}{2}$$

Use a hand calculator and carry one extra place.

$$x = \frac{3 \pm 5.744}{2}$$

$$x = \frac{8.744}{2}, \quad \frac{-2.744}{2}$$

$$x = 4.372, \quad -1.372$$

Round off to hundredths.

Ans. $x = 4.37$ or -1.37

108. $3x^2 - 6x + 2 = 0$ **109.** $x^2 + 3x - 5 = 0$

110. $5x^2 - x - 1 = 0$ **111.** $6x^2 = 9x + 12$

112. $7x^2 = 17 - 3x^2$ **113.** $x^2 - .2x - .06 = 0$

114. $-.3x^2 - .5x + 1 = 0$ **115.** $7x^2 = 9x - 2$

116. $2x(x - 5) - 3x^2 = (x - 1)(x + 3)$

Exercise 59. Equations in Quadratic Form

Written

Solve on the domain of real numbers:

Example: $x^4 - 7x^2 + 12 = 0$

$(x^2 - 4)(x^2 - 3) = 0$

$(x + 2)(x - 2)(x^2 - 3) = 0$

$x + 2 = 0$ or $x - 2 = 0$ or $x^2 - 3 = 0$

$x = -2$ or $x = 2$ or $x^2 = 3$

Ans. $\{\pm 2, \pm\sqrt{3}\}$

1. $x^4 - 5x^2 + 4 = 0$
2. $x^4 + 9 = 10x^2$
3. $4x^4 - 36 = 0$
4. $x^4 = 4x^2$
5. $16x^4 - 72x^2 = -81$
6. $x^6 - 2x^3 + 1 = 0$
7. $x^6 - 28x^3 + 27 = 0$
8. $4x^4 - 12x^2 + 9 = 0$
9. $x^4 - 3x^2 + 2 = 0$
10. $x^{10} - 31x^5 - 32 = 0$
11. $(x + 1)^2 + 2(x + 1) + 1 = 0$
12. $(x + 3)^2 + 3(x + 3) - 10 = 0$
13. $(2x - 1)^2 - 5(2x - 1) = 14$
14. $(x + \frac{1}{3})^2 + (x + \frac{1}{3}) - 6 = 0$
15. $(x^2 + 1)^2 - 6(x^2 + 1) + 5 = 0$
16. $(x^2 - 3)^2 - 3(x^2 - 3) = 18$
17. $(x^2 - x)^2 - 18(x^2 - x) + 72 = 0$
18. $(x^2 + x - 1)^2 - 6(x^2 + x - 1) = -5$

Exercise 60. Quadratic Inequalities

Oral

Solve each of the following on the replacement set $S = \{-5, -4, -3, -2, -1, 0, 1, 2, 3, 4, 5\}$.

1. $x^2 > 1$
2. $x^2 < 5$
3. $x^2 \geq 0$
4. $x^2 \geq 20$
5. $x^2 \leq -2$
6. $2 < x^2 < 10$
7. $3 \leq x^2 \leq 16$
8. $(x + 1)^2 > 10$
9. $(x - 1)^2 < 5$
10. $0 < (x + 1)^2 < 5$
11. If $ab > 0$, what can be said about a and b?
12. If $ab < 0$, what can be said about a and b?

Solve each of the following on the domain of real numbers and draw the graph of the solution set on a number line.

Example: $x^2 + 3x < 0$

$\qquad x(x + 3) < 0$

Since the product is negative, the two factors must have opposite signs.

$\qquad\qquad x < 0$ and $x + 3 > 0$ $\quad$ or $\quad x > 0$ and $x + 3 < 0$

$\qquad\qquad x < 0$ and $x > -3$ $\qquad$ or $\quad x > 0$ and $x < -3$

Ans. $\qquad\qquad -3 < x < 0$ $\qquad\qquad\qquad$ impossible

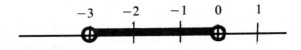

1. $x^2 > 4$
2. $x^2 < 25$
3. $x^2 \geq 100$
4. $x^2 \leq 16$
5. $x^2 < 7$
6. $x^2 > 12$
7. $x^2 + 4 < 0$
8. $x^2 + 9 > 0$
9. $(x + 1)^2 > 0$
10. $x(x - 2) < 0$
11. $x(x - 2) > 0$
12. $(x + 1)(x - 3) > 0$
13. $(x - 1)(x + 2) < 0$
14. $x^2 + 3x + 2 < 0$
15. $x^2 - 4x + 3 > 0$
16. $x^2 - 3x - 4 < 0$
17. $x^2 - 3x - 4 \geq 0$
18. $3x^2 \leq 9x$
19. $(1 - x)(2 + x) \leq 0$
20. $3 - 2x \leq x^2$
21. $x^2 - 2x + 1 < 0$
22. $5 - x^2 \leq 0$
23. $2x^2 - 5x + 2 \leq 0$
24. $x^2 - 3x - 1 \geq 0$

Exercise 61. Exponential and Radical Equations

Oral

Solve for x on the rational numbers.

1. $2^x = 2^3$
2. $2^x = 4$
3. $3^x = 3$
4. $3^{2x} = 3^4$
5. $2^x = 16$
6. $5^x = 125$
7. $3^{2x} = 27$
8. $5^x = 5^0$
9. $2^{x+1} = 1$
10. $2^x = \frac{1}{4}$
11. $10^x = 0.1$
12. $3^x = \frac{1}{3}$
13. $2^x = 0.5$
14. $x^{1/2} = 3$
15. $x^{1/3} = 2$
16. $x^{2/3} = 4$
17. $x^{-1/2} = 5$
18. $4^x = 8$
19. $x^{3/2} = 0$
20. $3^x = 1$
21. $\sqrt{x} = 4$
22. $\sqrt[3]{x} = 2$
23. $\sqrt{x} = -4$
24. $\sqrt[3]{x} = -2$
25. $\sqrt{x} = \sqrt{3}$
26. $\sqrt{x^2} = 9$
27. $\sqrt{|x|} = 5$
28. $\sqrt[3]{x} = \frac{1}{2}$
29. $\sqrt{x} = -1$
30. $\sqrt{-x} = 2$

Written

Solve for x on the domain of rational numbers. (The student is expected to place restrictions on the domain in problems **21–40**.)

Example: (a) $8^{x+1} = 16$ (b) $x^{3/2} = 27$

$(2^3)^{x+1} = 2^4$ $(x^{3/2})^{2/3} = 27^{2/3}$

$2^{3x+3} = 2^4$ **Ans.** $x = 3^2 = 9$

$3x + 3 = 4$

$3x = 1$

Ans. $x = \frac{1}{3}$

1. $x^{1/4} = 3$
2. $x = 16^{3/2}$
3. $2^x = 16$
4. $x^{3/5} = -8$
5. $x^{-3/4} = 27$
6. $4^x = 32$
7. $x^{-1} = 2$
8. $x^{5/2} = 32$
9. $x^{-1/2} = 5$
10. $x^{3/2} = 8$
11. $(\frac{1}{8})^x = 4$
12. $9^x = \frac{1}{27}$

13. $(\frac{1}{3})^{-x} = 27$

14. $(x + 2)^3 = 125$

15. $(x - 3)^{3/2} = 8$

16. $(x^2 - 1)^{-2} = \frac{1}{9}$

17. $(x^{-2/3} - 3)^2 = 1$

18. $3^{x-3} = 1$

19. $4^{2x} - 3(4^x) + 2 = 0$

20. $(x^{1/2} - \frac{1}{2})^{1/2} = \frac{1}{2}$

Example: $\sqrt{x - 1} + \sqrt{3x + 1} - 2 = 0$

The usual procedure is to square both sides, then CHECK the result. With three terms, put the two simpler on one side and isolate the most complicated before squaring.

$$\sqrt{3x + 1} = 2 - \sqrt{x - 1}$$

Square both sides.

$$3x + 1 = (2 - \sqrt{x - 1})^2$$
$$3x + 1 = 4 - 4\sqrt{x - 1} + x - 1$$
$$4\sqrt{x - 1} = 2 - 2x$$
$$2\sqrt{x - 1} = 1 - x$$

Square both sides again.

$$4(x - 1) = 1 - 2x + x^2$$
$$4x - 4 = 1 - 2x + x^2$$
$$0 = x^2 - 6x + 5$$
$$0 = (x - 5)(x - 1)$$
$$x - 5 = 0 \quad \text{or} \quad x - 1 = 0$$
$$x = 5 \quad \text{or} \quad x = 1$$

Each must be checked in the original equation.

$\sqrt{5 - 1} + \sqrt{15 + 1} - 2 \ ? \ 0$ $\sqrt{1 - 1} + \sqrt{3 + 1} - 2 \ ? \ 0$

$\sqrt{4} + \sqrt{16} - 2$ $0 + 2 - 2 = 0$

$2 + 4 - 2$

$4 \neq 0$ **Ans.** $x = 1$

5 is extraneous

21. $1 + \sqrt{x} = 5$

22. $\sqrt{3x - 2} = 7$

23. $\sqrt{3x - 1} = 3$

24. $\sqrt{49 - 8x} = 3$

25. $2\sqrt{3x} - 9 = 0$

26. $\sqrt[3]{x - 2} = -3$

27. $\sqrt{x^2 + 5} = 5 - x$

28. $\sqrt{x^2 - 8} = 8 - x$

29. $\sqrt{x + 14} - \sqrt{3x + 10} = 0$

30. $\sqrt{x - 1} = x - 1$

31. $2\sqrt{3x - 2} = \sqrt{2x - 3}$

32. $\sqrt{x + 5} = \sqrt{x} + 1$

33. $\sqrt{2x - 3} = 1 - \sqrt{2x}$

34. $\sqrt{x + 3} = 3x - 1$

35. $\sqrt{x + 7} = \sqrt{x} - \sqrt{7}$

36. $\sqrt{3x - 5} - \sqrt{x + 2} = 1$

37. $\sqrt{x^2 + 6} - x + 3 = 0$

38. $2x + 3 - \sqrt{2x + 3} = 12$

39. $\sqrt{\sqrt{\sqrt{9x + 3} + 1}} = 2$

40. $\sqrt{2x} - \sqrt{x + 1} = \dfrac{3}{\sqrt{x + 1}}$

Exercise 62. Simultaneous Quadratic Equations*

Written

Solve for x and for y:

Example: $x^2 + xy = 2$

$\qquad 2x - y = 5$

Solve the linear equation for either variable and substitute in the other. In this case solve for y in the second equation.

$$x^2 + xy = 2$$
$$\underline{\qquad\qquad y = 2x - 5}$$

$$x^2 + x(2x - 5) = 2$$

$$x^2 + 2x^2 - 5x - 2 = 0$$

$$3x^2 - 5x - 2 = 0$$

$$(3x + 1)(x - 2) = 0$$

$$3x + 1 = 0 \quad \text{or} \quad x - 2 = 0$$

$$x = -\tfrac{1}{3} \quad \text{or} \quad x = 2$$

$$y = -\tfrac{17}{3} \qquad y = -1$$

Ans.

x	2	$-\tfrac{1}{3}$
y	-1	$-\tfrac{17}{3}$

*Graphs of quadratic equations can be found in Exercise 68.

146

1. $x^2 + y^2 = 25$
   $x + y = 7$

2. $y = (x - 2)^2$
   $x - y = 2$

3. $x - y = 4$
   $xy = 12$

4. $xy + y^2 = 2$
   $3x - 2y = 1$

5. $x^2 + y = 2$
   $x + y = -4$

6. $y^2 - x = 4$
   $-x + 2y = 5$

7. $2xy - 5x^2 = 5$
   $3x - y = 2$

8. $x^2 - 2y^2 = 2$
   $x + y = 1$

9. $3x^2 - y^2 - 11 = 0$
   $2x - 3 = y$

10. $2y^2 - 10x^2 + 16y = 0$
    $3x - y = 4$

11. $x^2 - xy - 5y^2 = 1$
    $x - 5y = 2$

12. $y^2 - 8x^2 + y + 12x = 4$
    $6x - 2y = 4$

13. $x^2 - y^2 + x - y = 6$
    $2x - 3y = 1$

14. $3x - 2y = 7$
    $x^2 - y + xy = 11$

15. $x^2 - 4y^2 - 8 = 0$
    $\dfrac{x}{2} + 3y - 1 = 0$

16. $2x = 3y$
    $3(x - 2) + x^2 - y^2 = 3(x - 1)$

If both equations are quadratic, sometimes addition or subtraction will produce a linear equation in x and y, or a simple quadratic in just one variable.

Example: (a) $x^2 + 2y^2 = 11$

$\underline{x^2 - y^2 = 8}$ Subtract.

$$3y^2 = 3$$
$$y^2 = 1$$
$$y = \pm 1$$
$$x^2 = 9$$
$$x = \pm 3$$

x	3	3	-3	-3
y	1	-1	1	-1

(b) $(x - 3)(y + 2) = 18$

$\underline{ xy = 24}$

$xy - 3y + 2x - 6 = 18$

$\underline{ xy = 24}$

$$-3y + 2x - 6 = -6$$
$$2x - 3y = 0$$
$$x = \frac{3y}{2}$$

Substituting into $xy = 24$ gives

$$3y^2 = 48$$
$$y^2 = 16$$
$$y = \pm 4$$

Ans.

x	6	-6
y	4	-4

17. $x^2 + y^2 = 10$
$x^2 - y^2 = 8$

18. $x^2 - 3y^2 = 7$
$x^2 - y^2 = 25$

19. $xy = 2$
$xy + y + 3x = 7$

20. $xy = 15$
$(x - 3)y = 1$

21. $(x - 2)(y + 1) = 12$
$xy = 14$

22. $(x - 1)(y + 2) = 40$
$xy = 36$

23. $(x - 5)(y - 2) = 22$
$xy - 1 = 0$

24. $x^2 + x - y = 8$
$x - y = 6$

25. $x^2 + 2xy + y^2 = 4$
$x - y = 2$

26. $x^2 + 5xy + 6y^2 = 8$
$x + 3y = 16$

27. $x^2 + 2xy + y^2 + (x - y)^2 = 50$
$x + y = 7$

28. $2x - 3y = \frac{1}{2}$
$4x^2 + 9y^2 - 11xy = 2$

29. $3x^2 - 4xy + y^2 = 7$
$3x + y = 1$

30. $x^2 + 2xy = 3x + 2$
$3x + 2y = 7$

Exercise 63. Word Problems

Written

1. The square of a number added to 3 times the number equals 54. Find the number.

2. Find two consecutive numbers such that their product added to the smaller number equals 80.

3. Find a number which when added to its square equals 72.

4. On a 6 kilometer mountain climb, a party's average rate in kilometers per hour was 1 less than its time in hours. Find the average rate of the party.

5. Find two consecutive integers such that the sum of their squares added to the lesser number equals 21.

6. If 3 times a number added to $\frac{1}{2}$ of its square equals 80, find the number.

7. Find two consecutive even numbers the sum of whose squares is 100.

8. A folder of post cards sells for $1.20. If the number of cards is 7 more than the cost in cents of each card, find the number of cards in the folder.

9. Twice the sum of a number and its reciprocal equals $\frac{65}{4}$. Find the number.

10. The number of liters of gasoline used on a trip was 3 more than the cost in cents per liter. If the gasoline for the trip cost $9.90, how many liters were used?

11. The area of a lot that is 7 meters longer than it is wide is 144 square meters. Find its dimensions.

12. Find three consecutive numbers such that the square of the first number is 15 more than twice the sum of the other two numbers.

13. One number is 3 times as large as another number. Their product is 30 more than 3 times the larger number. Find the numbers.

14. Find a number such that twice that number added to 3 times its reciprocal equals $\frac{25}{2}$

15. Find two consecutive numbers such that their product is 8 more than twice their sum.

16. Find two numbers whose sum is $a + b$ and whose product is $2(ab - b^2)$.

17. The length of a strip of carpet is $5\frac{1}{2}$ times its width. If its area is $9\frac{7}{8}$ square meters, find its dimensions.

18. The sum of two numbers is 12. The sum of their squares is 4 more than twice their product. Find the numbers.

19. The denominator of a positive fraction is 6 more than its numerator. If the fraction is multiplied by its numerator, the result is 2 more than twice the original fraction. Find the fraction.

20. The denominator of a positive fraction is 2 more than its numerator. The fraction is $\frac{5}{8}$ less than its reciprocal. Find the fraction.

21. A rectangular field is 40 meters by 60 meters. If the length and the width of the field are increased by the same number of meters, the area will be doubled. By how many meters is each dimension increased?

22. The sum of the digits of a number is 10. The product of the digits is 12 less than the number. Find the number.

23. Find two consecutive whole numbers such that 5 times the larger divided by the square of the smaller gives 2 for a quotient and 2 for a remainder.

24. A rectangle is 2 cm longer than it is wide. By doubling the length of the rectangle and adding 3 cm to its width, the area is increased by 480 square centimeters. Find the original dimensions.

25. The sum of the digits of a number is 3. If the order of the digits is reversed, the result is 3 less than the product of the original number and its units' digit. Find the number.

26. Divide 78 into two positive factors such that the larger factor divided by the smaller factor gives a quotient of 2 and a remainder of 1.

27. A dealer bought a picture which he later sold for $24. If he gained a per cent equal to the cost in dollars of the picture, how much did the picture cost?

28. A rectangular garden is 8 meters wide and 10 meters long. If the length and the width are increased by the same number of meters, the area will be 40 square meters greater. By how many meters is each dimension increased?

29. If the sum of a certain number and 3 is multiplied by 9 minus the number, the result is 1 less than 3 times the number. Find the number.

30. A farmer ordinarily gets $135 for his apple crop. One year, when the price per barrel went up $.50, he found that he could keep 3 barrels for himself and still get the same amount for the rest. How many barrels does he usually sell, and at what price per barrel?

31. The product of two whole numbers exceeds twice their sum by 11, and twice the larger number is 1 less than 3 times the smaller. Find the numbers.

32. The expense of an entertainment costing $200 was to be divided equally among those present. If 20 more people than were expected came, reducing the cost per person by $.50, how many people finally came?

33. A steamer makes a trip of 2640 kilometers. If it should increase its average rate by 66 kilometers a day, it would take 2 days less for the trip. What is the usual number of days that the steamer takes for the trip?

34. Find the base and the altitude of a triangle the base of which is 5 centimeters less than its altitude and whose area is 88 square centimeters.

35. A man left $500 in a bank at simple interest for as many years as the per cent of interest that he received. If at the end of the time his principal and interest together amounted to $580, what was the rate of interest?

36. Two men can do a job together in $5\frac{5}{11}$ days. One man can do it alone in 2 days less than the other man. How long will it take each man to do the job alone?

37. A town appropriated $15,000 for repairing a section of road. As the construction cost $5 less a meter than was estimated, the town was able to

repair 100 meters more than had been planned. How many meters of road were repaired?

38. A fruit dealer bought melons for $35. Of these 8 were spoiled; but the dealer sold the rest for 30¢ apiece more than they cost him, gaining $7 on the transaction. How much did each melon cost him?

39. The width of a rectangle is 3 cm more than 75% of the length, and the area is 36 cm more than 18 times the width. What are the dimensions?

40. A field can be plowed in 3 hours with two tractors working together. One tractor would take $1\frac{3}{4}$ hours longer to do it alone than the other. How long would it take each tractor alone?

41. The perimeter of a rectangular platform is 10 meters 2 centimeters and the area is 440 square centimeters. Find its dimensions.

42. A square has 7 meters added to its width and 11 meters added to its length, making the resulting area 396 square meters. Find the area of the original square.

43. One man can split a cord of wood in 1 hour less than another man can. They work together 2 hours. Then the faster worker finishes alone in $3\frac{1}{4}$ hours. How long would it have taken each man to do the work alone?

44. A man bought a certain number of kilos of ham hocks for $4.80. The next day at a sale the price was 24¢ a kilo less. If the man had waited he could have purchased 1 kilo more for his $4.80. How many kilos did he buy?

45. A swimming pool 75 meters by 25 meters is surrounded by a tile platform of uniform width that has a floor space of 1725 square meters. Find the width of the platform.

46. A farmer ships 240 bushels of potatoes, half in bags and half in barrels. Each barrel holds 1 bushel more than each bag. If the farmer uses 32 more bags than barrels, how many bushels does a barrel hold?

47. In boarding up a square storeroom 7 meters high, the ceiling takes 60 square meters more lumber than one wall. Find the area of the floor space.

48. A boy started to divide 24 pieces of candy among some friends, but found that he must give each friend 1 piece less or 2 friends would not get any candy. How many friends had he if he divided the candy equally?

49. A storekeeper bought a lot of oranges for $6.00; but 10 of them spoiled and, although he sold the rest for 3¢ more apiece than they cost him, he lost 10% on the deal. How many oranges did he buy?

50. A man's stride is 20 cm longer than a boy's stride, and the man takes 500 less steps than the boy in walking 2 kilometers. How long is the boy's stride?

Exercise 64. Review Exercise on Quadratics

Written

(A)

Solve each of the following.

1. $x^2 + 9x = 22$

2. $\dfrac{x-1}{x} + \dfrac{x}{x-1} = \dfrac{5}{2}$

3. $\dfrac{5-x}{x-3} = \dfrac{4}{(x-1)(3-x)}$

4. $2\sqrt{x+2} + x = 1$

5. $(x+2)^2 \leq 25$

6. $x^4 - 13x^2 + 36 = 0$

7. $4x^2 + 4ax = b^2 - a^2$, where a and b are constants.

8. Solve for x and y: $\begin{cases} xy = 10 \\ x - y = 3 \end{cases}$

9. The difference of the cubes of two consecutive integers is 217. What are the numbers?

10. Two trains start from two stations at different rates of speed, each train going toward the other station. When they meet, one has traveled 108 kilometers farther than the other, and they finish the trip in 9 hours and 16 hours respectively. Find the rate of each train and the distance between stations.

(B)

State whether each of the following is TRUE or FALSE.

1. $(a + 2)$ is a factor of $a^4 - 13a^2 + 36$.

2. The equation $4x^2 + 5 = 1$ has no real solution.

3. When solving $x^2 - 8x = 1$ by completing the square, the next step is to add 16 to both sides.

4. To use the quadratic formula on $3x^2 - 4x = 7$; we would let $a = 3$, $b = -4$ and $c = 7$.

5. Three distinct real numbers will satisfy $x^4 = 9x^2$.

6. The solution of $x^2 < 5$ on the integers is $\{-2, -1, 0, 1, 2\}$.

7. If $27^x = 9$, then $x = \frac{2}{3}$.

8. $\sqrt{x+3} + 1 = 0$ has no real solution.

9. One solution of $12x^2 - 10x + \frac{1}{3} = 0$ is a positive number and the other is a negative number.

10. Seven times a certain integer is seven less than the square of the next larger integer. The integer could be either 6 or -1.

(C)

Multiple Choice: Select the correct answers for each of the following.

1. Solve for x: $6x^2 - 2 = x$

   (a) $\frac{1}{2}, \frac{2}{3}$ (b) $-\frac{1}{2}, \frac{2}{3}$ (c) $\frac{1}{2}, -\frac{2}{3}$

   (d) $-\frac{1}{2}, -\frac{2}{3}$ (e) $\frac{1}{3}, -1$

2. What is the difference between the areas of two squares if a side of the larger is $(m + 2)$ meters and a side of the smaller is $(2m - 3)$ meters?

   (a) $13 - m^2$ (b) $16m - 3m^2 - 5$ (c) $3m^2 - 16m + 5$

   (d) $3m^2 - 13$ (e) $5m^2 - 8m + 13$

3. Simplify: $(a^{-1} - b^{-1})^{-1}$

   (a) $\dfrac{ab}{b - a}$ (b) $\dfrac{ab}{a - b}$ (c) $\dfrac{ab}{a + b}$

   (d) $a - b$ (e) $\dfrac{1}{a - b}$

4. If Al can do a job in h hours and Bill can do the same job in k hours, the number of hours it will take them working together is

   (a) $\dfrac{h + k}{2}$ (b) $\dfrac{1}{h + k}$ (c) $\dfrac{hk}{h + k}$ (d) $\dfrac{h + k}{hk}$ (e) $h + k$

5. Simplify: $\left(\dfrac{\sqrt{x}\,y^{2/3}}{2x^{-1}}\right)^6$

   (a) $\dfrac{x^9 y^4}{2}$ (b) $2x^9 y^4$ (c) $\dfrac{64y^4}{x^9}$ (d) $\dfrac{x^9 y^4}{64}$ (e) $64x^9 y^4$

6. The tens' digit of a certain two digit number n, is one half the units' digit. Therefore n is always divisible by

   (a) 5   (b) 7   (c) 11   (d) 12   (e) 13

7. The solution to $x^2 - 6x + 7 = 0$ in simplest form is

   (a) $3 \pm \sqrt{2}$ (b) $-3 \pm \sqrt{2}$ (c) $3 \pm 2\sqrt{2}$

   (d) $1, -7$ (e) $-1, 7$

8. The value of x that satisfies $\sqrt{x - 8} = \sqrt{x} + 2$ is

   (a) No real number   (b) 0   (c) 8   (d) 9   (e) 36

9. The solutions of $2x^2 - xy = 6$ written in the form (x, y) are
   $$x - y = 1$$

   (a) $(1, 2), (-4, -3)$ (b) $(2, -4), (-3, 1)$

   (c) $(2, 1), (-3, -4)$ (d) $(-2, -3), (3, 2)$

   (e) $(-3, -2), (-4, 1)$

10. The real numbers in the solutions of $(x - 2)(x + 5) < 0$ are

(a) $2 < x < -5$ (b) $-5 < x < 2$ (c) $x < -5$ or $x > 2$
(d) $x > -5$ or $x < 2$ (e) $\{-4, -3, -2, -1, 0, 1\}$

(D)

Multiple Choice: Select the correct answer for each of the following.

1. Simplify: $\dfrac{x - 1}{x + 1} \sqrt{\dfrac{x + 1}{x - 1}}$

(a) 1 (b) $\dfrac{(x - 1)^2}{(x + 1)^2}$ (c) $\dfrac{\sqrt{x + 1}}{x + 1}$ (d) $\dfrac{\sqrt{x^2 - 1}}{x + 1}$ (e) $\dfrac{\sqrt{x^2 - 1}}{x - 1}$

2. Simplify: $1 / \left(\dfrac{1}{a} + \dfrac{1}{b} \right)$

(a) $\dfrac{1}{a} + \dfrac{1}{b}$ (b) $a + b$ (c) $\dfrac{ab}{a + b}$ (d) $\dfrac{a + b}{ab}$ (e) ab

3. Evaluate: $\dfrac{1}{8^{-2/3}} - 3x^0 + 27^{-1/3} - 1^{2/3}$

(a) $\frac{1}{3}$ (b) $2\frac{1}{3}$ (c) $-1\frac{5}{12}$ (d) 3 (e) 5

4. Simplify: $\dfrac{\sqrt{2} - \sqrt{3}}{\sqrt{2} + \sqrt{3}}$

(a) -1 (b) $2\sqrt{6} - 5$ (c) $5 - 2\sqrt{6}$ (d) $\sqrt{6} - 5$ (e) $\dfrac{2\sqrt{6} - 5}{5}$

5. If $a = 5$, $b = 7$, $c = 4$ and $s = \dfrac{a + b + c}{2}$, evaluate

$\sqrt{s(s - a)(s - b)(s - c)}$

(a) $4\sqrt{6}$ (b) $12\sqrt{12}$ (c) $8\sqrt{3}$ (d) $12\sqrt{6}$ (e) $4\sqrt{3}$

6. Solve: $x + y = 2a$
$\qquad\quad\; x - y = 2b$

(a) $x = 2a$ (b) $x = a$ (c) $x = 3a + b$ (d) $x = a + b$
$\quad\;\; y = 2b$ $\quad\;\; y = b$ $\quad\;\; y = -a - b$ $\quad\;\; y = a - b$

(e) $x = a - b$
$\quad\;\; y = a + b$

7. Solve: $2x = x^2 - 3$

(a) $(3, -1)$ (b) $(-3, 1)$ (c) $(2, -1)$
(d) $(3, 1)$ (e) $(-3, -1)$

8. In five tests Mary had an average of 82. On the final exam, which counts as much as 3 tests, she made 71. To the nearest integer, her final average is

(a) 76   (b) 77   (c) 78   (d) 79   (e) 80

9. Solve the equations on the domain of the positive reals.

$$xy = 24$$
$$y = x - 5$$

(a) $x = 3$ (b) $x = -3$ (c) $x = 8$ (d) $x = 12$ (e) $x = 8$
    $y = 8$ $y = -8$ $y = -3$ $y = 7$ $y = 3$

10. The solutions of $2x^2 - 3x - 3 = 0$ are

(a) $\dfrac{3 \pm \sqrt{33}}{4}$ (b) $\dfrac{-3 \pm \sqrt{33}}{4}$ (c) $\dfrac{3 \pm \sqrt{15}}{2}$

(d) $\dfrac{3 \pm \sqrt{33}}{2}$ (e) $\dfrac{-3 \pm \sqrt{15}}{4}$

RELATIONS AND FUNCTIONS

Exercise 65. Relations and Functions

Oral

Determine whether each of the following sets describes a relation or not. Which of those that are relations are functions?

1. $\{(0, 1), (1, 2), (2, 3)\}$ 2. $\{(1, 2), (1, 3)\}$

3. $\{0, 1, 2, 3\}$ 4. $\{(-1, 1), (1, -1)\}$

5. $\{(2, 1), (2, 2), (3, 2)\}$ 6. $\{2, 3\}$

7. $\{(1, 2), (2, 2), (3, 2)\}$ 8. $\{(3, 5), (4, 5), (5, 5)\}$

9. $\{1, (2, 3)\}$ 10. $\{(x, 3) : x \text{ is an integer}\}$

11. $\{xy : x \text{ and } y \text{ are natural numbers}\}$ 12. $\{(1, 2, 3), (4, 5, 6)\}$

13. $\{(x, y): x \text{ is an integer and } y = 2x\}$ 14. $\{(x, y): y = x^2\}$

15. $\{(x, 3x) : |x| < 3 \text{ and integral}\}$ 16. $\{(2a, 2): a \text{ is an integer}\}$

17. $\{x + y : 0 < x < 1 \text{ and } 0 < y < 1\}$ 18. $\{(x - y): y = |x|\}$

19. $\{2x - 3 : x \text{ is an integer}\}$ 20. $\{(x, y) : x = y^2\}$

The domain of each of the following functions is the set of natural numbers. (Some of the requested function values may not be defined.)

21. If $f(x) = x + 1$; find $f(1)$, $f(2)$, $f(0)$, $f(10)$.

22. If $g(x) = 2x + 3$; find $g(1)$, $g(\frac{1}{2})$, $g(2)$, $g(10)$.

23. If $h(x) = 2x^2 - x + 1$; find $h(1)$, $h(2)$, $h(-2)$, $h(3)$.

24. If $f(x) = \dfrac{1}{x} - x$; find $f(1)$, $f(2)$, $f(3)$, $f(10)$.

25. If $f(x) = 3x$ and a is a natural number; find $f(2a)$, $2f(a)$, $f(a^2)$, $[f(a)]^2$.

26. If $f(x) = 3x - 1$ and a is a natural number; find $f(2a)$, $2f(a)$, $f(a^2)$, $[f(a)]^2$.

27. $f = \{(0, 2), (1, -1), (2, 3), (3, -1), (4, 2), (5, 3)\}$. What is the domain of f? What is the range of f? Find $f(0)$, $f(4)$, $f(2)$, $f(-1)$, $f(5)$.

28. $g = \{(-1, 2), (0, 5), (1, -2), (3, 5)\}$. What is the domain of g? What is the range of g? Find the values of $g(-1)$, $g(3)$, $g(0)$, $g(1)$, $g(2)$.

29. The domain of g is the set of positive integers. Let $g(x) = 0$ if x is prime, and $g(x) = 1$ if x is not prime. Find $g(1)$, $g(2)$, $g(3)$, $g(4)$, $g(5)$, $g(6)$, $g(7)$, $g(35)$, $g(47)$. Is g a function or relation? Why?

30. The domain of F is the set of positive integers. Let $F(x) = 1$ if $(-1)^x$ is positive and $F(x) = 0$ if $(-1)^x$ is negative. Find $F(1)$, $F(2)$, $F(3)$, $F(4)$, $F(234)$, $F(467)$.

31. A boy weighs himself every morning for a week and records his weights as follows: Monday 131, Tuesday 132, Wednesday 131, Thursday 130, Friday 129, Saturday 131, Sunday 130. Is the relationship between the days and his weights a relation or a function? What is the domain and range?

32. A college student records the number of letters he sends and receives each day as follows.

d: day	s: sent	r: received
Mon	2	1
Tue	0	1
Wed	0	2
Thu	1	0
Fri	0	1
Sat	1	1
Sun	2	0

Consider the set of ordered pairs (r, s) from the table. Is this relation a function? What is the domain and the range of this relation? Consider the set of ordered pairs (d, s). Is this a relation or a function?

If the domain of each of the following functions is the set of positive integers, determine the range in each case.

33. $f(x) = x + 1$

34. $f(x) = 2x$

35. $f(t) = 2t + 1$

36. $f(a) = \dfrac{1}{a + 1}$

37. $f(x) = \dfrac{2x + 2}{x + 1}$

38. $f(x) = x^2 - 1$

Written

Each of the following functions has as its domain the set of all rational numbers except zero. (Some of the function values might not be defined.)

Example: If $f(x) = \dfrac{x^2 + 2}{3}$; find the values of $f(-1), f(0), f(a + 1)$.

$$f(-1) = \frac{(-1)^2 + 2}{3} = \frac{1 + 2}{3} = 1$$

$f(0)$ is undefined because 0 isn't in the domain.

$$f(a + 1) = \frac{(a + 1)^2 + 2}{3} = \frac{a^2 + 2a + 1 + 2}{3} = \frac{a^2 + 2a + 3}{3}$$

1. If $f(x) = \dfrac{3 - 2x}{3}$; find the value of $f(0), f(-1), f(-2), f(2)$.

2. If $g(x) = 2x - x^3$; find the value of $g(-1), g(1), g(2), g(-2)$.

3. If $h(x) = \dfrac{1}{x^2} - x^2$; find the value of $h(1), h(-1), h(2), h(\sqrt{2})$.

4. If $g(x) = \dfrac{1}{1 + x^2}$; find the value of $g(1), g(0), g(-1), g(2), g(-2)$.

5. If $f(x) = 3x - 2$; find $f(\frac{1}{3}), f(\frac{2}{3}), f(\frac{3}{2}), f(-1)$.

6. If $f(x) = x^2 - \dfrac{1}{x}$; find $f(1), f(2), f(\frac{1}{2}), f(-1)$.

7. If $f(x) = 2x^3 - \dfrac{1}{x^2}$; find $f(\frac{1}{2}), f(2), f(3), f(-\frac{1}{3})$.

8. If $f(x) = 2x$; find $f(a + b), f(a) + f(b), f(ab)$, and $f(a)f(b)$.

9. If $g(x) = 2x + 1$; find $g(a + b), g(a) + g(b), g(ab)$, and $g(a)g(b)$.

10. If $h(x) = x^2$; find $h(a + b), h(a) + h(b), h(ab)$, and $h(a)h(b)$.

Example: If $f(x) = x + 3$ and $g(x) = 1 - 4x$, find the values of $f(g(x))$ and $g(f(x))$.

$f(g(x)) = f(1 - 4x) = (1 - 4x) + 3 = 4 - 4x$
$g(f(x)) = g(x + 3) = 1 - 4(x + 3) = 1 - 4x - 12 = -11 - 4x$

11. If $f(x) = 2x + 1$ and $g(x) = x^2$, find the values of $f[g(a)]$ and $g[f(a)]$.

12. If $f(x) = 2x$ and $g(x) = \dfrac{x}{2}$, find the values of $f[g(a)]$ and $g[f(a)]$.

158

13. If $f(x) = 2x$, $g(x) = 2x + 1$, and $h(x) = x^2$, find the value of $f(g[h(a)])$.

14. If $f(x) = 2x$, $g(x) = 2x - 1$, and $h(x) = \frac{1}{2}x^2$, find the value of $h(f[g(a)])$.

15. If $f(x) = \dfrac{x}{2}$, $g(x) = x + 1$, and $h(x) = 2x$, find the value of $h(g[f(a)])$.

16. Functions f and g are given as follows:

$$f = \{(1, 3), (2, 1), (3, 2)\}$$
$$g = \{(1, 1), (2, 3), (3, 2)\}$$

(a) Determine the function s defined by $s(x) = f(x) + g(x)$.

(b) Determine the function p defined by $p(x) = f(x) \cdot g(x)$.

(c) Find the values of $f[g(1)]$, $f[g(2)]$, $f[g(3)]$.

(d) Determine $g[f(x)]$ for each x in the domain of f.

17. The functions f and g are given as:

$$f = \{(x, f(x)) : f(x) = 2x - 1 \text{ and } x = 0, 1, 2, 3, 4\}$$
$$g = \{(x, g(x)) : g(x) = x + 1 \text{ and } x = 2, 3, 4, 5, 6\}$$

Write out f and g as sets of ordered pairs. What is the domain of f and the domain of g? What is the domain of h where $h(x) = g(x) + f(x)$? Write out h as a set of ordered pairs. Write h in the same form as f and g were given. Do the same for F if $F(x) = f[g(x)]$ and for G if $G(x) = g[f(x)]$.

18. The functions f and g are defined by the formulas $f(x) = 2x + 1$ and $g(x) = 2 - 3x$ for all x. If we define the function $f + g$ as $[f + g](x) = f(x) + g(x)$ and the function fg as $[fg](x) = f(x)g(x)$, find formulas for $f + g$, fg, $2f + 3g$ and $3f + 2g$. Find a formula for $f \circ g$, where $f \circ g$ is defined as $[f \circ g](x) = f[g(x)]$. Find a formula for H, where $H = g \circ f$.

Determine the largest subset of the real numbers which can be the domain in each of the following functions.

Example: $f(x) = \sqrt{x - 1} + \dfrac{1}{x - 4}$

For $\sqrt{x - 1}$ to be defined, we must have $x - 1 \geq 0$; that is, $x \geq 1$. For $\dfrac{1}{x - 4}$ to be defined, we must have $x - 4 \neq 0$; that is, $x \neq 4$. Therefore, the domain is $x \geq 1$ and $x \neq 4$.

19. $f(x) = \dfrac{1}{x}$ **20.** $g(x) = \sqrt{x}$ **21.** $F(x) = \dfrac{1}{x + 1}$

22. $G(x) = \sqrt{1 - x}$ **23.** $f(x) = \dfrac{1}{x + 1} + \dfrac{1}{x - 1}$

If the domain in each of the following functions is the set of non-negative integers, determine the range for each.

24. $f(x) = \dfrac{1}{x + 3}$ **25.** $f(x) = 3 - x$

26. $g(x) = 20 - 7x$ **27.** $g(x) = \dfrac{x^2 - 4}{x + 2}$

28. $h(x) = \dfrac{x^2 + 2x + 1}{x + 1}$

29. The table below determines a function g. State the domain and range of g and find a formula for the rule of correspondence.

t	1	2	3	4	5
$g(t)$	0	3	8	15	24

30. If f is defined by the formula $f(x) = 2x - 3$ for all x, find $f(2)$, $f(6)$, $f(0)$, $f(-1)$, $f(x + 1)$, $f(x^2)$, $f\left(\dfrac{x}{2}\right)$, $f(3x)$.

31. g is a function whose domain is all real numbers. If $g\left(\dfrac{x}{2}\right) = 2x - 3$, determine $g(x)$, $g(2x)$, $g(1)$, $g(3)$, $g(0)$.

32. If h is a function whose domain is all real numbers and $h(3x) = 3x^2 - 6x$, find $h(x)$, $h(2)$, $h(0)$, $h(-1)$, $h(a)$.

33. If $f(x) = \sqrt{5 - x}$ and both x and $f(x)$ are real numbers, find the restrictions on the domain and range of f.

34. If $g(x) = \sqrt{x^2 - 4}$ and x and $g(x)$ are real numbers, find restrictions on the domain and range of g.

35. If $f(x) = |x| - 1$ and x and $f(x)$ are real, find the maximal real domain and the range of f.

36. If $f(x) = x^2 + 1$, find the maximal real domain and the range of f.

37. If $f(x) = x^3 - x$ show that $f(-x) = -f(x)$ for all real x.

38. If $f(x) = x^4 - 2x^2 + 6$, show that $f(x) = f(-x)$ for all real x.

A zero of a function is the number from the domain which gives the value zero from the range. Determine the zeros, if any, of the following functions whose domains consist of all allowable real numbers.

Example: $f(x) = \dfrac{x}{x + 2} - \dfrac{3}{x - 2} + \dfrac{12}{x^2 - 4}$

The domain is all the reals except ± 2. $f(x) = 0$ when

$$\frac{x}{x + 2} - \frac{3}{x - 2} + \frac{12}{x^2 - 4} = 0$$

$$x(x - 2) - 3(x + 2) + 12 = 0$$

$$x^2 - 5x + 6 = 0$$

$$x = 2 \text{ or } x = 3$$

Ans. Since $2 \notin$ domain, the only zero is 3.

39. $f(x) = 2x - 1$

40. $f = \{(0, 1), (1, 2), (2, 3)\}$

41. $g = \{(-1, 1), (0, 2), (1, 0)\}$

42. $f(x) = x^2 - 9$

43. $g(x) = \dfrac{1}{x - 1} + \dfrac{1}{x + 1}$

44. $f(x) = x - \dfrac{1}{x}$

45. $g(x) = x^2 + 2x + 3$

46. $h(t) = |t| - t$

47. $F(x) = \dfrac{x^2 - 1}{x + 1}$

48. $G(x) = \dfrac{x^2 + 1}{x + 1}$

49. $G(x) = \sqrt{x + 1} - 3$

50. $F(x) = \sqrt{x + 3} + 1 - 3x$

GRAPHS

Exercise 66. Graphs of Linear Equations

Oral

If the four quadrants of the plane are named I, II, III, and IV as in the diagram, determine the quadrant or axis in which each of the following points are located.

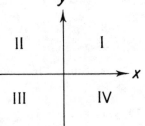

1. $A = (0, 1)$
2. $B = (2, 0)$
3. $C = (-3, 0)$
4. $D = (0, 5)$
5. $E = (2, 1)$
6. $F = (2, -1)$
7. $G = (-2, 1)$
8. $H = (-3, -2)$
9. $I = (3, 2)$
10. $J = (3, -2)$
11. $K = (-5, -5)$
12. $L = (-2, 3)$

Determine the slope and y-intercept for each of the following.

13. $y = 2x + 3$
14. $y = 4 - x$
15. $y = \frac{1}{2}x + 7$
16. $y = 3x$
17. $y = 3$
18. $2y = x - 4$
19. $3y = 6 - x$
20. $-2y = 3x - 5$
21. $x + y = 5$
22. $x - y = 3$

23. If (x, y) is a point whose coordinates satisfy the equation $y = 2x + 1$, find y if $x = 0$, and if $x = 2$. Determine the value of y of corresponding to each x in the following table.

x	0	2	−1	−2	3	5
y						

Do the same as in example 23 for each of the following equations.

24. $y = 3x + 2$
25. $2x + y = 1$
26. $2x + 3y = 6$
27. $3x - 4y = 12$
28. $3x + 5y = 7$
29. $5x - 6y = 30$
30. $3x + 2y = 6$

162

Which of the following pairs of equations are inconsistent (equations of parallel lines), which are dependent (equations of the same line), and which are independent (equations of intersecting lines)?

31. $x + y = 2$
$\quad\ \ x + y = 3$

32. $x - y = 5$
$\quad\ \ x - y = 7$

33. $2x - y\ \ = 8$
$\quad\ \ 6x - 3y = 24$

34. $x + y = 5$
$\quad\ \ x - y = 5$

35. $x = 3$
$\quad\ \ y = 5$

36. $y = 2x + 3$
$\quad\ \ y = 2x + 7$

37. $y = x\ \ - 2$
$\quad\ \ y = 2x - 4$

38. $y = 4$
$\quad\ \ y = -4$

39. $\ \ y = 3x - 1$
$\quad\ \ 3x = y - 1$

40. $\dfrac{x}{2} + \dfrac{y}{3} = 2$
$\quad\ \ 3x + 2y = 12$

Give an example of each of the following.

41. An equation of a horizontal line through $(2, 3)$.

42. An equation of a vertical line through $(-2, -3)$.

43. An equation of a line through the origin with slope 1.

44. An equation of a line through the origin with slope 2.

45. An equation of a horizontal line through the origin.

Written

1. (a) Plot the points $(0, 0)$, $(1, 2)$, $(3, 6)$, $(-2, -4)$.
  (b) Plot the points $(1, 2)$, $(2, 0)$, $(3, -2)$, $(4, -4)$.
  (c) Plot the points $(-6, -5)$, $(-3, -2)$, $(0, 1)$, $(3, 4)$.

For each of the pairs of points in problems 2-15; do (a), (b), and (c).
  (a) Determine the slope.
  (b) Determine the equation of the line through the two points.
  (c) Draw the graph.

Example: $(5, 2)$, $(2, -3)$

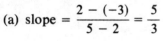

  (a) slope $= \dfrac{2 - (-3)}{5 - 2} = \dfrac{5}{3}$

(c)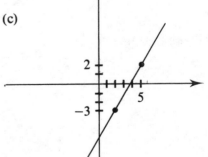

  (b) Use the point-slope formula:

$$y - y_1 = m(x - x_1)$$
$$y - 2 = \tfrac{5}{3}(x - 5)$$
$$3y - 6 = 5x - 25$$
$$5x - 3y = 19$$

163

2. (2,3), (0,0)   **3.** (−1,5), (0,0)

4. (6,2), (5,2)   **5.** (6,2), (5,1)

6. (−1,2), (3,5)   **7.** (−2,−3), (−5,−4)

8. (−2,−5), (1,−7)   **9.** (9,−3), (7,−1)

10. (73,27), (23,−13)   **11.** (17,−5), (6,−13)

12. (5,−2), (5,3)   **13.** (−2,3), (4,−3)

14. (0,5), (3,−7)   **15.** (−2,1), (−2,0)

For each of the following equations:
(a) determine the slope of the graph
(b) determine the y-intercept of the graph
(c) determine the x-intercept of the graph
(d) draw the graph

16. $y = 2x + 3$ **17.** $y = 2x + 5$

18. $y = -3x + 6$ **19.** $2x - 3y = 12$

20. $\dfrac{x}{3} + \dfrac{y}{2} = 1$ **21.** $x = 2y + 4$

22. $\dfrac{2x}{3} + \dfrac{3y}{4} = 1$ **23.** $3x + 2y = 5$

24. $2x - 3y = 0$ **25.** $4x - 6y = 10$

Draw the graphs of the equations:

Example: $y = |x| + 2$.

Plot several points and draw a broken line connecting them.

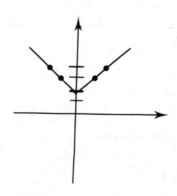

26. $y = |x - 2|$

27. $y = 3 - |x + 1|$

28. $y = |x| - 3$

29. $|x + 2| + y = 5$

30. $y + 3 = \frac{1}{2}|x - 2|$

31. $y - 1 = 2|x - 1|$

32. $x + 1 = |y - 3|$

33. $x - 2 = 2|y + 1|$

Determine an equation for each of the following lines.

Example: The line through (5, 2) with slope of $\frac{5}{3}$.

The equation of any line with slope a/b always has the form $ax - by = k$ where k is some constant. In this case $5x - 3y = k$. Since the point (5, 2) lies on the line, its coordinates must satisfy the equation

$$5 \cdot 5 - 3 \cdot 2 = k$$

$$19 = k$$

Therefore the equation is $5x - 3y = 19$.

The slope-intercept method would give:
$y - 2 = \frac{5}{3}(x - 5)$ which is the same equation in a different form.

34. The line through (0,0) with slope -1.

35. The line through (2,3) with slope -1.

36. The line through $(-2,-3)$ with slope -1.

37. The line through (2,3) with slope 3.

38. The line through (2,3) with slope -3.

39. The line through (2,3) with slope $-\frac{1}{3}$.

40. The line through $(-1,5)$ with slope -2.

41. The line through (5,6) with slope $\frac{2}{3}$.

42. The line through $(-1,0)$ with slope 0.

43. The line through $(-1,-5)$ with slope $-\frac{2}{7}$.

Draw on the same axes the graphs of the following pairs of equations.
Find the coordinates of the points, if any, which lie on both lines.
Sketch the graph of each equation on the same axes and estimate the co-
ordinates of the point of intersection.

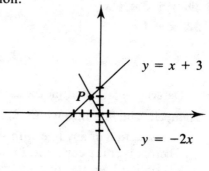

$y = x + 3$

$y = -2x$

Example: $x - y = -3$

$2x + y = 0$

Ans. $P = (-1,2)$

44. $x + y = 6$
$x - y = 2$

45. $y = 2x + 3$
$y = 3x + 2$

46. $3x + 2y = 6$
$4x - 3y = 8$

47. $3x - 2y = -7$
$2x - 4y = -10$

48. $2x + y = 6$
$2x + y = 8$

49. $3x + 7y = 0$
$4x - 15y = 0$

50. $x - 3y = 7$
$2x - 6y = 14$

51. $2x + 5y = -11$
$3x - 2y = 12$

52. $7x - 3y = 10$
$4x + 3y = 1$

53. $3x - 6y = 9$
$8y - 4x = 12$

54. $\dfrac{x}{2} + \dfrac{y}{3} = \dfrac{10}{3}$
$2x - y = 4$

55. $3x - 6y = 9$

$4x - 8y = 12$

56. $2x - 3y = 10$
$3x + 2y = 2$

57. $2x = 4(2y + 2)$
$3(x - 3y) + 2 = 17$

Draw graphs of the following pairs of equations and solve the equations
simultaneously by noting the points of intersection.

58. $y = |x|$
$x = 3y - 4$

59. $y = |x - 1|$
$y = x + 1$

60. $y - 1 = \tfrac{1}{2}|x - 2|$
$y = 4$

61. $y - 1 = \tfrac{1}{2}|x - 2|$
$3y + x = 10$

62. $y = |x|$
$y = 2 - |x|$

63. $x - 2y = 6$
$y = |x - 6|$

166

Exercise 67. Graphs of Linear Inequalities

Oral

Describe the region in the plane determined by each of the following.

1. $x > 3$ 2. $y > -2$ 3. $x \le -1$
4. $y \le 2$ 5. $y = x$ 6. $y > x$
7. $y < x$ 8. $y = 2x - 3$ 9. $y \ge 2x - 3$
10. $y \le 2x - 3$ 11. $x + y > 4$ 12. $x - y \le 3$
13. $\{(x,y) : y < 2x\}$ 14. $\{(x,y) : y \ge x + 1\}$

Written

In the plane shade the regions which are determined by each of the following inequalities.

Example: $3x + 4y > 12$.

First solve for y: $y > -\frac{3}{4}x + 3$.
Then sketch the graph of $y = -\frac{3}{4}x + 3$, and shade the region above the line.

1. $y \le 4$ 2. $2x \ge 5$ 3. $y < 2x + 3$
4. $y < 3 - 2x$ 5. $y > 3x - 4$ 6. $2x - 3y \le 6$
7. $2x + y \le 0$ 8. $3x + 4y \ge 12$ 9. $3x + 6 \le 2$
10. $x - 3y \ge 6$ 11. $y \le |x|$ 12. $y \ge |2x| - 1$

In the plane determine and shade the regions whose points satisfy simultaneously all the inequalities of each set.

Example: $-3 < x \le 3$; $y < x + 2$ and $y \ge -\dfrac{x}{3} - 2$

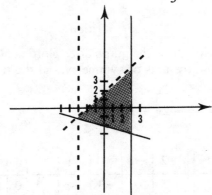

13. $-1 \le x \le 3$ and $y > 0$ **14.** $0 < x \le 5$ and $-2 \le y \le 2$

15. $-2 < x < 2$ or $-1 < y < 1$

16. $y \le x$
  $y \ge 0$
  $x \le 5$

17. $x + y > 0$
  $x \le 0$
  $y - 2x < 4$

18. $2x - 3y \ge -6$
  $2x + y \ge 2$
  $2x - y \le 2$

19. $x \ge 0$
  $y \ge 0$
  $x - y \ge -2$
  $3x - y \le 9$
  $5y + x \le 20$

20. $x \ge 4$
  $y \ge 1$
  $y \le 8$
  $x \le 10$
  $x + y \le 13$

Exercise 68. Graphs of Quadratic Equations

Oral

Determine the x and y intercepts of each of the following.

1. $y = x^2$
2. $y = (x - 1)^2$
3. $y = (x + 2)^2$
4. $y = (x - 1)(x + 2)$
5. $x^2 + y^2 = 9$
6. $x^2 + y^2 + 16 = 0$
7. $x^2 + y^2 = 25$
8. $4x^2 + y^2 = 36$
9. $4x^2 + 9y^2 = 36$
10. $x^2 - y^2 = 16$
11. $4x^2 - y^2 = 36$
12. $y^2 - x^2 = 9$
13. $xy = 12$
14. $x^2 + y^2 = 0$
15. $x^2 - y^2 = 0$

Written

For each equation draw the graph after plotting at least six points. From the graph determine the axis of symmetry and the turning point.

Example: $y + 3 = x^2 - 2x$

$\qquad y = x^2 - 2x - 3$

x	-2	-1	0	1	2	3	4
y	5	0	-3	-4	-3	0	5

The axis of symmetry is $x = 1$.
The turning point is $(1, -4)$.

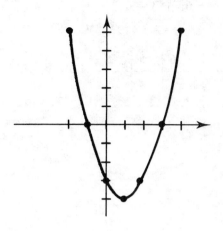

1. $y = x^2$ for $-4 \le x \le 4$
2. $y = 2x^2$ for $-3 \le x \le 3$
3. $y = \frac{1}{3}x^2$ for $-4 \le x \le 4$
4. $y = (x - 1)^2$ for $-2 \le x \le 4$
5. $y = x^2 - 1$
6. $y = 2(x - 1)^2$
7. $y = \frac{1}{3}(x - 1)^2$
8. $y = 3(x - 2)^2$
9. $y = 2(x + 2)^2$
10. $y - 3 = 2(x + 2)^2$
11. $y = (x - 3)^2$
12. $y = x^2 - 6x + 9$
13. $y = 2(x + 1)^2$
14. $y = 2x^2 + 4x + 2$
15. $3y = x^2 + 4x + 4$
16. $y = x^2 + 1$
17. $y = (x - 1)(x - 2)$
18. $y = -x^2$
19. $y = 4 - x^2$
20. $y = -x^2 - 1$
21. $y = -2(x - 1)^2$
22. $y = -3(1 - x)^2$
23. $y + x^2 - 2x = 0$
24. $y = x^2 - 4x + 3$
25. $y = x^2 - 5x - 6$
26. $y = -3(x - 2)(x - 3)$
27. $y = x^2 + 4x + 5$
28. $y = 3x^2 - 6x + 1$

Example: $x + y^2 + 6y + 3 = 0$

$$x = -y^2 - 6y - 3$$

x	−3	2	5	6	5	2
y	0	−1	−2	−3	−4	−5

The axis of symmetry is $y = -3$.
The turning point is $(6, -3)$.

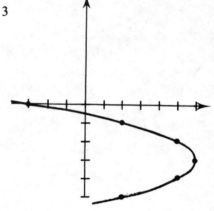

29. $x = y^2$

30. $x = (y - 2)^2$

31. $x = y^2 - 4y + 3$

32. $y^2 - 2x + 4 = 0$

33. $y^2 + 4y + x = 5$

34. $x = y^2 + 4y + 5$

35. $x = (y + 3)(y - 2)$

36. $y^2 - 3x = 0$

37. $y^2 - 2y = x + 7$

38. $x - 3 = 3(y - 1)^2$

For each equation draw the graph after plotting enough points to determine the shape.

39. $x^2 + y^2 = 4$

40. $x^2 + y^2 = 25$

41. $x^2 + y^2 = 49$

42. $xy = 6$

43. $xy = -3$

44. $4x^2 + 9y^2 = 36$

45. $x^2 + y = 4$

46. $x + y^2 = 4$

47. $2x^2 + 2y^2 = 10$

48. $x^2 - y^2 = 4$

Solve the following pairs of equations graphically and check by the algebraic solution.

49. $x^2 = 3 - y$
$x - y = -1$

50. $x^2 = y + 8$
$2x - y = 5$

51. $x^2 + y^2 = 25$
$2x - y = 5$

52. $x^2 = y + 4$
$2x - y = 5$

53. $x^2 + y = 2$
$x + y = -4$

54. $x^2 = y$
$3x - y = 2$

55. $x^2 + y^2 = 50$
$x + y = 8$

56. $x = y^2 - 2y$
$2y - x = 4$

57. $y = x^2 + x - 1$
$2x - y = -1$

58. $2y = x^2 + 2x + 3$
$2x + y = -3$

59. $x^2 + y^2 = 25$
$xy = 12$

60. $x = y^2 - 3y - 4$
$2x + y = 4$

Exercise 69. Graphs of Quadratic Inequalities

Written

Use a graph in two unknowns to solve the following inequalities in one unknown.

Example: $x^2 - 2x - 3 < 0$.

First sketch the graph of $y = x^2 - 2x - 3$, showing intercepts and turning point, as in **Exercise 68**. The portion of the graph where $y < 0$ lies between $x = -1$ and $x = 3$, thus the solution is $-1 < x < 3$.

1. $3x^2 - x - 2 \geq 0$ 2. $6x^2 + 5x - 4 \leq 0$

3. $x^2 + 2x < 15$ 4. $x^2 + 7x > 18$

5. $x^2 - 4x \geq 3x - 12$ 6. $2x^2 + 3x \leq 3 - 2x$

Shade the region determined by each of the following.

Example: $y < x^2 - 2x - 3$.

Sketch the graph of $y = x^2 - 2x - 3$. Since our graph should show the y-values that are *less* than these, we shade the region below the graph.

7. $y > x^2$ 8. $y \leq x^2$ 9. $y < x^2 + 1$

10. $y < x^2 - 3$ 11. $y < x^2 + 4x + 5$ 12. $y \geq x^2 - 4x + 3$

13. $y \geq x^2 - 5x - 6$ 14. $y \leq x^2 - 5x + 6$ 15. $x^2 + y^2 \leq 9$

16. $x^2 + y^2 > 16$ 17. $x^2 + y^2 \geq 25$ 18. $4x^2 + y^2 < 16$

19. $1 < y < 3$ and $y \geq x^2$ 20. $-2 \leq x \leq 2$ and $x^2 + y^2 < 16$.

21. $-2 < x < 0$ and $y < x^2$ 22. $y \leq x + 2$ and $y \geq x^2$

23. $-1 < y < 1$ and $x^2 + y^2 \leq 9$ 24. $x + y > 1$ and $y < 3 - x^2$

25. $x - y > 1$ and $y \geq x^2$ 26. $x - y \leq 1$ and $y \leq x^2$

Exercise 70. Graphs of Functions and Relations

Written

Draw the graphs of the following functions. Note carefully the domain of each function. If the domain is large sometimes only part of the graph should be drawn.

Example: D_f = non-negative integers.

$$f(x) = 3 - 2x$$

x	0	1	2	3
$f(x)$	3	1	-1	-3

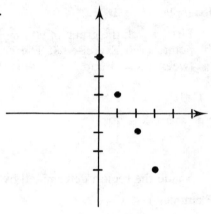

The graph is a set of isolated points to the right of the *y*-axis.

1. $f = \{(1,0), (2,1), (3,2), (-1,6), (0,5), (-2,-1)\}$
2. $f = \{(x,y) : y = 2x - 1 \text{ and } -2 \le x \le 3\}$
3. $D_f = \{x : 0 \le x \le 5\}, f(x) = \dfrac{2x - 3}{4}$
4. $D_f = \{x : -3 \le x \le 2\}, f(x) = 4x + 3$
5. $D_f = \{-3, -2, -1, 0, 1, 2, 3\}, f(x) = 4x + 3$
6. D_f = all reals, $f(x) = 2x$
7. D_f = integers, $f(x) = 2x + 1$
8. D_f = positive integers, $f(x) = 2x + 3$
9. D_f = all reals, $f(x) = 2x + 3$
10. D_f = all reals, $f(x) = 3 - 4x$
11. D_f = all reals, $f(x) = |x|$
12. $D_f = \{x : -3 \le x \le 3\}, f(x) = |x| + 2$
13. $D_f = \{x : -3 \le x \le 3\}, f(x) = |x - 1|$
14. $D_f = \{x : -2 \le x \le 2\}, f(x) = |2x - 1|$
15. $D_f = \{x : -3 \le x \le 3\}, f(x) = -|x - 1|$

16. $D_f = \{x : 0 \le x \le 6\}, f(x) = \frac{1}{2}|x - 3|$

17. D_f = all reals, $f(x) = |x + 2|$

18. D_f = all reals, $f(x) = |2x + 3|$

19. $D_f = \{x : -2 \le x \le 6\}, f(x) = |x| + x$

20. D_f = all reals, $f(x) = x + |x - 2|$

21. $D_f = \{x : 0 < x \le 10\}, f(x) =$ postage on a first class letter. Rates in 1976 are 13¢ for the first ounce and 11¢ for each ounce or fraction thereafter.

In problems **22–30**: D_f = all reals.

22. $f(x) = x - |x|$

23. $f(x) = x - |2x|$

24. $f(x) = |x - 1| + 1$

25. $f(x) = 2|x - 3| - 3$

26. $f(x) = -|x + 1| + 1$

27. $f(x) = 2 - |2 - x|$

28. $2f(x) = |2x - 3|$

29. $f(x) = \left| \dfrac{x + 6}{2} \right|$

30. $f(x) = \left| \dfrac{x}{2} - 3 \right| + 1$

Draw the graphs of the following functions whose domains are all reals. Use the graph in each case to determine those values of x for which the function values are greater than or equal to zero.

Example: $f(x) = (3 - x)(2 + x)$

x	-3	-2	-1	0	1	2	3
$f(x)$	-6	0	4	6	6	4	0

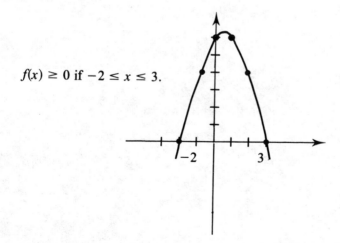

$f(x) \ge 0$ if $-2 \le x \le 3$.

31. $f(x) = 4 - x^2$

32. $f(x) = x^2 - 9$

33. $f(x) = x^2 - 3x$

34. $f(x) = 4x - 2x^2$

35. $f(x) = (x - 1)(x + 3)$

36. $f(x) = -(x - 1)(x + 3)$

37. $f(x) = 6 - 5x - x^2$

38. $f(x) = 6 - 2x$

39. $f(x) = 2 - |x|$

40. $f(x) = 4 - |x - 1|$

In each of the following problems a function f is defined over a certain domain. In each case draw the graphs of

$$f = \{x, f(x)\}, \quad g = \{x, -f(x)\}, \quad G = \{x, |f(x)|\}$$

41. $f(x) = 3x - 6$, $D_f = \{x : -1 \leq x \leq 3\}$

42. $f(x) = 2 - 3x$, $D_f = \{x : 0 \leq x \leq 3\}$

43. $f(x) = x^2 + 1$, $D_f = \{-2 \leq x \leq 2\}$

44. $f(x) = (x + 1)(x - 3)$, $D_f = \{-2 \leq x \leq 4\}$

45. $f(x) = (3 - x)(2 + x)$, $D_f = \{-3 \leq x \leq 4\}$

46. $f(x) = x^2 + 2x - 3$, $D_f = \{-4 \leq x \leq 2\}$

47. $f(x) = |x - 2| - 2$, $D_f = \{-1 \leq x \leq 5\}$

48. $f(x) = (x - 4)x^2$, $D_f = \{-1 \leq x \leq 5\}$

49. $f(x) = (x^2 - 4)x$, $D_f = \{-3 \leq x \leq 3\}$

50. $f(x) = (x^2 - 4)x^2$, $D_f = \{-3 \leq x \leq 3\}$

RIGHT TRIANGLE TRIGONOMETRY

Exercise 71. Right Triangle Trigonometry

Oral

1. In the adjoining figure state the value of each of the following in terms of a, b, and c: sin A, cos B, tan A, tan B.

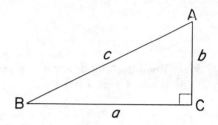

2. Use the figure to determine the value of sin α, cos γ, tan β, sin δ.

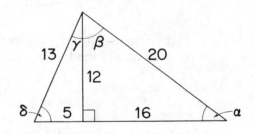

3. Use the figure to determine tan A, sin A and cos A.

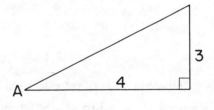

4. Use the figure to determine tan B, sin B, cos B.

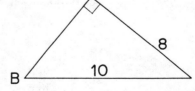

5. Use the figure to determine $\sin C$, $\cos C$, and $\tan C$.

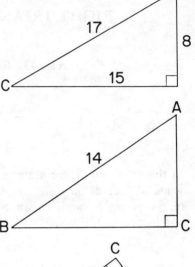

6. In the adjoining figure it is given that $\sin A = \frac{1}{2}$. Find BC.

7. In the adjoining figure it is given that $\tan A = \frac{2}{3}$. Find AC.

8. In the table on page 225 find:

$\sin 18°$, $\cos 46°$, $\tan 32°$, $\sin 72°$, $\cos 72°$, $\cos 60°$, $\cos 45°$, $\tan 21°$, $\cos 21°$, $\cos 43°$, $\tan 30°$, $\cos 56°$, $\tan 60°$, $\sin 45°$.

Written

In problems **1–10** refer to right triangle ABC. Do not use tables.

Example: If $a = 10$ and $b = 20$, find c, $\sin A$, $\cos A$, and $\tan A$.

From the Pythagorean Theorem, $c^2 = a^2 + b^2$

$$c^2 = 100 + 400 = 500$$
$$c = 10\sqrt{5}$$

$$\sin A = \frac{\text{opp}}{\text{hyp}} = \frac{a}{c} = \frac{10}{10\sqrt{5}} = \frac{\sqrt{5}}{5}$$

$$\cos A = \frac{\text{adj}}{\text{hyp}} = \frac{b}{c} = \frac{20}{10\sqrt{5}} = \frac{2\sqrt{5}}{5}$$

$$\tan A = \frac{\text{opp}}{\text{adj}} = \frac{a}{b} = \frac{10}{20} = \frac{1}{2}$$

176

1. If $a = 4$ and $b = 6$, find c, $\sin A$, and $\tan B$.

2. If $a = 8$ and $c = 17$, find b, $\sin B$, $\tan A$, and $\cos B$.

3. If $\sin A = \frac{3}{4}$ and $a = 8$, find c, b, and $\cos B$.

4. If $\cos B = \frac{4}{5}$, find $\sin B$ and $\tan A$.

5. If $a = 1$ and $c = 2$, find $\tan A$, $\sin A$, and $\cos A$.

6. If $a = 4$ and $b = 4$, find $\sin B$, $\tan A$ and $\sin A$.

7. If $b = 6$ and $c = 16$, find $\tan A$ and $\tan B$.

8. If $a = 5$ and $b = 10$, find $\sin A$ and $\tan A$.

9. If $\tan B = \frac{1}{2}$ and $c = 10$, find a and b.

10. If $\sin A = \frac{2}{3}$ and $b = 4$, find a and c.

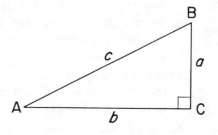

In problems **11–20** refer to the right triangle ABC with altitude CD. Use the table on page 000 to find the measures of the sides and angles requested. To indicate that the measure of the angle A is $32°$, we will write $m \angle A = 32$. Measures of angles should be determined to the nearest degree and measures of sides to the nearest unit.

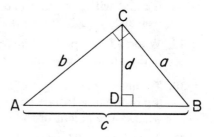

11. $m \angle A = 30$, $a = 15$. Find b, d, $\angle B$.

12. $b = 17$, $a = 14$. Find $\angle A$, d.

13. $m \angle B = 26$, $c = 30$. Find a, b, d.

14. $a = 41$, $b = 40$. Find $\angle B$, c.

15. $m \angle A = 47$, $d = 20$. Find b and a

16. $c = 36$, $m \angle B = 36$. Find a, d, $\angle A$.

17. $a = 10$, $b = 20$. Find $\angle A$, $\angle B$, c.

18. $b = 13$, $a = 5$. Find c and d.

19. $a = 20$, $b = 18$. Find $\angle C$ and d.

20. $a = 36$, $m \angle A = 20$. Find b and c.

21. From a point on the level ground 150 meters away from the wall of a building, the angle between the lines to the base and the top of the building is 27°. How high is the building?

22. A cog railway rises at a constant angle of 21°. If the station at the top of the mountain is 1550 meters higher than the base station, what is the length of the railway?

23. How far off the ground is the top of a vertical pole if a guy rope from the top to a point 19 meters from the foot makes an angle of 61° with the ground? (Assume the ground is level.)

24. If a staircase to a landing 10 meters above the floor is 15 meters long, at what angle to the floor is the staircase pitched?

25. From a point on the ground 12 meters from the bottom of a wall of the angle of elevation of the top of the wall is 49°. How long a ladder would be needed to reach the top of the wall from that point?

26. A rectangular plot of ground is 28 meters wide and 77 meters long. If a diagonal path is laid out across the plot, what angle does it make with the longer side?

27. An observer 1000 meters away from a point on the ground that is directly below a plane finds the angle of elevation of the plane to be 85°. How high up is the plane?

28. If a ladder 11 meters long rests with one end against the wall of a building and with the other end on the ground 4 meters from the foot of the wall, what angle does it make with the ground?

29. When a fence post 1.7 meters high casts a shadow 2.3 meters long, what is the angle of elevation of the sun?

30. To measure the height of a tree, a man finds the angle of elevation of the top of the tree from a point 110 meters from the base. If this angle is 33°, what is the height of the tree?

31. A straight road leads up from one town to another at an average grade of 11°. If the distance between the towns by the road is 2¾ kilometers how many meters higher is the second town than the first?

32. A uniformly inclined road 346 meters long is built to reach the level of a bridge 27 meters above a railroad track. Find the angle of the slope of the road.

33. Two roads intersect at right angles. A straight path leaves one road 340 meters from the intersection and meets the other road 436 meters from the intersection. What angle does the path make with each road?

34. A man wishes to find the distance between two houses on opposite shores of a lake. He walks from one house a distance of 350 meters

along the shore in a direction at right angles to the line between the houses. He then finds that from his present position the angle between the lines to the two houses is 74°. What is the distance between the houses?

35. A roof measures 6.6 meters from the ridge pole to the eaves. If the ridge pole is 3 meters higher than the eaves, at what angle is the roof pitched?

36. The observation room of a fire tower on a hill is ⅜ of a kilometer above the surrounding country. If a fire warden in the tower finds the angle of depression of a fire to be 8°, how far from the tower is the fire?

37. A section of road 985 meters long is to be built to cut off a right angled corner. If this section leaves one of the roads at a point 436 meters from the corner, at what angle does it meet the other road.

38. A guy rope from the top of a derrick post 78 meters above the ground makes an angle of 73° with the post. How far from the foot of the post does it touch the ground?

39. A man in a plane 5 kilometers above the level of the ocean observes the angle of depression of a submarine on the surface to be 13°. How far must he fly to be directly above the submarine?

40. A chute from the top of a tower on a diving raft is to be inclined at an angle of 50° to the horizontal. How high must the top of the tower be from the water to get a slide fifteen and a half meters long?

41. Two men are 432 meters apart, one directly east of the other. One man walks directly north for a distance of 230 meters and stops. In what direction must the second man walk to meet the first?

42. A man leaves a straight road and walks 736 meters in straight line at an angle of 22° from the road. How far is he from the nearest point on the road?

43. A logging railroad follows the contours of a valley to maintain an even grade from a town to a lumber camp that is 689 meters higher than the town. If the road is 6 km long, what is the angle of its grade?

44. If a dam 50 meters high backs up a lake 357 meters long in a valley, what is the average slope of the valley?

45. What is the angle of elevation of the sun when the shadow cast by a post is two thirds as long as the post?

46. A boat travelling 9 kilometers per hour leaves a point on the Equator at an angle of 14°. How far will the boat be from the nearest point on the Equator after 2 days?

47. A stay wire attached to a pole at a point 78 meters above the ground makes an angle of 75° with the pole. How long is the wire if its other end is fastened to a post at a point 3 meters above the ground?

48. A man standing 100 meters away from the base of a tree finds that the angle between the horizontal and the line from his eyes to the top of the tree is 24°. If the man's eyes are 1.7 meters above the ground, how high is the tree?

49. A balloon is 2736 meters above the ground. If two observers on opposite sides of the point on the ground directly below the balloon find its angle of elevation from their respective positions to be 47° and 38°, how far apart are the observers?

50. A man wishes to measure the height of a hill. He takes two points on the same level 500 meters apart and in the same direction from the hill. He finds that the angles of elevation of the top of the hill from these points to be 28° and 41°. What is the height of the hill?

ELEMENTARY STATISTICS

Exercise 72. Elementary Statistics

Oral

In these problems you are asked to make some guesses about certain situations. Try to make your guesses reasonable, that is you should be able to give some reason why you chose one answer rather than another. Later on in the written problems you will have a chance to see whether your answer seems to check with what actually happens.

1. A boy tosses six pennies together and counts the number of heads which appear at each toss.

    (a) What is the fewest number of heads which might appear?

    (b) What is the largest number of heads which might appear?

    (c) What is the most likely number of heads to appear?

    (d) If the boy makes 100 tosses what do you think the average number of heads would be?

2. If the boy tosses five pennies at a time instead of six answer the same four questions as in Problem 1.

    Are the answers to (c) and (d) the same in Problem 1?

    Are the answers to (c) and (d) the same in Problem 2?

3. A boy tosses one die (one of a pair of dice) and notes the number from 1 to 6 which appears.

    (a) What is the smallest number which might appear?

    (b) What is the largest number which might appear?

    (c) Which number is most likely to appear?

    (d) If he throws the die fifty times, what do you think the average of all the numbers which appear would be?

4. A man deals a hand of five cards from an ordinary deck of playing cards and counts the number of black cards which appear.

    (a) What is the smallest number of black cards which might appear?

    (b) What is the largest number?

    (c) What is the most likely number?

(d) Suppose the man deals fifty hands returning the cards to the deck and shuffling before each new deal. What do you think the average number of black cards per hand would be?

5. A man deals a hand of five cards as above and this time counts the number of spades which appear. Answer the same four questions as in Problem **4**.

6. The following words are frequently used in statistics. You should be able to say what they mean. Tally; frequency distribution; histogram; frequency polygon; cumulative frequency polygon; range; mean; median; mode; quartile; percentile. If you do not know the meaning of these words, most of them are defined in the Written Problems **9**, **10**, **11** and **12**.

Written

1. One author of this book actually tossed six coins and counted the number of heads on each toss. He did this 50 times with the following results.

Number of heads	0	1	2	3	4	5	6
Number of tosses	0	4	14	15	15	2	0

How do these results of what actually happened compare with the answers to the questions of Problem **1** which you gave?

2. Toss six pennies 50 times and make a count of your results similar to that above. Do you get exactly the same answers? Make histograms of the results in Problems **1** and **2** and compare them.

3. Do the same with five coins. Compare your results with those of several other members of your class.

4. Toss a die fifty times, answer the questions of Oral Problem **3** and compare your results with answers you gave there.

5. Do the same for cards as suggested by problems **4** and **5** of the Oral Problems.

6. Make histograms, frequency polygons and cumulative frequency polygons for the results in Problems **4** and **5**.

7. In a certain book, the number of letters of the first word on each of 25 consecutive pages was determined. The results were:

7, 6, 4, 2, 3, 2, 8, 4, 8, 7, 10, 4, 10, 3, 4, 10, 6, 5, 2, 9, 4, 3, 6, 4, 11

How long was the shortest word? the longest? What was the most common word length, what was the average word length? Make a frequency distribution of the results and draw a histogram. Do you think this was a child's book or an adult's book? Why?

8. One semester a mathematics class of 30 boys had five tests and one final examination which counted as much as three tests. The boys kept track of the grades and at the end of the term made up the following table.

Grade	test 1	test 2	test 3	test 4	test 5	exam
A	2	0	5	9	2	3
B	5	4	2	6	6	4
C	13	10	15	12	18	11
D	7	5	5	1	3	6
E	1	3	3	2	0	4
F	2	8	0	0	1	2

Which was the easiest test? Which the hardest? Counting an A as 95, B as 85, C as 75 etc., what was the class average on each test and on the examination? If Johnnie's grades were A, B, C, B, B with C on the exam, what should his final grade be? How about Tom with F, D, C, D, C and C on the exam or Steve who got C, F, A, D, B and A on the exam? Draw a frequency polygon for the distribution of grades on each test.

The following table contains information for the next set of problems. In a class of 22 boys their age, height and weight were listed.

Boy	Age		Height in inches	Weight in lbs.
	yrs.	mo.		
Alfred	14	1	66	140
Bob	14	4	68	147
Charles	14	2	66	156
Dave	14	3	60	110
Earnest	13	11	59	95
Fred	14		61	118
George	14	2	65	139
Harry	14	2	66	146
Ike	15	1	66	134
James	14	6	67	147
Kim	14	5	66	146
Larry	14	4	68	153
Monty	13	11	61	122
Nat	14	7	60	102
Oliver	14	8	70	170
Pete	14	6	66	144
Rich	14	9	68	158
Sam	14		62	120
Tom	14	2	64	132
Vic	14	3	65	141
Walt	14	4	62	119
Zab	14	5	65	130

9. Make a tally of the number of boys at each age. Such a tally is called a *frequency distribution table* of the ages. Draw a bar graph of the tally. Such a bar graph is called a *histogram* of the distribution.

10. Use the histogram to determine the most common age in the class. This is the *mode* of the distribution. How old is the youngest boy? How old is the oldest boy? The difference in ages of the youngest and oldest boys is the *range* of the distribution. What is the range? The average age is called the *mean* of the distribution of ages. What is the mean?

11. Make a *cumulative frequency table* of the ages, i.e., a table showing at each age the total number of boys having that age or less. Draw a *cumulative frequency polygon*, i.e. plot a point above each age indicating its cumulative frequency and connect successive points by line segments.

12. The *median* age of the distribution is the age such that half the boys are younger and half older. The first, second and third quartiles are the ages such that one-fourth, two-fourths and three-fourths of the boys are younger. Look at the cumulative frequency polygon you drew in Problem 11 and estimate the median age. Estimate the quartiles. Compare the second quartile and the median. Compare the range of ages of the boys in the second and third quartiles to the total range you got in Problem 10. What is the ratio of these ranges? What does this tell you about the distribution?

13, 14, 15, 16. Study the distribution of heights of the class in the same manner as you did the ages in Problems 9, 10, 11, 12.

17, 18, 19, 20. Group the weights of the boys by ten pound intervals such as 90–99, 100–109, etc. Make a tally of the number of boys in each weight class. Use the values 95, 105 etc., as an approximation to the weight of each boy in that class. Study the distribution of weights as you did that of the ages in Problems 9, 10, 11, 12.

EXERCISES AND EXAMINATIONS

Exercise 73. Review Exercises

Review Exercise (A)

1. (a) Factor completely: $4m^2 - 10m - 6$
   (b) Factor completely: $x^2 + ax + bx + ab$
   (c) Determine the coordinates of the vertex of the parabola
   $$y = x^2 + 2x - 4.$$

2. (a) Factor completely: $8a^3 - b^3$
   (b) If $f(y) = y^2 - 9y$, find $f(\tfrac{1}{3})$.
   (c) Find the solution set for the inequality: $\dfrac{k-2}{2} > \dfrac{4k-3}{4}$

3. (a) Multiply: 3023_4 times 32_4
   (b) Express 241_5 as a numeral in the decimal system.
   (c) If $a = -3$, $c = -2$, and $d = 6$, evaluate t if $t = \dfrac{-a(d - c^2)}{cd}$.

4. (a) Find all values of x which satisfy: $-3x + 7 \geq \dfrac{9 - 6x}{-3}$

   (b) At sea, the distance of the horizon varies directly as one's height above the water. If at a height of 5 meters the horizon is 12 kilometers distant, what is its distance as seen from a lighthouse 28 meters above sea level?

5. Solve for x, y, and z, and CHECK:
   $$2x + y = 8$$
   $$4y + 5z = 13$$
   $$-4x + z = -5$$

6. (a) Divide $a^6 - 2a^3b^3 + b^6$ by $a^2 - 2ab + b^2$.
   (b) Solve for y and CHECK:
   $$(2y + 3)^2 - 5(3y - 7) - (2y - 1)(2y - 5) = 3$$

7. (a) Factor completely: $x^3 + 2x^2 - x - 2$
   (b) A tank contains 24 liters of a nitric acid solution which is 12% acid. How much water must be added to make the solution 8% acid?

8. (a) Factor completely: $4a^2 - 9b^2 + 6b - 1$

   (b) Simplify: $\dfrac{2}{x - 3a} + \dfrac{2a}{x^2 - 4ax + 4a^2} - \dfrac{x - a}{6a^2 - 5ax + x^2}$

9. (a) Solve for x: $\dfrac{x - 1}{x} + \dfrac{x}{x - 1} = \dfrac{5}{2}$

   (b) Graph the equation: $y = -2|x + 3|$.

10. (a) Solve for x: $3x^2 - 2x - 2 = 0$

    (b) Determine the *integers* in the solution of set of $|x - 3| < 4$.

11. (a) Evaluate: $8^{2/3} + 1^{2x} - 3x^0$

    (b) Multiply: $\sqrt[3]{12x^2y^4} \cdot \sqrt[3]{4xy^2}$

    (c) Express in simplest form with positive exponents: $\dfrac{1 - a^{-2}}{1 + a^{-1}}$

12. (a) Solve for n : $n - \sqrt{2n + 7} = 4$

    (b) Solve for x in terms of a: $\dfrac{x + a}{4} - \dfrac{x + 2}{x + a} = \dfrac{x - a}{4}$

13. (a) Simplify: $\left(\dfrac{x^{-1} \cdot \sqrt[3]{x}}{x^2} \right)^{-3}$

    (b) Rationalize the denominator and simplify: $\dfrac{2\sqrt{2} + 6}{2\sqrt{2} - 1}$

    (c) Find the values of x which satisfy $x^2 - 5x - 6 > 0$.

14. (a) Combine: $\sqrt{\dfrac{2}{5}} + \sqrt{490} - \dfrac{2}{\sqrt{10}}$

    (b) In triangle ABC with $AC = 3$, $AB = 5$ and $\angle C = 90°$, find the values of: (i) $\sin B$; (ii) $\cos B$.

15. (a) If $A = \{x: x$ is a positive integer$\}$ and $B = \left\{ \dfrac{x}{2} : -3 < x < 5 \right\}$, then list the elements of $A \cap B$.

    (b) Determine: (i) the slope, and (ii) the coordinates of the x intercept of a line passing through the points $(-3, 4)$ and $(5, -4)$.

    (c) Sketch a graph of the function F if $F(x) = 2|x - 3|$, for $-2 \le x \le 8$.

16. (a) Solve for y: $\dfrac{y}{2} - \dfrac{y - 2}{3} = \dfrac{2y - 2}{4}$

    (b) Prove: The sum of two positive consecutive even integers is divisible by an odd integer other than 1.

17. (a) Express the following repeating decimal as a quotient of two relatively prime integers: $1.166666666 \ldots$

    (b) The ratio of the ten's and unit's digits of a two digit number is $2 : 3$. The number with its digits reversed is 27 greater than the original number. Find the number.

18. A man drives to a certain place at the rate of 90 kilometers per hour. He returns by a road that is 8 kilometers longer at the rate of 72 kilometers per hour and takes 1 hour longer than in going. How long is each road?

19. (a) Solve for x only:
$$\begin{cases} \dfrac{s}{x} + \dfrac{r}{y} = 5 \\[2mm] \dfrac{r}{x} + \dfrac{s}{y} = 5 \end{cases}$$

(b) A man can do a piece of work in 8 days, his son can do it in 12 days. They start working together and after a certain time the son is called away and his father finishes the work in 3 more days. How many days to they work together?

20. If the operation "hatch" is defined on the set of real numbers by:
$$a \mathbin{\#} b = \frac{a + b}{3}$$

(a) Is $\#$ commutative? Justify your answer.

(b) Write the distributive property of ordinary multiplication over $\#$.

(c) Does the distributive property hold for ordinary multiplication over "hatch", for real numbers a, b, and c? Justify your conclusion.

(d) Does $\#$ operation have a unique identity element? If so, what is it?

21. Neatly graph the solution set for the following: $y \le 2x + 4$
$$y > -3$$
$$6x + 5y \le 30.$$

22. A ship is to steam from A to B, a distance of 1200 kilometers. Half way through the voyage she doubles her speed. Thus the ship arrives at B one day and one hour earlier than she would have if she had maintained her original speed for the whole trip. Find her original speed.

23. Simplify:
$$\left[\frac{\dfrac{x}{y} + x}{y - \dfrac{1}{y}} - 1 \right] \div \left[\frac{x^2 - 2xy}{1 - y} - (y + 1) \right]$$

24. (a) Two persons, A and B, together have $6 less than a third person C. If B gives $5 to A, A's money will then be half of C's. If instead, A gives $5 to B, A's money will then be one-third of B's. How many dollars has each?

187

(b) A tower, whose top is 30 meters above the level of the water stands on the shore of a lake. If the angle of elevation of the top of the tower from a boat on the lake is $11° 20'$, find the distance from the boat to the foot of the tower. (Nearest meter)

25. (a) Simplify: $\left(\dfrac{2}{x-3} - \dfrac{3}{2-x} - \dfrac{2x-7}{x^2-5x+6}\right) \div \left(\dfrac{1}{x+3} + \dfrac{1}{3-x}\right)$

    (b) Solve for x and y: $\dfrac{5}{x} + \dfrac{3}{y} = 1; \dfrac{2}{x} - \dfrac{1}{y} = 7$

Review Exercise (B)

1. (a) Subtract the sum of $a^2 - a + 2$ and $2a^2 - 5$ from $2a^2 - 7$.

   (b) Divide $6x^3 - 5x + x^2 - 2$ by $2x + 1$.

2. (a) Simplify: $x - (3 - [2x - 4(1 - 2x) + 7])$

   (b) Factor: $9a^2 - 36b^2$

   (c) If $x = -2$ and $y = 3$, find the value of $2y^2 - 3x^2y - x^3$.

3. Factor completely:

   (a) $8x^3 + 27y^3$

   (b) $a^2 - b^2 - 2b - 1$

   (c) $2ax - 6x - 2ay + 6y$

4. (a) Solve the inequality: $\dfrac{2-x}{3} \leq \dfrac{4x-3}{2}$

   (b) Simplify: $1 + \dfrac{2x}{2x-1} - \dfrac{8x^2-2}{4x^2-1}$

5. (a) If x varies directly as y and x equals 810 when y equals 18, find y when x equals 10.

   (b) Solve for x: $3x^2 - 6 = 2 - 10x$

6. (a) Define: The graph of an equation.

   (b) Let $A = \{(x, y): x \text{ and } y \text{ are real numbers and } 3x + 2y \leq 0\}$,

   $B = \{(x, y): x \text{ and } y \text{ are real numbers and } 2x - y > -3\}$.

   Sketch A and B on the xy plane and indicate those points which are elements of $A \cap B$.

7. (a) Factor: $5a^3 - 20ab^2$ (b) Factor: $a^2 + 2px - p^2 - x^2$

   (c) Evaluate: $4^{3/2} + 7x^0 + [2^{-1} - 4^{-1}]^{-1}$

8. (a) Rationalize the denominator and simplify: $\dfrac{\sqrt{3}}{3 + \sqrt{3}}$

   (b) Solve for x: $3 - \dfrac{3x}{4} > 2$

9. Solve for x and check: $\dfrac{2x + 3}{3} - \dfrac{x + 7}{2} - \dfrac{3(x - 1)}{4} = 0$

10. (a) Define: prime number.

    (b) Factor: $4x^2 - 20xy + 25y^2$

    (c) Factor: $15 - x - 2x^2$

    (d) For what values of x will $|x - 5| = 4$ be true?

11. (a) Simplify: $(3xy^2)^3(-x^2)^2$

    (b) Find the Highest Common Factor (also sometimes called the Greatest Common Divisor) and the Least Common Multiple for the numbers: 42, 70, and 154.

    (c) If 12 is 3 less than $5k$, find the value of $(2 - 3k)^3$.

12. Solve for M and check: $(M + 1)^2 - (M - 2)(2M + 1) = 8 - M(M - 3)$

13. (a) Find two consecutive odd integers such that five times the smaller diminished by two times the larger exceeds the sum of the two numbers by five.

    (b) 40 kilos of salt water is 25% pure salt. How much pure water must be added to the mixture so that it will be 10% pure salt?

14. (a) Factor: $8a^3 - b^3$

    (b) Solve for x: $x^2 - 7x = 18$

    (c) For what values of x will $2x - 5 < 13$ be true?

    (d) Henry was x years old y years ago. How old will he be z years from now?

15. (a) Simplify: $\left[\dfrac{3x^2 - 5x + 2}{1 - x^2}\right] \div \left[\dfrac{2 - x - 3x^2}{(1 + x)^2}\right]$

    (b) Find the equation of the line passing through the point (2, 3) and having its slope equal to $\frac{2}{3}$.

    (c) Give an example of a dependent set of linear equations.

16. Mr. French invested $7,300, part at 5% and the remainder at 6%. His yearly income is $34 greater than if he had invested all his money at 5%. How much was invested at each rate?

17. Solve the following set of equations:

$$\begin{cases} 4(3 + x) + 6(y - 1) - 12 = 0. \\ \dfrac{2x - 5y}{7} - \dfrac{x - 2y}{5} = \dfrac{4}{7} \end{cases}$$

18. Solve for x and check:

$$\frac{2}{2x - 1} + \frac{2}{2x - 7} = \frac{4x^2 - 1}{4x^2 - 16x + 7} - 1$$

19. (a) Consider the function $y = -x^2 + 2x + 3$. Draw a rough sketch of the graph of the function, find the coordinates of the turning point (vertex) and find the coordinates of the point or points where the graph crosses the x-axis.

(b) Write the equation of the graph at the right.

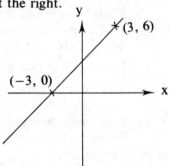

20. (a) Simplify: $\sqrt{12} - \dfrac{4}{\sqrt{3}} + \dfrac{3\sqrt{6}}{\sqrt{2}} - \dfrac{\sqrt{27}}{3}$

(b) Solve for x: $\sqrt{3x^2 + 4} = 2 - x$

21. (a) If y varies inversely as the square root of x and y is equal to 8 when x is 2, find y when x is 8.

(b) Alan does a job in 4 days that Bill can do in 6. They work together a number of days and finish five-sixths of the job. How many days did they work together?

22. (a) In the triangle at the right, C is the right angle, side a is $\sqrt{3}$ cm and side c is $\sqrt{5}$ cm. Find $\sin A$ and $\tan A$ in simplest radical form.

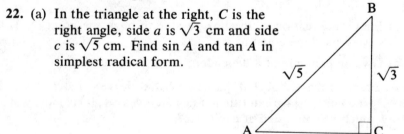

(b) A boy finds the angle of elevation to his kite to be $34° \, 20'$. If the kite is 49 meters high, how much string would be needed if the string is assumed to be taut?

23. Joe and Sam can paint Mr. Brown's garage in 7 hours if they work together. But after working together for 2 hours Joe has to leave and Sam finishes the job alone in 15 hours. How long would it have taken Joe to do the job if he did it alone?

24. (a) If x, y, and c are real numbers, prove: If $x > y$ then $x + c > y + c$.

   (b) Read the following statements and state whether they are true or false. Justify your answer with a sentence, statement, or counter example.

   (i) If x is any integer, then $8x^2 + 8x + 1$ is an odd integer.

   (ii) There is no rational number between $\frac{2}{3}$ and $\frac{3}{5}$.

   (iii) If x is a member of the set A where
   $A = \{x : x \text{ is an integer and } |x| < 3\}$, then $\dfrac{x^2 - 4}{x + 1}$ must be a rational number.

25. (a) The following statements are both false. Give counter examples to show this.

   (i) The product of any two irrational numbers is irrational.

   (ii) The sum of any two irrational numbers is irrational.

   (b) Prove: If a and b are even numbers and a is greater than b then $4a - 3b$ is even.

26. Define the operation # for all rational numbers a and b as follows: $a \# b = a + ab + b$.

   (a) Evaluate $3 \# 7$.

   (b) Illustrate by one example using the numbers 1, 2 and 3 that the operation # is associative.

   (c) Solve for $x : x \# 7 = 3$.

27. (a) Simplify: $\left(\dfrac{3}{x + 2} + \dfrac{x}{x - 2}\right) \div \dfrac{x^2 - 4x + 3}{x^2 - x - 6}$

   (b) Solve the following for a and b: $\begin{cases} \dfrac{3}{2a} - \dfrac{6}{b} = 0 \\ \\ \dfrac{3}{a} - \dfrac{4}{b} = 2 \end{cases}$

28. Solve the following equation for x.

   (a) Express the roots in simplest radical form.

   (b) Approximate these roots to the nearest tenth.

$$\frac{4}{2x - 1} + \frac{3x}{2x + 1} = \frac{5x^2 + 1}{4x^2 - 1}$$

29. A boy started to ride his bicycle to his grandmother's house, 24 kilometers away, at the rate of 8 kilometers per hour. After riding part of the way, he has a flat tire and he has to push his bicycle the remainder of the trip at 3 kilometers per hour, thus arriving at his grandmother's house 50 minutes later than he would have had he ridden the whole way. How far had he ridden when his tire went flat?

30. (a) If x, and y represent real numbers, define $x > y$. Prove that if x, y and c are real numbers and $x > y$ and $c < 0$, then $xc < yc$.

(b) If x and y are real numbers and if $x > y$, decide whether the following are positive or negative. If it cannot be decided say "Unknown".

(i) $x + y$ (ii) $|y - x|$ (iii) xy

(iv) $\dfrac{1}{y - x}$ (v) x and y if $\dfrac{x}{y} < 0$

Review Exercise (C)

Multiple Choice: Select the correct answer for each of the following.

1. Express 11010_2 in base 10

(a) 8   (b) 10   (c) 13   (d) 26   (e) 50

2. Simplify: $2 - [3p - (4p - 7)] - 5(p + 3)$

(a) $-4p - 20$ (b) $-4p - 6$ (c) $-12p - 2$ (d) $-12p - 20$
(e) $4p - 20$

3. Subtract the sum of $2x^2 + 3x - 4$ and $x^2 - 1$ from $2x^2 - 3x$

(a) $5 - 6x - x^2$ (b) $x^2 - 6x + 3$ (c) $x^2 + 6x - 5$
(d) $x^2 - 3x + 3$ (e) $4x^2 - 5$

4. Divide $x^3 - 19x + 30$ by $x + 5$

(a) $x^2 + 5x - 6$ (b) $x^2 - 5x - 6$ (c) $x^2 - 5x + 6$
(d) $x^2 + 5x + 6$ (e) $x^2 + 6$

5. Find the GCD and LCM of 60, 90, 450

(a) 30 and 900   (b) 60 and 450   (c) 60 and 900
(d) 30 and 450   (e) 15 and 900

6. If $a = 2$, $b = -3$ and $c = \frac{1}{2}$, evaluate $ab^2 - (a + b)^5 + a^2bc$

(a) -25 (b) 11   (c) 13   (d) 25   (e) 31

7. Simplify: $(\frac{1}{2}a^2b^5)^3 \cdot (-4a)^2$

(a) $-8a^6b^{15}$ (b) $-a^8b^{15}$ (c) $8a^6b^5$
(d) a^8b^{15} (e) $8a^7b^8$

8. The prime factors of $9y^2 - 42y + 49$ are
   (a) $(3y + 7)^2$ (b) $(3y + 7)(3y - 7)$ (c) $(9y - 7)^2$
   (d) $(3y - 7)^2$ (e) $(y - 7)(9y - 7)$

9. Jane is y years old. Joe is z years older than Jane was x years ago. How old is Joe now?
   (a) $y + z - x$ (b) $y - z + x$ (c) $y + z + x$ (d) $y - z - x$
   (e) $-y + x + z$

10. Factor completely: $12a^2 - 75$
    (a) $12(a^2 - 6)$ (b) $3(4a^2 - 25)$ (c) $4(3a^2 - \frac{75}{4})$
    (d) $3(2a - 5)^2$ (e) $3(2a - 5)(2a + 5)$

11. Solve $|x - 4| = |-8|$
    (a) 12 only   (b) 4 only   (c) 12 and 4
    (d) -4 only   (e) -4 and 12

12. Solve for x: $ax + a^2 = 2az + ab$
    (a) a (b) $a + b$ (c) $2a - b$ (d) $a - b$ (e) b

13. Factor: $24m^2 + m - 10$
    (a) $(8m - 5)(3m + 2)$ (b) $(8m + 5)(3m - 2)$ (c) $(6m + 1)(4m - 10)$
    (d) $(12m - 5)(2m - 2)$ (e) $(8m - 5)(3m - 2)$

14. Solve for a: $3a^2 - (a - 6)(3a + 4) = 8a$
    (a) $-\frac{12}{7}$ (b) 4   (c) no solution   (d) -4 (e) $\frac{12}{11}$

15. Find the number such that the product of its additive inverse with its multiplicative inverse is 15 less than twice the number.
    (a) 4   (b) 5   (c) 6   (d) 7   (e) 8

16. Express $1.121212 \ldots$ as the ratio of two relatively prime integers.
    (a) $\frac{28}{25}$ (b) $\frac{37}{33}$ (c) $\frac{112}{100}$ (d) $\frac{112}{99}$ (e) $\frac{38}{33}$

17. Use the rule method to describe the following set of numbers: 4, 6, 8, 10, . . .
    (a) $\{2x \mid x$ is an integer$\}$ (b) $\{2x \mid x$ is a positive integer$\}$
    (c) $\{2x + 2 \mid x$ is an integer$\}$ (d) $\{2x + 2 \mid x$ is a positive integer$\}$
    (e) $\{x + 3 \mid x$ is a positive integer$\}$

18. Multiply: $(2x - 3)(x + 2)$
    (a) $2x^2 - 5x - 6$ (b) $2x^2 - x + 6$ (c) $2x^2 - x - 6$
    (d) $x^2 + x - 6$ (e) $2x^2 + x - 6$

19. Compute $\sqrt{56}$ to the nearest tenth.
    (a) 7.4   (b) 7.5   (c) 7.6   (d) 7.7   (e) 7.8

20. Solve for x: $-2(x - 1) > 4$

    (a) $x < -1$ (b) $x > -1$ (c) $x < -3$

    (d) $x > -3$ (e) $x < -2$

21. Subtract $3a^2b - 4ab - 3ab^2$ from $2a^2b - 3ab^2 + 4b^2$

    (a) $5a^2b - 4ab - 6ab^2 + 4b^2$ (b) $a^2b - 4ab - 4b^2$

    (c) $-a^2b + 4ab + 4b^2$

    (d) $-a^2b + 4ab - 6ab^2 + 4b^2$ (e) $-a^2b - 4ab - 4b^2$

22. For what values of x will $|x - 2| = 3$?

    (a) 1, 2   (b) 5, 2   (c) -1, 5   (d) -1, -5 (e) 1, -5

23. If $2z + 1$ is an odd integer, express the next two even integers greater than $2x + 1$.

    (a) $2x$, $2x + 2$ (b) $2x + 1$, $2x + 3$ (c) $2x + 1$, $2x + 2$

    (d) $2x + 2$, $2x + 3$ (e) $2x + 2$, $2x + 4$

24. If $k = -2$, $m = 0$ and $n = 3$, evaluate: $4km - k^3n - (kn)^2 - k^2$

    (a) -16 (b) -64 (c) 56   (d) 64   (e) -8

25. Divide $6x^3 - 5x + x^2 - 2$ by $2x + 1$

    (a) $3x^2 + x - 2$ (b) $3x^2 - x - 2$ (c) $3x^2 - x + 2$

    (d) $3x^2 + x + 2$ (e) $3x - 2$

26. Simplify: $(3ab^2)^3(-a^2)^2$

    (a) $-27a^{12}b^6$ (b) $27a^{12}b^6$ (c) $-27a^3b^5$

    (d) $27a^3b^5$ (e) $27a^7b^6$

27. If you bought p kilos of nuts at $3y$ cents per kilo and $2p$ kilos at $2y$ cents per kilo, what would be the total cost of your purchase?

    (a) $6py$ (b) $7py$ (c) $8py$ (d) $9py$ (e) $10py$

28. Express the number whose unit's digit is d and whose ten's digit is one more than the units digit.

    (a) $10t + u$ (b) $10t + d$ (c) $10d + d$

    (d) $11d + 1$ (e) $11d + 10$

29. Find the G.C.D. and the L.C.M. of 42, 70, 168.

    (a) 7 and 165   (b) 14 and 165   (c) 14 and 840

    (d) 7 and 840   (e) 42 and 168

30. Solve for y: $\dfrac{y}{2} - \dfrac{y - 2}{3} = \dfrac{y - 1}{2}$

    (a) $\frac{5}{2}$ (b) $\frac{7}{2}$ (c) $-\frac{1}{2}$ (d) 1   (e) $\frac{1}{2}$

31. If 10 is 4 more than $2a$, find the value of $5 - 3a$.

    (a) 20   (b) 14   (c) -16 (d) -4 (e) 0

32. Write the equation of a line whose graph goes through the origin and has a slope of zero.

(a) $y = 0$ (b) $x = 0$ (c) $x + y = 0$ (d) $x - y = 0$ (e) $y = 2x$

33. The factors of $4x^2 - 16x + 15$ are

(a) $(3 - 2x)(5 - 2x)$ (b) $(3 + 2x)(5 + 2x)$ (c) $(15 - 4x)(1 - x)$
(d) $(3 - 2x)(5 + 2x)$ (e) $(3 + 2x)(5 - 2x)$

34. If $a = \frac{1}{4}$, find the value of $a^2 - \left(\dfrac{4}{a} + \dfrac{a}{4}\right)$.

(a) $-16\frac{1}{8}$ (b) $16\frac{1}{8}$ (c) $-15\frac{7}{8}$ (d) -16 (e) $\frac{1}{16}$

35. The factors of $9n^2 - 4a^2 + 30n + 25$ are

(a) $(3n + 5 - 2a)^2$ (b) $(3n - 5 + 2a)^2$
(c) $(3n + 5 - 2a)(3n - 5 + 2a)$ (d) $(3n + 5 - 2a)(3n + 5 + 2a)$
(e) $(3n - 5 - 2a)(3n + 5 + 2a)$

36. Simplify: $\dfrac{2 + 2^{-1} + 2^0}{2^{-2} + 2}$

(a) $\frac{7}{4}$ (b) $\frac{5}{4}$ (c) $\frac{9}{14}$ (d) $\frac{14}{9}$ (e) $\frac{9}{2}$

37. Solve for x: $3 - \dfrac{3x}{4} > 2$

(a) $x < \frac{4}{3}$ (b) $x > \frac{4}{3}$ (c) $x < \frac{3}{4}$
(d) $x > -\frac{4}{3}$ (e) $x < -\frac{4}{3}$

38. Simplify: $2 - \dfrac{3a}{a - 2} - \dfrac{6}{2 - a}$

(a) 1 (b) -1 (c) $2 - a$ (d) $a - 2$ (e) $\dfrac{a + 2}{a - 2}$

39. What values may x have in order that $\dfrac{4 - 3x}{2} \le 11$?

(a) $x \le -6$ (b) $x \le \frac{1}{8}$ (c) $x \ge \frac{1}{8}$
(d) $x \ge -6$ (e) $x \le -\frac{1}{8}$

40. The rate of a car rolling down a hill in neutral is directly proportional to the time it rolls. If, on a certain slope, its speed at the end of 3 seconds is 12 meters per second, in how many seconds will it be traveling 32 meters per second?

(a) 4   (b) 5   (c) 6   (d) 7   (e) 8

41. Simplify: $\sqrt{147} - \sqrt{\frac{25}{3}} + 6(3)^{-1/2}$

(a) $\dfrac{4}{3\sqrt{3}}$ (b) $22\sqrt{3}$ (c) $\dfrac{20\sqrt{3}}{3}$ (d) $\dfrac{22\sqrt{3}}{3}$ (e) $6\sqrt{3}$

42. Find the coordinates of the y-intercept of $3x - 5y = 7$.

    (a) $(\tfrac{7}{3}, 0)$ (b) $(0, -\tfrac{7}{5})$ (c) $(0, \tfrac{7}{3})$ (d) $(-\tfrac{7}{5}, 0)$ (e) $(\tfrac{7}{3}, \tfrac{7}{5})$

43. Simplify: $\dfrac{2\sqrt{3} - \sqrt{2}}{\sqrt{3} + 2\sqrt{2}}$

    (a) $\sqrt{6} - \sqrt{2}$ (b) $\sqrt{6} - 2$ (c) $2 - \sqrt{6}$

    (d) $\dfrac{2 - 3\sqrt{6}}{-5}$ (e) $\dfrac{14 - 4\sqrt{6}}{-5}$

44. The sum of two numbers is 243. If twice the larger is 14 less than three times the smaller, find the smaller number.

    (a) 14   (b) 100   (c) 109   (d) 134   (e) 143

45. A man can do a job in 6 days and his son can do the same job in 9 days. How many days will it take them both to do the job working together?

    (a) 15   (b) $\tfrac{15}{2}$ (c) 7   (d) $\tfrac{18}{5}$ (e) 3

46. Determine the values of x which make $x(x + 1) = 0$ a true equation.

    (a) 0 only   (b) 1 only   (c) 0 and 1   (d) 0 and -1 (e) 1 and -1

47. Express 330_4 as a numeral in base 7 by first writing it in base 10.

    (a) 14   (b) 60   (c) 84   (d) 114   (e) 141

48. Express $1.27\overline{27}$ as a ratio of two relatively prime integers.

    (a) $\tfrac{3}{11}$ (b) $\tfrac{4}{3}$ (c) $\tfrac{14}{11}$ (d) $\tfrac{127}{99}$ (e) $\tfrac{127}{100}$

49. Write the equation of a line whose graph passes through $(1, -3)$ and $(5, 9)$.

    (a) $3x + y = 6$ (b) $3x - y = 6$ (c) $3x - y = -10$

    (d) $x - 3y = 10$ (e) $x + 3y = 6$

50. If x varies inversely as y, and x equals 4 when y is 6, how much will x equal when y is 24?

    (a) $\tfrac{1}{16}$ (b) $\tfrac{1}{4}$ (c) 1   (d) 16   (e) 32

Review Exercise (D)

Multiple Choice: Select the correct answer for each of the following.

1. The prime factors of $a^5 - 16a$ are

    (a) $a(a^4 - 16)$ (b) $a(a^2 + 4)(a^2 - 4)$

    (c) $a(a^2 + 4)(a + 2)(a - 2)$ (d) $(a^4 + 16)(a - 1)$

    (e) $a(a^2 - 4)^2$

2. The prime factors of $x^2(t - s) - y^2(t - s)$ are

(a) $(x^2 - y^2)(t - s)$ (b) $(t - s)(x + y)(x - y)$
(c) $xy(t - s)$ (d) $x^2y^2(t - s)$
(e) $(t + s)(x + y)(x - y)$

3. Solve for x: $5 - x > \dfrac{2x - 3}{-7}$

(a) $x > \frac{38}{9}$ (b) $x < \frac{38}{9}$ (c) $x < \frac{32}{5}$ (d) $x > \frac{32}{5}$ (e) $x > 0$

4. The value of $4^{-3/2} - \sqrt[3]{8^2} + 4$ is

(a) $\dfrac{-23}{16}$ (b) 8   (c) -11 (d) 0   (e) $\frac{1}{8}$

5. The value of $\dfrac{3^{-1} - 2^{-1}}{3^{-1} + 2^{-1}}$ is

(a) $-\frac{1}{5}$ (b) $\frac{1}{5}$ (c) 5   (d) -5 (e) 0

6. One factor of $27x^3 - y^6$ is

(a) $(3x - y)$ (b) $(3x + y)$
(c) $(9x^2 + 3xy + y^2)$ (d) $(9x^2 + 3xy^2 + y^4)$
(e) $(9x^2 - 3xy^2 + y^4)$

7. Rationalize the numerator: $\dfrac{2 - \sqrt{6}}{2}$

(a) $\dfrac{1}{2 - \sqrt{6}}$ (b) $\dfrac{1}{\sqrt{6} - 2}$ (c) $\sqrt{6} + 2$

(d) $\dfrac{-1}{\sqrt{6} + 2}$ (e) $\dfrac{1}{\sqrt{6} + 2}$

8. Solve for x: $2x(x + 2) = 7$

(a) $\dfrac{2 \pm 3\sqrt{2}}{2}$ (b) $\dfrac{-2 \pm 3\sqrt{2}}{2}$ (c) $2 \pm 3\sqrt{2}$

(d) $-2 \pm 3\sqrt{2}$ (e) No real solution

9. Leslie had $40 more than Ida. If Ida had $10 more than one third as much as Leslie, how much did Ida have?

(a) $5   (b) $25   (c) $35   (d) $65   (e) $75

10. Add: $\dfrac{3}{a + 3} - \dfrac{2}{3 - a} - \dfrac{12}{a^2 - 9}$

(a) $\dfrac{5}{a + 3}$ (b) $5(a - 3)$ (c) $\dfrac{a - 27}{a^2 - 9}$ (d) $\dfrac{5a - 9}{a^2 - 9}$ (e) 5

11. Write in simplest form with positive exponents.
$(a^{1/2}b^{-3}c^{-5})^3 \cdot (a^{3/2}b^{-10}c^{20})^{-1}$

(a) abc^5 (b) $\dfrac{b}{c^5}$ (c) bc^5 (d) $\dfrac{c^5}{b}$ (e) $\dfrac{ab}{c^5}$

12. Which point does NOT lie on the graph of $4x + 5y = 53$?

(a) $(-3, 11)$ (b) $(2, 7)$ (c) $(5, 4)$

(d) $(7, 3)$ (e) $(12, -1)$

13. Simplify: $\dfrac{a^2 - 2a + 1}{a^4 b - b} \cdot \dfrac{a^2 b + b}{a^2 - a}$

(a) $\dfrac{a}{a + 1}$ (b) $\dfrac{1}{a(a + 1)}$ (c) $\dfrac{a - 1}{a^2 - 1}$ (d) $\dfrac{a - 1}{a(a^2 - 1)}$ (e) $\dfrac{1}{a + 1}$

14. Solve for x: $5 - x = \sqrt{2x^2 + 1}$

(a) -2 (b) 2 (c) $2\sqrt{6}$ (d) -12 (e) 15

15. If $A = \{x : x$ is an odd natural number less than 10$\}$ and

$B = \{y : y$ is a prime number less than 15$\}$, then $A \cap B$ is

(a) $\{2, 3, 5, 7\}$ (b) $\{1, 3, 5, 7, 9\}$ (c) $\{3, 5, 7\}$

(d) $\{1, 9\}$ (e) $\varnothing$

16. Solve for x: $-2[3x - 4(5 - x)] + 4 = 3(1 - x)$

(a) $-\frac{41}{5}$ (b) $-\frac{41}{3}$ (c) $\frac{41}{13}$ (d) $\frac{29}{11}$ (e) 4

17. Solve for x: $2 - |x - 9| = 0$

(a) 11 (b) $7, 11$ (c) $7, 9$ (d) 7 (e) $9, 11$

18. Joe is now 12 years older than Nancy. In 7 years Joe will be twice as old as Nancy will be then. Nancy's age now is

(a) 5 (b) 17 (c) 19 (d) 26 (e) 31

19. Solve for x: $\frac{5}{8}(x + 5) - \frac{1}{4}(3x - 5) = x - 1$

(a) $\frac{18}{12}$ (b) 7 (c) $\frac{12}{11}$ (d) -131 (e) 56

20. A train leaving Canton for Dover, 200 kilometers away, met with an accident 40 kilometers from Dover. It was able to proceed at half its original speed and reached Dover one hour late. The rate of the train in kilometers per hour before the accident was

(a) 10 (b) 20 (c) 30 (d) 40 (e) 50

*Reprinted with permission of the National Association of Independent Schools, 4 Liberty Square, Boston, Massachusetts.

Exercise 74. Sample NAIS Examinations*

Mathematics III Algebra

1. Two numbers in the ratio of 7 to 4 have a sum of 198. Find the numbers.
2. State whether each of the following numerals is positive or negative:

   (a) $(-5)^{16}$ (b) $-3(-4)^9$
   (c) $(-2)^{10}$ (d) -2^{10}

3. Perform the indicated operations:

   (a) $(6 - 9)(4 - 2)$ (b) $6 - 9(4 + 2)$
   (c) $(6 - 9)4 - 2$ (d) $(6 - 6)(4 + 2)$

4. Perform the indicated operations:

   (a) 2.91×100 (b) $(2.5 \times 76) + (7.5 \times 76)$
   (c) $5.7 \div 1000$ (d) $2^4 \times 5^4$

5. Replace the question mark in each case below with any numeral that will make the resulting statement true:

   (a) $\dfrac{5\frac{1}{3}}{2\frac{1}{3}} + ? = 4$ (b) $\dfrac{4.63}{0.2} < ? < 39.1 - 15.94$

6. Name the property illustrated by each of the following:

   (a) $ab = ba$ (b) $a(b + c) = a\,(c + b)$
   (c) $a(b + c) = ab + ac$ (d) $(a + b) + c = a + (b + c)$

7. For what values of x, if any, are the following statements true?

   (a) $5x = -10$ (b) $(x)\left(\dfrac{1}{x}\right) = 1$

   (c) $3x > 2x$ (d) $x + 5 = x$
   (e) $x^2 \geq 0$ (f) $|x| < 0$

8. State the restriction, if any, on the value of n if each of the following represents a real number:

   (a) $\dfrac{7}{n}$ (b) $\dfrac{n}{7}$ (c) $\dfrac{7}{n - 7}$ (d) $\dfrac{7}{n^2 + 1}$

9. Write an expression using the letter k that must be

   (a) odd for any integer k

   (b) equal to zero for any integer k

   (c) equal to one for any integer k provided $k \neq 0$

   (d) negative for any integer k provided $k \neq 0$

10. If 5 is 4 less than 3 times a, find the value of $2 - 3a$.

11. Simplify each of the following:

   (a) $2(a + 3b) - (2a - b)$

   (b) $\dfrac{15x^3}{3x} - (0.1x)^2$

12. Solve for x:

   (a) $\dfrac{x - 2}{3} - \dfrac{x + 1}{4} = 4$

   (b) $\dfrac{10}{x - 3} + \dfrac{4}{3 - x} = 6$

13. Solve each of the following equations for b, giving the results in simplest form:

   (a) $A = bh$

   (b) $P = 2b + 2h$

   (c) $A = \frac{1}{2}bh$

   (d) $A = \frac{1}{2}h(a + b)$

14. Solve for x:

   (a) $x - 4.2x = 0.8x - 12$

   (b) $x(x - 4) = 0$

15. Solve for x, giving answer in simplified radical form: $6x - x^2 = 1$

16. Solve for x, giving answer in simplified radical form:

   (a) $x\sqrt{5} = 3x + 4$

   (b) $\sqrt{x} = 2\sqrt{3} - \sqrt{6}$

17. Solve for x:

   (a) $x^2 - 4x = a^2 - 4$

   (b) $x^2 + x = ax + a$

18. Solve for t:
   $0.3(2t - 20) + 5 \le 0.1(t - 60)$

19. On a real-number line graph the solution set of:
   $|1 - x| > 3$

20. On a real-number line graph the intersection of the solution sets of the following inequalities:

   $x + 2 \ge -4$ and $x - 3 < 4$

21. Write a simple sentence that is equivalent to each of the following compound sentences:

   (a) $x \not> a$ and $x \not< a$

   (b) $m \not\equiv n$

22. Copy the diagram shown at right twice and then shade in the following sets:

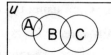

   (a) $(A \cap B) \cup C$
   (b) $A \cap C$

23. Solve the following system of equations:
$$\begin{cases} 3x + 5y = 11 \\ 4x - 3y = 5 \end{cases}$$

24. Factor completely:

    (a) $x^3 - 9x$ (b) $3 + 4x - 7x^2$

25. (a) In a coordinate system plot the four points:

        $A:(4, 3)$ $B:(-1, 3)$ $C:(-3, -3)$ $D:(2, -3)$

    (b) Find the area of parallelogram $ABCD$

    (c) Find the area of triangle BCD

26. Simplify each of the following:

    (a) $4(5 - c) - 3\{8 - 7(c - 2)\}$ (b) $\dfrac{p + prt}{p}$

27. Express each of the following as single fractions in simplest form:

    (a) $\dfrac{5}{3x} + \dfrac{10}{3x}$ (b) $\dfrac{a}{b} \div \dfrac{c}{d}$ (c) $\dfrac{1}{2x} - \dfrac{3}{x}$ (d) $\dfrac{x}{5} + 4$

28. Simplify each of the following:

    (a) $\dfrac{x^2 + x}{2 + 2x}$ (b) $\dfrac{9x}{3x - 15} \cdot \dfrac{(x - 5)^2}{2(5 - x)}$

29. Simplify each of the following:

    (a) $\dfrac{2x^2}{x^2 - y^2} + \dfrac{y}{y - x}$ (b) $\dfrac{a^3 + 6 - 3a - 2a^2}{a - 2}$

30. Simplify each of the following:

    (a) $\dfrac{5a^2}{b^2 - 36} \div \dfrac{25ab - 25a}{b^2 - 7b + 6}$ (b) $\dfrac{2b}{a - b} - \dfrac{2a}{a - b}$

31. (a) Simplify: $\dfrac{a + 2 - \dfrac{1}{a - 2}}{1 + \dfrac{1}{4 - a^2}}$

    (b) Give all restrictions on the value of a in the above fraction.

32. Find the ratio $y : x$ in each case below:

    (a) $5x = 4y$ (b) $\tfrac{1}{3}x = y$ (c) $\dfrac{x}{y} = 0$ (d) $2x = \tfrac{1}{2}y$

33. Simplify each of the following:

    (a) $2\sqrt{150} - \tfrac{3}{8}\sqrt{96}$ (b) $\sqrt{\tfrac{1}{8}}$

    (c) $5\sqrt{10}[2\sqrt{5} - \sqrt{15}]$ (d) $\dfrac{1}{\sqrt{4} + 1}$

34. If the first of 3 consecutive even numbers is divided by 4, the second by 6 and the third by 8, the sum of the quotients equals 29. Find the numbers.

35. A certain eighth-grade class contains n boys. There are 5 fewer girls in the class than boys.

    (a) What is the smallest possible value for n?

    (b) Express the ratio of girls to boys.

    (c) Express the ratio of girls to total eighth graders.

    (d) If the ratio of boys to girls is 3 to 2, how many students are in the class?

36. Answer each of the following questions in as specific terms as possible.

    (a) What is the effect on the area of a square if the measure of its side is doubled?

    (b) What is the effect on the volume of a rectangular solid if the measure of its length and width are doubled but its height remains unchanged?

37. In a certain two-digit number written in base-ten notation, the unit's digit is two less than the ten's digit. Three times the square of the unit's digit increased by the sum of the digits of the number equals the number with its digits reversed. Find the number.

38. Ten years from now Bob will be five-sixths as old as George will then be. Five years ago Bob was two-thirds as old as George was at that time. How old is each now?

39. Bert had some nickels and dimes worth $2.80. If the nickels were replaced by dimes and the dimes by nickels, the value would be $3.50. Find the number of nickels and dimes that he had originally.

40. A jet plane going 500 mph passes an observation tower 36 minutes before another jet that is going 600 mph. How long will it be after the first jet passes the tower before the second jet catches up to the first?

41. A merchant bought some shirts for $120. The next day at a sale the price charged for each shirt was reduced by $1. The merchant figured that, at the sale price, he could have bought 10 more shirts for $120. How many shirts did he buy originally?

Mathematics IV Algebra*

1. Determine the smallest number such that the sum of three times the number and twice its reciprocal is $\frac{25}{2}$.

*Reprinted with permission of the National Association of Independent Schools, 4 Liberty Square, Boston, Massachusetts.

2. Write an equation for the straight line shown in the graph at right.

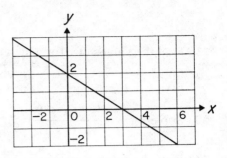

3. If a polynomial is divided by $2x - 3$, the quotient is $3x^3 + 5x - 2$ and the remainder is -4. What is the polynomial?

4. Factor over the integers, if possible:

(a) $x^2 - 6x - 91$ (b) $2(x - 3)^2 + 18(x - 3) + 40$

5. Factor over the integers, if possible:

(a) $(x^2 - 4)(x^2 - 4) - 5(x^2 - 4)$ (b) $(x - 3)^2 - ax + 3a$

6. Factor over the integers, if possible:

(a) $x^2 - 64x$ (b) $2x^3 + 128$

7. Simplify: $\dfrac{x^4 - x^2 + x + 1}{x^3 - x^2 + 1}$

8. Simplify:

(a) $x + y - \dfrac{2xy}{x + y}$ (b) $\dfrac{3}{x - 2} - \dfrac{5x + 10}{x^2 - 4}$

9. Simplify:

(a) $\dfrac{6a - 3(2b - a)}{5(2b - 3a)}$ (b) $\dfrac{\dfrac{x}{y} + 4}{16 - \dfrac{x^2}{y^2}}$

10. Here is a proof that the sum of -3 and 5 is 2. It depends upon the basic properties of the integers under addition. You are to supply a reason justifying each step in the proof.

(1) $-3 + 5 = -3 + (3 + 2)$
(2) $ = (-3 + 3) + 2$
(3) $ = 0 + 2$
(4) $ = 2$

11. Find the solution set for each of the following:

(a) $\dfrac{2x}{3} + \dfrac{5 - x}{4} = 0$ (b) $3(x - 2) + (x - 2)^2 = (x - 2)$

12. Find the values of x for which each of the following statements is true:

(a) $x^2 = 1$　　　　　　(b) $\sqrt{x^2} = 1$　　　　　　(c) $x - 1 > 0$

(d) $x^2 - 1 < 0$　　　　(e) $x^2 - x < 0$

13. Solve for x: $\dfrac{x^2 - 6x + 9}{x - 3} = 2x^2 - 13x + 21$

14. Find the solution set for $\sqrt{2x - 1} = \dfrac{x - 3}{2}$

15. Solve for x:

(a) $2x^2 - 4x - 7 = 0$　　　　　　(b) $x^2 - 7x + 10 < -2$

16. Find the solution set for each of the following:

(a) $|6 - 3x| < 12$　　　　　　(b) $8 \left| \dfrac{x - 5}{2} \right| - 7 = 17$

17. Find the solution set for the system of equations:

$$\begin{cases} 2x + \dfrac{2y}{3} = \dfrac{10}{3} \\[2mm] \dfrac{x}{3} + \dfrac{y}{3} = 3 \end{cases}$$

18. Solve for r: $\dfrac{F}{f} = \dfrac{R + r}{r}$

19. For what values of x are the following statements true?

(a) $p - x = p + 4$　　　　　　(b) $-2 + x = -[2 + |x|]$

(c) $p > q$ and $px > qx$　　　　(d) $p > q$ and $(x + 2)p < (x + 2)q$

20. Solve for x: $\dfrac{2}{x + 1} + \dfrac{1 - x}{x} = \dfrac{1}{x^2 + x}$

21. Simplify:

(a) $(3^{-2})(3x^0)$　　　　　　(b) $\dfrac{2^{-1} + 2^{-2}}{2^{-2}}$

22. Simplify:

(a) $\dfrac{a^{-1}}{a + a^{-1}}$　　　　　　(b) $x^{1/2}(x^{3/2} + x^{-1/2})$

23. Simplify:

(a) $\dfrac{\sqrt{2}}{2 + \sqrt{8}}$　　　　　　(b) $\sqrt{112} - \dfrac{8}{\sqrt{28}}$

24. Solve for x:

(a) $(64)^x - (\tfrac{1}{4})^{-2} = 0$　　　　　　(b) $(4x - 3)^{1/2} = x^0$

25. (a) Given that $f\left(\dfrac{x}{2}\right) = \dfrac{x^2 - 4x + 6}{2}$, find $f(x)$.

(b) If $f(x) = 2x^2 + 9x - 2$ and $g(x) = 2x^2 + 5x + 6$, find the set of real numbers, x, such that $f(x) \geq g(x)$.

26. If $(3, -b)$ and $(3, b)$ are both members of function f, what must be true of the real number b?

27. The sum of two positive numbers in the ratio $2 : 3$ is n. Find the smaller number.

28. Prove that, if a and b are integers, $2a + 3(b + 4a) = 14a + 3b$. Give a reason for each step in your proof.

29. (a) The consecutive vertices of a quadrilateral are $(-3, 2)$, $(0, -2)$, $(6, 2)$, and $(3, 6)$. Which of the following words best describes it?

   (1) Trapezoid   (2) Parallelogram   (3) Rhombus
   (4) Rectangle   (5) Square

(b) Give the coordinates of the point of intersection of the diagonals in the quadrilateral described in part (a).

30. Write an equation for the straight line that is parallel to the line $2x - 3y = 12$ and has a y-intercept of 3.

31. Graph $y = \frac{1}{2}(x + |x|)$ given that $-3 \leq x \leq 3$.

32. The value of 14 coins, consisting of nickels, dimes and quarters, is $1.65. Find the number of dimes, if the number of nickels is one less than twice the number of quarters.

33. What number divided by one-third of itself is seven?

34. A function f is defined by the equation $f(x) = \sqrt{x + 4}$. In the universe of real numbers, find the domain and range of f.

35. If $f(x) = x^3 - 3x + \dfrac{3}{x} - \dfrac{1}{x^3}$, show that $f(a) = f\left(-\dfrac{1}{a}\right)$ if $a \neq 0$.

36. There are 20 problems on a certain mathematics examination. The correct solution of all the word problems constitutes 25% of the total credit. If all problems count the same and if no problems are deleted, how many word problems would have to be added to the examination to make the correct solution of all the word problems account for 40% of the final grade?

37. A man travels for four hours at a certain rate of speed. His brother travels for two hours at a rate of eighteen miles per hour decreased by twice the rate at which the first man travelled. If the product of the distances each travelled is more than 288, how fast did the first man travel?

38. U = {red, orange, yellow, green, blue, violet}. List the elements of A under the following conditions:

B = {orange, green} and $A \cap C$ = {orange} and $\overline{A \cup C}$ = {green} and $B \cup C$ = {red, orange, green, blue}.

39. A grocer had two boxes of apples. Box A contained twenty more apples than box B. The grocer took two-fifths of the apples in box A and transferred them to box B. After doing that, he took ten of the apples in box B and put them in box A. He then found that the two boxes contained the same number of apples. How many apples were in box A originally?

40. Write a set of inequalities that describes the shaded region in the graph at right.

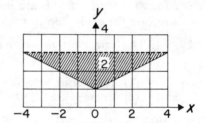

Exercise 75. Mid-Year Examinations

Mid-year Examination (A) $1\frac{1}{2}$ hours

1. (a) Remove parentheses and simplify:

$5a - [2b - \{-b - 2(2b - a) + 7\}]$

(b) Perform the indicated operation:

$(12x^4y^4 - 14x^5y^3 - 2x^2y^2) \div (-2x^2y^2)$

2. (a) If $r = -1$, $s = 2$, and $t = -3$, evaluate the following expression:

$2rt^2 + rs^2 - 2r^2s - t^3$.

(b) Divide $(2a^2 - 12 + a^5 - a^3 + 8a)$ by $(a^2 + 3 - 2a)$.

3. Factor the following expressions completely:

(a) $6a^2 + ab - 15b^2$ (b) $3x^3 + 24$ (c) $4x^4 - 17x^2 + 4$

4. (a) Simplify: $\dfrac{\dfrac{m^2 + n^2}{n} - 2m}{\dfrac{1}{m} - \dfrac{1}{n}}$

(b) Solve for x: $\dfrac{x - b}{a} = \dfrac{x - a}{b}$, $a \neq b$, $a \neq 0$, $b \neq 0$

5. (a) Express the perimeter of a rectangle having a length of t feet and a width of k yards.

(b) If $2x + 1$ represents an odd integer write the next two larger even integers.

(c) If a apples cost c cents, how much do t apples cost?

(d) What is the largest prime number whose square is less than 800?

6. Simplify: $\dfrac{a + 3}{a^2 + a - 2} - \dfrac{3a - 4}{a^2 - 3a + 2} - \dfrac{2a + 7}{4 - a^2}$

7. When \$1100.00 is invested, part at 5% and the remainder at $3\frac{1}{2}$%, the yearly income is \$49.00. How much is invested at each rate?

8. Solve for y and CHECK: $\dfrac{4y}{y + 2} - \dfrac{y - 22}{2y^2 + 3y - 2} = 4 + \dfrac{1}{1 - 2y}$

9. Donner is 5 years older than Blitzen and Dasher is 3 years older than the sum of the ages of the other two. Four years from now, the sum of the ages of the three reindeer will be 23 more than 6 times Blitzen's age one year ago. Find their present ages.

10. (a) Given $a = b$ (i) For what value or values of x is $a + x = b + x$?

    (ii) For what value or values of x is $\dfrac{a}{x} = \dfrac{b}{x}$?

    (iii) For what value or values of x is $a + 2x = b + x$?

(b) What is the value of k if 3 is a root of the equation:

$$\frac{2}{x^2} = \frac{x}{3} + 7k\,?$$

(c) Find y if $y = 679^2 - 669^2$

Mid-year Examination (B) $1\frac{1}{2}$ hours

1. (a) Subtract $3a^2b - 4ab - 3ab^2$ from $2a^2b - 3ab^2 + 4b^3$.
   (b) Divide $x^3 - x^2 - 10x + 12$ by $x - 3$.

2. (a) If $a = -2$, $b = 0$ and $c = 3$, evaluate $4a^2b - a^3c^2 - (ac)^2 - a^2$.
   (b) Simplify: $4xy - [3y(x + y) + 4xy - 3x(y - 2x)]$

3. (a) Multiply $(-2x^2y)^2$ by $(-xy^2)^3$.
   (b) Define: "rational number."   (c) Multiply 524_6 by 24_6

4. Factor each of the following expressions completely.
   (a) $9y^2 + 12y + 4$ (b) $3a^2 - 12b^4$ (c) $8x^2 - 2xy - 3y^2$

5. (a) For what values of x will $|x + 3| = 7$ be true?

(b) For what values of x will $3x + 2 > 7$ be a true statement?

(c) Find the G.C.D. and the L.C.M. for the numbers 42, 56 and 98.

6. Solve for x and CHECK: $\dfrac{3x + 8}{5} + \dfrac{2x}{15} - \dfrac{7x - 2}{10} = \dfrac{5x + 6}{6}$

7. (a) By saving 50 cents each week Al will have enough money for the prom. If he sells his skates for \$5.50 and saves only 30 cents a week, he will have \$1.50 more than enough. How many weeks are there until the prom?

(b) A ski tow charges x dollars for the first ride and d cents for each ride thereafter. Express the cost of t rides in dollars. Assume that $t > 1$.

8. Solve for x: $(x + 1)(x - 1) - (2x + 1)(x + 2) + 3(x + 1)^2 = 3$

9. (a) Joe can do a job alone in 4 days that Bill can do alone in 5 days. How long will it take them to do the job if they work together?

(b) Jane is now eight years older than Dick. Seven years ago she was three times as old as Dick was then. Find their present ages.

10. (a) Prove: $x \cdot 0 = 0$ for any rational number x.

(b) Consider the operation $*$ defined for all rational numbers as follows:

$a * b = 2ab - 3a$. Answer the following and show your work.

(i) Is the operation $*$ commutative?

(ii) Is the operation $*$ distributive over addition; that is, does $a * (b + c) = (a * b) + (a * c)$ for any rational numbers a, b and c?

Mid-year Examination (C) $1\frac{1}{2}$ hours

Part I (60%)

1. Factor: $2y^2 - 18$

2. Simplify: $(-2xy^2)^3 \cdot (-3x^2y)^2$

3. If $x = -1$, $y = -2$, and $z = 3$, find the value of $2xy^2 + 2xz^2 - xyz$.

4. Divide $6x^3 - 7x^2 - 14x + 15$ by $3x - 5$.

5. Subtract twice $2x^2 - 2x + 6$ from the sum of $2x - 4x^2 + 8$ and $8x^2 - 6x + 5$.

6. Find all values of x for which $x + 1 < 5$.

7. Find the highest common factor of 56, 70 and 84.

8. Define: multiple of a number.

9. Simplify: $x - \{2x + 1 - [x - 2 - (x - 3) + x] - 2x\}$

10. Factor: $a^6 - 27b^3$

11. A number increased by one-fifth of its additive inverse is 8. Find the number.

12. Find all values of x satisfying $|x - 3| = |-7|$.

13. If t is an odd number find the sum of the next two even numbers.

14. Factor: $36x^2 + 3xy - 14y^2$

15. If Joe can shovel a walk in 4 hours and his little sister Ann can do it in 6 hours, how long would it take them to do the job if they worked together?

Part II (40%)

16. Solve for x and check: $\dfrac{2x - 1}{3} - \dfrac{x + 10}{6} = \dfrac{10 - 3x}{5} - \dfrac{x + 40}{2}$

17. The operation $*$ is defined for all integers as $a * b = a^2 + ab + b^2$.

    (a) Find the value of $(-3) * (2)$.

    (b) Is $*$ a commutative operation? Justify.

    (c) Solve for x: $2 * x = 19$

18. In my piggy bank I found 36 coins made up of nickels, dimes and quarters. The total value of the coins is \$3.30. If the number of nickels is one more than twice the number of dimes, how many quarters are there?

19. Solve and check: $3(4x - 3)^2 - (x + 6)(x - 5) = 47x^2 - 16$

20. John started out on a 60 mile trip at a certain rate of speed, but after 25 miles he had an accident which delayed him 30 minutes. By filling his gas tank with jet-fuel he was able to double his speed for the rest of the trip and actually arrived at his destination three eighths of an hour earlier than had he gone the entire distance at the initial rate of speed. Find the initial rate of speed.

Mid-year Examination (D) $1\frac{1}{2}$ hours

1. a) Simplify: $2(a - 3)^2 - (3a - 5)(2a + 1)$

   b) Simplify: $7 - \{x - 3(2x - 1)\} - 2(x + 2)$

2. a) If $a = -2$ and $b = 3$ find the value of $2a^2 + 3ab - |a - b|$.

   b) Subtract $a^2 - 3a + 5$ from $a^3 - 2a - 7$.

3. Factor: a) $3x^2 - 75$
              b) $x^3 - 13x^2 - 30x$
              c) $6b^2 + 11b - 10$

4. If $A = \{x \in R : |x| < 4\}$, and $B = \{x \in R : -2 \leq x < 6\}$.

   Find: a) $A \cap B$; b) $A \cup B$.

5. a) If the length of a rectangle is 3 less than four times the width, express the perimeter in terms of the width.

   b) A red die and a green die are rolled. What is the probability that the sum of the spots showing is 12?, 8?, 8 or 12?

6. Solve for x, $x \in R$: $\dfrac{3x - 2}{4} - \dfrac{2x + 5}{3} = \dfrac{x - 3}{2} + 1$

7. a) Express $0.23\overline{636}$ as a quotient of two relatively prime integers.

   b) Solve for x, $x \in R$: $\dfrac{2 - 5x}{3} > 1 - x$

8. A cab driver finds at the end of the day that he has \$3.20 worth of change, made up of nickels, dimes and quarters. If the number of quarters is four less than the number of dimes and the number of nickels is three more than twice the number of dimes, how many nickels does he have?

9. Copy the steps and give the reason for each step in the proof of the following theorem: If $a - c = b - c$, then $a = b$.

   Proof: 1) $a - c = b - c$
            2) $(a - c) + c = (b - c) + c$
            3) $(a + \bar{c}) + c = (b + \bar{c}) + c$
            4) $a + (\bar{c} + c) = b + (\bar{c} + c)$
            5) $a + 0 = b + 0$
            6) $a = b$

10. A man drove from Boston to New York by a certain route at the rate of 60 kilometers per hour and then returned by a route that was 30 kilometers longer at the rate of 90 kilometers per hour. If his return trip took two hours less time, find the length of each route.

PART I (60%)

1. a) Write the additive inverse of $a + b$.
   b) Remove parentheses and simplify: $-(x - y) - x(y - 1)$.

2. Subtract the sum of $3a^2c - 7ab + 3b^2$ and $6ab - 3b^2 + 5ac$ from $2a^2c + 4ab + 5ac$.

3. a) Simplify: $(x - 2)^2 + (x + 1)(x - 1)$
   b) Factor completely: $2t^2 - 18$

4. a) How much is $(x + 2)$ kilos of coffee worth at C cents per kilo?

   b) How many hours does it take to drive M kilometers at 10 kilometers per hour?

   c) Express the perimeter of a rectangle if its width is x centimeters and its length is y centimeters

5. If $A = -2$ and $B = -3$, find the value of: $\dfrac{A^2 - 4A + 2}{AB - B - 2}$

6. a) Factor: $16a^2 - 24ab + 9b^2$
   b) Simplify: $(2x)^3(-5x^2)(-x)^2$

7. The sum of two number is 47. If twice the larger is subtracted from three times the smaller the result is then 11. Find the numbers.

8. a) Express $3.27\overline{27}$ as a quotient of two integers.

   b) Solve for x: $1 - \dfrac{x}{2} > 2(x - 7)$

9. Multiply: $2x^3 - 3x + 2$ by $x^2 - 1$.

10. a) Factor: $6a^2 - a - 35$
    b) Solve for x: $3x^2 - (x - 6)(3x + 4) = 8x$

11. In your test booklet write the missing reasons for the proof of the following theorem.

Theorem: For all real numbers a, $a \cdot 0 = 0$.

	Statements		Reasons
1.	$0 + 0$	$= 0$	1. ?
2.	a	$= a$	2. Reflexive property of $=$.
3.	$a(0 + 0)$	$= a \cdot 0$	3. ?
4.	$a \cdot 0 + a \cdot 0$	$= a \cdot 0$	4, ?
5.	$a \cdot 0 + a \cdot 0$	$= a \cdot 0 + 0$	5. ?
6.	$\therefore \quad a \cdot 0$	$= 0$	6. ?

12. a) Solve for x: $a(1 + bx) = 3a + b$

   b) Solve for y: $\dfrac{y - 4}{5} - \dfrac{3y - 2}{20} = \dfrac{2y + 5}{10}$

13. Six years ago Pete was four times as old as Ted.

   a) If x equals Ted's age six years ago, express Pete's age now.

   b) If two years from now Pete will be twice as old as Ted, find how old each will be then.

14. Two sets of real numbers are defined as follows:

$$\text{set } A = \{x : |x| \leq 5\}$$
$$\text{set } B = \{x : -x + 2 > 0\}$$

   a) Graph set A and set B on the same real number line. (Properly label end points and clearly indicate which set is A, and which is B.)

   (b) On a separate real number line graph the set $A \cap B$.

   (c) Write, in set notation, the set $A \cup B$.

Exercise 76. Final Examinations

Final Examination (A) $1\frac{1}{2}$ hours

Part I (60%)

1. Factor completely: (a) $9 - x^6$ (b) $m^2 + 3m - 28$

2. Find the value of $\dfrac{ab}{c} + ab^2 + b^3 c^2$, when $a = 3$, $b = -2$, $c = \frac{1}{2}$.

3. Divide $a^5 + 2a^2 - a^3 + 10a - 12$ by $a^2 + 3 - 2a$.

4. Solve for z: $3 - \dfrac{z^2 - 3z}{2} = z$

5. Simplify: (a) $\dfrac{(2x)^2(x^6)^{1/2}}{x^4}$ (b) $(a + a^{-1})^{-1}$

6. Solve for x in terms of a: $\dfrac{x + a}{2} - \dfrac{2}{x + a} = \dfrac{x - a}{2}$

7. Determine the solution set for each of the following:
   (a) $|2x - 1| = \tfrac{1}{2}$ (b) $4x + 5 \geq 6x - 4$

8. Solve for y in simplest radical form: $3y^2 = 2y + 6$

9. Let us define the symbol $\boxed{x}$ to mean, the smallest integer greater than x.
   Find $\boxed{-2}$, $\boxed{\sqrt{60}}$, and $\boxed{\pi}$.

10. Simplify: $9\sqrt{\dfrac{2}{3}} + \sqrt{24} - \dfrac{12}{\sqrt{6}}$

11. Solve for x and y: $\begin{cases} 4x + 3y = -3 \\ 5x - 2y = 25 \end{cases}$

12. Simplify: $\dfrac{t}{t - h} - \dfrac{2th}{t^2 - h^2} - \dfrac{2t}{t + h}$

13. Rationalize the denominator and simplify: $\dfrac{4 + \sqrt{2}}{3 - \sqrt{2}}$

14. Factor:
    (a) $4a^2 - 2bc - c^2 - b^2$ (b) $y^2 + ay - 4z^2 - 2az$

15. State the coordinates of the intercepts and the slope of the straight line $2x - 3y - 6 = 0$.

Part II (40%)

16. Solve for x: $\dfrac{x}{x^2 + 2x - 3} - \dfrac{3}{x^2 - 2x + 1} = \dfrac{1}{x - 1}$

17. If a boy walks from his home to the next town at 3 miles per hour and returns at the rate of 4 miles per hour, he will take 5 minutes longer than when he goes there and back at $3\tfrac{1}{2}$ miles per hour. How far away is the next town?

18. (a) Find the solutions of $2x + 3y = 21$ that belong to the set of positive integers.

   (b) If $A = \{(x, y) : x \text{ and } y \text{ are real, and } 2x - y < 6\}$, sketch the graph of A.

19. The operation $*$ is defined for all non-negative real numbers as follows:

$$x * y = \sqrt{x^2 + y^2}$$

   (a) Find $2 * 3$.

   (b) State the commutative law for $*$.

   (c) There is an identity element I such that $I * r = r * I = r$ for any non-negative real number r. Find I.

   (d) Is there a $*$-inverse element for each non-negative real number? Justify your answer.

   (e) Solve for x: $x * 1 = 4 * 7$

Final Examination (B) $1\frac{1}{2}$ hours

1. (a) Factor completely: $4a^2 - 25b^2 + 2a + 5b$

   (b) Simplify: $\dfrac{3\sqrt{3}}{\sqrt{2}} + 2\sqrt{75} - \dfrac{3}{\sqrt{27}}$

2. (a) Solve for x: $x(x - 6) = x - 12$

   (b) Simplify: $\dfrac{\sqrt{2} - 2}{3\sqrt{2} + 2}$

3. (a) If the price of a diamond varies directly as the square of its weight and if a diamond weighing 18 grains is worth \$810, how much does a diamond worth \$120 weigh?

   (b) Simplify: $\left(\dfrac{x^6 y^{-2}}{9}\right)^{-1/2}$

4. Consider the graph of the equation: $y = x^2 - 6x - 7$.

   (a) Find the coordinates of its x and y intercepts;

   (b) Make a rough sketch of the graph;

   (c) Find the coordinates of the vertex;

   (d) Name the curve.

5. (a) Solve: $|x - 4| > 7$.

   (b) Find value(s) for y which satisfy: $\sqrt{3y^2 - 9y} = y - 3$

214

6. A two digit number is 6 less than 4 times the sum of its digits. If twice the units digit is divided by the tens digit, the quotient is 5 and the remainder is 1. Find the number.

7. (a) Simplify: $\dfrac{1 - x^3}{x^2 - 1} \div \left[3 - \dfrac{3}{x + 1}\right]$

   (b) Solve the following equation: $a = \dfrac{3 + a}{a}$, expressing the roots in simplest radical form.

8. (a) From the top of a lighthouse 153.8 feet high, the angle of depression of a passing boat is measured to be 13°20'. How far from the base of the lighthouse is the boat?

angle	sine	cosine	tangent
12°	.208	.978	.213
13°	.225	.974	.231
14°	.242	.970	.249
55°	.819	.574	1.428
56°	.829	.559	1.483
57°	.839	.545	1.540

   (b) Consider the graph of $2x + 3y = -7$, and the graph of
$$3x + ky = 2.$$

   For what value of k do the graphs fail to intersect?

9. Solve the following equation and CHECK:
$$\frac{2x}{2x + 3} - \frac{1 - x}{2 - x} = \frac{7}{6 + x - 2x^2}$$

10. (a) If the operation # is defined for all real numbers a and b as follows:
$$a \# b = (ab)^{-1/2}$$

   SHOW whether or not # is an associative operation.

   (b) If 5 men and 2 boys work together, a piece of work can be completed in one day; and if 3 men and 6 boys work together it can also be completed in one day. How long would it take one boy alone to do the work?

1. (a) Solve for x: $5x^2 + 2 = 11x$

   (b) Factor completely: $x^2 - y^2 - ax + ay$

   (c) $A = \{2, 3, 4, 5, 6, 7, 8, 9\}$

   $B = \{2x + 1: -2 < x < 4 \text{ and } x \text{ is an integer}\}$

   Find: $A \cap B$.

2. (a) Add and simplify: $6\sqrt{\dfrac{3}{2}} - \sqrt{24} + \dfrac{1}{\sqrt{6}}$

   (b) Evaluate: $3a^0 - 8^{2/3} + (\tfrac{4}{9})^{-1/2}$

   (c) Express in simplest form with positive exponents: $\left[\dfrac{2a^{-1}c^{-1/2}}{b^2}\right]^{-2}$

3. (a) Solve for y by completing the square: $y^2 - 6y + k = 0$

   (b) If y is inversely proportional to the square root of x, and $y = 6$ when $x = 25$, find x when $y = 3\tfrac{1}{3}$.

4. (a) Determine the coordinates of all intercepts and of the vertex (turning point) of the parabola: $y = 12 + 4x - x^2$.

   (b) Find the values of x which satisfy: $x^2 - 3x - 10 > 0$

5. (a) Multiply: $\sqrt[3]{a^2b} \cdot \sqrt{ab}$, if $a > 0$ and $b > 0$.

   (b) Express in simplest form with a rational denominator: $\dfrac{6}{5 + 2\sqrt{7}}$.

6. (a) Factor: $x^2 - 2yz - y^2 - z^2$

   (b) Solve for n: $b = \dfrac{2}{n}(n + a)$

   (c) In the triangle at the right, if $a = 9$, $b = 12$, and $C = 90°$, find the numerical value of: (i) $\tan B$, and (ii) $\cos A$.

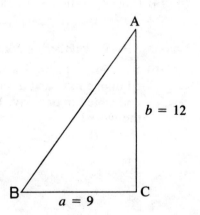

A

$b = 12$

B $a = 9$ C

7. (a) Simplify: $\dfrac{8a^3 - 1}{4a^2 - 1} + \dfrac{2}{2 + \dfrac{1}{a}}$

   (b) Solve for all a which satisfy: $\sqrt{a + 4} - 1 = \sqrt{a}$

8. (a) Jar A contains a solution that is 60% acid. Jar B contains an 80% acid solution. How much must be taken from each jar to obtain 2 quarts of a 75% acid solution?

(b) Solve for x in simplest radical form: $\dfrac{x-5}{3-x} + \dfrac{4}{x^2 - 4x + 3} = 0$

9. (a) The two operations $\oplus$ and $\odot$ are defined for all positive real numbers a and b as follows:

$$a \oplus b = \frac{a}{b} \quad \text{and} \quad a \odot b = \sqrt{ab}\,.$$

(i) What is the name of the following relationship:
$$a \odot (b \oplus c) = (a \odot b) \oplus (a \odot c)?$$

(ii) Is the above relationship true for all positive real numbers? Why or why not?

(b) The angle of elevation of the top of a pole is $44°10'$ when measured from a point on level ground 50 feet from the foot of the pole. Find, to the nearest tenth of a foot, the length of rope required to reach from the ground observation point to the top of the pole.

angle	sine	cosine	tangent
43°	.682	.731	.933
44°	.695	.719	.966
45°	.707	.707	1.000
46°	.719	.695	1.035

10. Abe and Ben work together on a job for 12 days and then Abe stops and Ben finishes the job in 2 more days. Find the time it would take each to do the job alone if Ben takes 15 days longer than Abe when they each work alone.

Final Examination (D) $\qquad$ $1\frac{1}{2}$ hours

1. (a) Factor completely: $x^3 - 16x$

(b) Factor completely: $a^2 - b^2 - 1 + 2b$

(c) Evaluate: $(-8)^{2/3} - (.5)^{-2} + 3x^0$

2. (a) Simplify: $(-3a^2 b^{4/3} c^{n-1})(6b^{1/3} c^n)^{-1}$

(b) Simplify: $\sqrt[3]{\frac{3}{4}} \div \sqrt[3]{\frac{3}{64}}$

(c) Simplify: $\dfrac{6}{\sqrt{3}} + \sqrt{147} - 3\sqrt[4]{9}$

3. (a) Solve for y in the simplest radical form: $3y^2 - 4y - 5 = 0$

(b) Let $A = \{x : |x - 3| \le 4,\ x \text{ being an integer}\}$

$B = \{x : x^2 + 2x < 7,\ x \text{ being an integer}\}$

List the elements of A, B and $A \cap B$.

4. (a) If $f(x) = \dfrac{3x + 4}{2}$, write and simplify $f\left(\dfrac{2a - 4}{3}\right)$.

(b) Find x in terms of a if: $\dfrac{1}{a} + \dfrac{1}{m} = 1$ and $\dfrac{1}{x} + \dfrac{1}{2m} = 1$.

5. (a) Solve for x: $\sqrt{x + 5} - \sqrt{x} = 1$

(b) Simplify: $\left(1 - \dfrac{a - 12b + 2c + 2}{a + 2}\right) \div \left(\dfrac{ac + 2c - 6ab - 12b}{a^2 + 4a + 4}\right)$

6. (a) Sketch the graph of $y = x^2 + 2x - 3$, and label the vertex, the axis of symmetry and the intercepts.

(b) Show that the point $(2,5)$ lies on the curve in part (a). Find the equation of the line through $(2,5)$ and $(-3,0)$.

7. (a) Express with a rational denominator: $\dfrac{3\sqrt{2}}{\sqrt{2} - \sqrt{5}}$

(b) The operation $a * b = \dfrac{3ab}{2}$ is defined on the real numbers.

   (i) Find the identity element for $*$.

   (ii) Does every number have an inverse for $*$?

8. (a) Rectangle $ABCD$ (see diagram) has side $AB = \sqrt{11}$ inches and side $AD = 5$ in. Express $\cos \alpha$ and $\tan \alpha$ in simplest radical form.

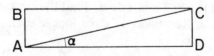

(b) A 22 foot ladder leans against a house making an angle of 51°40′ with the ground. How high up the building will the ladder touch?

	sin	cos	tan
50°	.766	.643	1.192
51°	.777	.629	1.235
52°	.788	.616	1.280

218

9. (a) The weights of two boys are in the ratio of 8 : 13. If they each reduce by 6 pounds, their weights are in the ratio of 3 : 5. Find their weights now.

   (b) Solve for x: $\dfrac{2(x - 7)}{(x - 4)(x + 7)} + \dfrac{2 - x}{4 - x} - \dfrac{x + 3}{x + 7} = 0$

10. A man walked 6 miles at a certain rate of speed. If he had gone 2 miles per hour faster, he would have taken 30 minutes less time. What was the time for the original trip?

Final Examination (E) $1\frac{1}{2}$ hours

1. (a) Find the value of: $(2^{3/2} \cdot 2^{1/5} \cdot 4^{-1})^{-10}$

   (b) In the right triangle shown,
   find:

   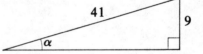

   (i) $\cos \alpha$

   (ii) $\tan \alpha$

2. (a) Factor: (i) $x^4 + xy^3$

   (ii) $x^2 - y^2 + 16 - 8x$

   (b) Simplify: $81^{3/4} - (4x)^0 - 25^{-1/2}$

3. (a) If $f(x) = 4x + 1$ and $g(x) = x^2$, calculate

   (i) $f(3)$ (ii) $g(3)$ (iii) $f[g(3)]$

   (b) Sketch the graph of the function $f(x) = x^2 + 4x - 5$, and give the coordinates of the vertex.

4. (a) Simplify: $\dfrac{1}{\sqrt{21} + 2\sqrt{5}}$

   (b) Calculate $\sqrt{21}$ by linear interpolation.

   (c) Simplify: $\sqrt[3]{54} - \sqrt[3]{250} + \sqrt[3]{\tfrac{1}{8}}$

5. How many pounds of water must be added to 70 pounds of brine which is 15% salt in order to make it 10% salt by weight?

6. (a) Solve for x: $\sqrt{x - 3} = x - 9$

   (b) For which real numbers x is $x^2 > -2x + 35$?

7. Simplify: $\left(1 + \dfrac{5x + 4}{x^2 - 3x - 4}\right)\left(1 - \dfrac{x - 16}{x - x^2}\right) \div \left(\dfrac{2x^2 + 6x + 8}{x^2 + x}\right)$

8. *A* goes to visit *B*, making the five mile trip on foot. He saves one hour on his return trip, as *B* drives him back on his scooter. The scooter goes 16 m.p.h. faster than *A* walks. Find the rates of both parts of the trip.

9. (a) Sketch the set of points (x,y) satisfying all three of the following inequalities:

$$x \geq 0, \quad y \geq 2, \quad y \geq -\tfrac{1}{2}x + 4$$

(b) Find the coordinates of the vertices of the region in part (*a*).

10. Solve the following equation for *x*:

$$\frac{x + 3}{x - 3} + \frac{5}{x} = 3 - \frac{7}{x(x - 3)}$$

Final Examination (F)   1½ hours

Part I (80%)

1. Simplify: $2\sqrt{8a^3} - 2a\sqrt{\dfrac{a}{2}} - \sqrt[3]{54a^4}$

2. Write an equation of the line parallel to $2x - 5y = 6$ which passes through the origin.

3. Simplify: $\dfrac{6a}{4 - 3a} + \dfrac{8}{3a - 4}$

4. If *x* varies directly as y^2 and $x = 8$ when $y = 2$, find *x* when $y = 5$.

5. Factor completely: (a) $2x^2 - 18$
                         (b) $3xy - y - 6x^2 + 2x$

6. Simplify: $\sqrt{49} - \dfrac{2}{3 - \sqrt{7}}$

7. Find the discriminant of the following and use it to discuss the solutions:

$$2x^2 - 3x + 4 = 0$$

8. Simplify the following expression: $\left(\dfrac{(8a)^2 x^0}{27a^{-4}y^3}\right)^{-1/3}$

9. Show that $\sqrt{x - 8} = \sqrt{x + 2}$ has no solutions.

10. If *p* is a real number greater than zero, what can be said about *q* if:

(a) $p + q = 0$ (b) $pq = 0$ (c) $\dfrac{p}{q} = 1$

(d) $pq < 0$ (e) $p - q \geq p$

220

11. Simplify: $\left(\dfrac{a^2}{b^3} + \dfrac{1}{a}\right) \div \left(\dfrac{a}{b^2} - \dfrac{1}{b} + \dfrac{1}{a}\right)$

12. Solve the following system of equations for y in terms of a and b.

$$\frac{1}{x} + \frac{1}{y} = a$$

$$\frac{1}{x} - \frac{1}{y} = b$$

13. The ratio of the ten's digit to the unit's digit of a two digit number is 2 to 3. If the digits are reversed, the resulting number will be 27 larger than the original number. Write the equation or equations you would use to find the original number. (DO NOT SOLVE.)

14. If $f(x) = \dfrac{x}{x-1}$, evaluate:

    (a) $f(3)$ (b) $f(1)$ (c) $f\left(\dfrac{x}{x-1}\right)$

15. Find the length of the shadow cast by a 50 foot flagpole standing on level ground when the sun is 40° above the horizon.

	sin	cos	tan
40°	0.64	0.77	0.84
50°	0.77	0.64	1.19

16. Given the functions $s(x) = x^2$, $t(x) = x + 2$ defined on the reals. Sketch:

    (a) $s \circ t$ (b) $t \circ s$ (c) $t \circ (s \circ t)$ (d) $s \circ (t \circ s)$

Part II (20%)

17. A right triangle has two legs equal in measure. If the hypotenuse is 3 inches longer than either leg, find the length of a leg.

18. A bus driving from Boston to Philadelphia (288 miles) travels 8 miles per hour faster going than returning. If the return trip takes 3 hours longer than going, find the average rate of speed in each direction.

19. Using the same axis system sketch the following sets. Be sure to label axes and intercepts.

    (a) $A = \{(x,y) : x + y > 5\}$

    (b) $B = \{(x,y) : y \le -x^2 + 4x + 5\}$

    (c) $A \cap B$

1. (a) If 10 is 4 more than $2a$, find the value of $5 - 3a$.

    (b) Write the equation of a line whose graph goes through the origin and has a slope of zero.

    (c) Determine whether or not $3 - 2x$ is a factor of $4x^2 - 16x + 15$. (Show your work.)

2. If $A = \{x \mid 0 < x \le 27$, and x is an integer$\}$, and

    $B = \{\odot \mid \odot$ is an integral perfect square less than 65$\}$,

    (a) list the elements of B using the roster method;

    (b) determine $B \cap A$;

    (c) state the number of elements in $A \cup B$.

3. (a) Graph on the number line, the solution set of: $7 > |x - 1|$, where x is a real number.

    (b) Find the coordinates of the x and y intercepts of the graph of:
    $$y = x^2 - 4$$

4. (a) Solve the following for all values of k which make it valid:
    $$\frac{k - 2}{2} > \frac{4k - 3}{4}$$

    (b) Find $f(\frac{1}{3})$, if $f(y) = y^2 - 9y$.

    (c) If y is an integer, is $(2y + 1)^2$ always odd, always even, or one cannot tell? (Show your work.)

5. Solve for x and y:
    $$\begin{cases} x - \dfrac{5y + 2}{2} = -4 \\ \\ y - \dfrac{2x - 3}{7} = 3 \end{cases}$$

6. (a) Express $1.27\overline{27}$ as a ratio of two relatively prime integers.

    (b) Write the equation of a line whose graph passes through $(1, -3)$ and $(5, 9)$.

7. A man drives to a certain place at the rate of 80 kilometers per hour. He returns by a road that is 3 kilometers longer at the rate of 64 kilometers per hour and takes 30 minutes longer than in going. How long is each road?

8. (a) If p pounds of apples cost d dimes, how many cents will 2 pounds cost?

(b) Solve for y and CHECK:

$(2y + 3)^2 - 5(3y - 7) - (2y - 1)(2y - 5) = 3$.

9. (a) If x varies inversely as y, and x equals 4 when y is 6, how much will x equal when y is 24?

(b) Carefully graph the solution set of the system to the right, labelling axes and important points.

$$\begin{cases} y \geq \dfrac{x}{2} \\ y < 2x + 8 \\ 3x + 2y < 16 \end{cases}$$

10. Two persons, A and B, together have \$6 less than a third person C. If B gives \$5 to A, A's money will then be half of C's. If instead, A gives \$5 to B, A's money will then be one-third of B's. How many dollars has each?

Final Examination (H) $1\frac{1}{2}$ hours

Part I (60%)

1. Factor completely: $9y^2 - 36x^2$

2. Simplify: $(-2a^2c)^3 \div \dfrac{4a^5}{c^3}$

3. Solve for x: $\dfrac{4 - x}{5} > x + 2$

4. Factor: $6y^2 + y - 35$

5. Write the equation of the straight line passing through the points $(0,4)$ and $(3,-2)$.

6. Simplify: $\dfrac{x - 1}{x - 3} + \dfrac{2}{3 - x}$

7. Factor: $x^3 + 27$

8. Solve simultaneously: $\begin{cases} 4x - 3y = 17 \\ 2x + y = 1 \end{cases}$

9. If $f(x) = 3x - 7$, (a) find $f(-3)$; (b) find x if $f(x) = 8$.

10. Factor: $a^2 - a - d^2 + d$

11. Divide: $21x^3 - 20x^2 + 13x - 6$ by $3x - 2$.

12. If A travels for 3 hours at 40 kph and then speeds up to 50 kph for 2 hours, how far did he travel?

13. Factor completely: $a^4 - 12a^2 + 27$

14. Solve for y in terms of x: $3x - 2(y - 4) = -(y + 2x)$

15. Simplify: $\left(\dfrac{1}{c} - 1\right) \div \left(5 - \dfrac{5}{c}\right)$

Part II (40%)

16. John is 8 more than 3 times as old as his son. Six years ago John was 13 times as old as his son. How old is John now?

17. Solve for x: $(2x - 3)^2 - 2(2x - 3) = 3$

18. Simplify: $\dfrac{1}{a^2 - 3a + 2} - \dfrac{5}{a - 2} + \dfrac{2}{1 - a^2}$

19. If $A = \{(x,y) \mid y \geq 3x + 7\}$, $B = \{(x,y) \mid 2x + 3y \leq 21\}$, and $C = \{(x,y) \mid x \geq -3\}$, then on the same set of axes sketch the graph of $A \cap B \cap C$.

20. A 12 liter solution is 75% acid. How many liters of solution that is 20% acid needs to be added to the 75% acid solution to end up with a solution that is 50% acid?

TABLE I
Values of Sines, Cosines, Tangents, Cotangents

Angle	sin	cos	tan	cot	
1°	.0175	.9998	.0175	57.2900	89°
2°	.0349	.9994	.0349	28.6363	88°
3°	.0523	.9986	.0524	19.0811	87°
4°	.0698	.9976	.0699	14.3007	86°
5°	.0872	.9962	.0875	11.4301	85°
6°	.1045	.9945	.1051	9.5144	84°
7°	.1219	.9925	.1228	8.1443	83°
8°	.1392	.9903	.1405	7.1154	82°
9°	.1564	.9877	.1584	6.3138	81°
10°	.1736	.9848	.1763	5.6713	80°
11°	.1908	.9816	.1944	5.1446	79°
12°	.2079	.9781	.2126	4.7046	78°
13°	.2250	.9744	.2309	4.3315	77°
14°	.2419	.9703	.2493	4.0108	76°
15°	.2588	.9659	.2679	3.7321	75°
16°	.2756	.9613	.2867	3.4874	74°
17°	.2924	.9563	.3057	3.2709	73°
18°	.3090	.9511	.3249	3.0777	72°
19°	.3256	.9455	.3443	2.9042	71°
20°	.3420	.9397	.3640	2.7475	70°
21°	.3584	.9336	.3839	2.6051	69°
22°	.3746	.9272	.4040	2.4751	68°
23°	.3907	.9205	.4245	2.3559	67°
24°	.4067	.9135	.4452	2.2460	66°
25°	.4226	.9063	.4663	2.1445	65°
26°	.4384	.8988	.4877	2.0503	64°
27°	.4540	.8910	.5095	1.9626	63°
28°	.4695	.8829	.5317	1.8807	62°
29°	.4848	.8746	.5543	1.8040	61°
30°	.5000	.8660	.5774	1.7321	60°
31°	.5150	.8572	.6009	1.6643	59°
32°	.5299	.8480	.6249	1.6003	58°
33°	.5446	.8387	.6494	1.5399	57°
34°	.5592	.8290	.6745	1.4826	56°
35°	.5736	.8192	.7002	1.4281	55°
36°	.5878	.8090	.7265	1.3764	54°
37°	.6018	.7986	.7536	1.3270	53°
38°	.6157	.7880	.7813	12799	52°
39°	.6293	.7771	.8098	1.2349	51°
40°	.6428	.7660	.8391	1.1918	50°
41°	.6561	.7547	.8693	1.1504	49°
42°	.6691	.7431	.9004	1.1106	48°
43°	.6820	.7314	.9325	1.0724	47°
44°	.6947	.7193	.9657	1.0355	46°
45°	.7071	.7071	1.0000	1.0000	45°
	cos	sin	cot	tan	angle

ANSWER
KEY

Answers for odd number problems and review exercises.

Exercise 1, page 1

1. 86
3. 300
5. 100
7. 27
9. $1\frac{3}{8}$
11. 1
13. 8
15. 0
17. 54
19. $-\frac{2}{3}$
21. -37
23. 4

25. 16
27. 5
29. 18
31. 9
33. -2
35. $\frac{17}{3}$
37. $\frac{1}{8}$
39. -18
41. $\frac{25}{6}$
43. -24
45. $-\frac{79}{3}$

Exercise 2, page 3

1. $a + 2b - 5c$
3. $7l - 5m - 2n - 4p$
5. $-6x^2 + x - 4$
7. $-8x^3 - 13x^2 - x - 2$
9. $-21ax - 25y$
11. $2x^3 - 3x^2 - 13x - 6$
13. $6.5 + 1.1x - 9.5y$
15. $7ax^2 - 5a^2x - 5ax$

Exercise 3, page 5

1. $3a^2 - 7ab - 18b^2$

3. $x^2 - 12xy + 7y^2 - 15$

5. $11a^2 - 15a^2b - 4ab^2 - 14b^2$

7. $-7mn - 4b^2y^2 - 4by^2$

9. $-7abc + 2bc + 5ab$

Exercise 4, page 6

1. $-33m + 55n - 65p$

3. $-2.5x^2 - 1.2x - 1.63$

5. $-51y^2 + 80y^3 - 29.5 + 57y$

7. $9a + 9b$

9. $-6n$

11. $-4y^2 + 6.6xy - 2x^2$

13. $19ax^2 - 31ax - 14x^2 + 16a^2x$

15. $12p$

17. $-5a - 25x - y$

19. $8n - 6a$

Exercise 5, page 8

1. $-2560abc$

3. $-48a^4 + 112a^3 + 728a^2$

5. $-\frac{2}{3}a^3b + a^2b^2 - 3ab^3$

7. $-9a^5b^6c^2$

9. $ax - 2ay - bx + 2by - cx + 2cy$

11. $x^3 + y^3$

13. $-15a^2 - 26ab + 21b^2$

15. $x^4 + 4x^3 + 5x^2 + 5x + 6$

17. $x^4 - y^4$

19. $3a^4 + 11a^3b + 21a^2b^2$
$+ 22ab^3 + 8b^4$

21. $a^6 - 1$

23. $x^4 + x^3 - 4x^2 + 5x - 3$

25. $-3a^8 + 16a^6 - 4a^5 + 35a^4$
$- 11a^3 - 65a - 52$

27. $-m^6 - 4m^5 + 10m^4 + 11m^3$
$- 10m^2 - 8m$

29. $-6a^4 - 20a^3b - 6a^2b^2$

31. $45a^2 - 15ac - 60c^2$

33. $a^4 - 2a^2b^2 + b^4$

Exercise 6, page 10

1. $-3b$

3. $\frac{3}{2}y^4 - 3y^2 + x$

5. $-40m$

7. $x - 2$

9. $2a + 4$

11. $2x - 3$

13. $-2x + 5$

15. $2x + 3y$

17. $a + 10b$

19. $m - 3n$

21. $x + 2y$

23. $x^2 - 9x - 4$

25. $x - 1 - \dfrac{4}{x - 1}$

27. $x^2 + 2x + 3 + \dfrac{7}{x - 2}$

29. $x - 2 - \dfrac{2}{x + 5}$

31. $m - n$

33. $a - 3b + 2$

35. $x^2 + xy + y^2$

37. $-3x + 4 + \dfrac{14}{2x^2 - 5x - 7}$

Exercise 7, page 13

1. $9x^2 - 5x + 3$

3. $26p + 10$

5. $28y^2 - 11$

7. $-10x^2 + 3xy + 4y^2$

9. $-.6x + .35$

11. $2\frac{2}{3}a + 6$

13. $2x^3 - 2x^2 + 3x - 2$

15. $-5m - 13n$

17. $-5x + 25$

19. $-3y - 5$

21. $-18x^2 + 16x - 27$

23. $16a^2 - 15a$

25. $-2a - 12b$

27. $-15a^2 + 8a$

29. $12b - 3a$

Exercise 8, page 14

1. $(3a - 2b + 7c) + (a - 7b - c)$

3. $(3a - 2b) + (3a + 2b)$

5. $(m^2 - 8m + 2) - (-m + 13m^2 + 9)$

7. $(9a + 7m) - (9a - 7m)$

9. $(a + b - c)(a - b + c)$

11. $(x - y)[3(x - y)]$

13. $(a + b + 3a + 3b) \div (-a - b)$

15. $(a - 9)(-4a + 1) - (a - 5)(-2a + 7)$

17. $(3 - 2a + 5b)z + (4 + a - 2b)x$

19. $(4m + 5a - 13)z - (3a - 4m - 11)x$

21. $-(3a^2 + 10a)x + (4b^2 - 18b)y - (2 - a)z$

23. $-(1 - a - a^2)y - (3 + 4a - 17a^2)x$

25. $(a^2b - ab^2 - 3a)y - (ab^2 - 7a^2b)x$
    $\quad - (3ab - 14)x$

27. $-3x^2 + 6x - 4$

29. $-12x^2 - 6x + 24$

31. $3x^2 - 6x + 4$

33. $3x^2 - 3x - 10$

Exercise 9, page 16

1. $9a^2 + 2ab + \dfrac{b^2}{9}$

3. $81x^4 + 18x^2ab^2 + a^2b^4$

5. $x^8 + 14x^4y^2 + 49y^4$

7. $x^2 + .4xy + .04y^2$

9. $25 + .3a + .0009a^2$

11. $a^2b^2c^2 + 6abcx + 9x^2$

13. $9r^4s^2 + 42r^3s^4 + 49r^2s^6$

15. $x^2 + 2xy + y^2 + 6x + 6y + 9$

17. $4x^2 + 4ax + a^2 + 20x + 10a + 25$

19. $4m^2 + 12mn + 9n^2 + 16m$
    $\quad + 24n + 16$

21. $4r^2 + 20rs + 25s^2$
    $\quad + .4r + s + .01$

23. $4a^2 + 4ab + b^2 + 12a + 6b + 9$

25. $r^2 + 2rs + s^2 + 6rt + 6st + 9t^2$

27. $\dfrac{9m^2}{4} - 3mn + 4n^2$

29. $.0064c^2 - .016cd + .01d^2$

31. $\dfrac{p^2}{4} - .2pq + .04q^2$

231

33. $a^2 - 2ab + b^2 - 2a + 2b + 1$

35. $4p^2 + 4pq + q^2 - 20p - 10q + 25$

37. $1 - 2a - 2b + a^2 + 2ab + b^2$

39. $x^2 + 2xy + y^2 - 2xz - 2yz + z^2$

41. $m^2 + 6mn + 9n^2 - 12m$
$\quad - 36n + 36$

43. $49x^2 + 28xy + 4y^2 - 81a^2$

45. $x^4 + 2x^2y + y^2 - a^4$

47. $4x^2 - 4xy + y^2 - a^2$

49. $121r^2 - 4a^2 - 4am - m^2$

51. $1 - a^2 - 2ab - b^2$

53. $4 + 4b + b^2 - a^2$

55. $m^2 - 2mn^2 + n^4 - a^4 + 2a^2b - b^2$

57. $a^2 + 2a + \frac{7}{16}$

59. $m^2 - \dfrac{2m}{3} - \dfrac{8}{9}$

61. $y^2 + \dfrac{24y}{5} - 1$

63. $x^2 + .8x - .24$

65. $a^2 + 4.1a + .4$

67. $p^2 - .2pq - .08q^2$

69. $a^2 + ab - ac - bc$

71. $x^2 - ax + 2bx - 2ab$

73. $a^2 + 2ab + b^2 + 5a + 5b - 14$

75. $x^2 + 5xy + 5x + 6y^2 + 12y + 6$

77. $x^2 - 4xy + 4y^2 + 4x - 8y - 5$

79. $9x^2 + 6xz + z^2 - 9xy - 3yz + 2y^2$

Exercise 10, page 19

1. $\frac{1}{4}x^2 + .04xy + .0016y^2$

3. $a^6 - 17a^3/3 - 30$

5. $4x^2 + .58x - .003$

7. $4m^2 + 2mn - 6mp - 3np$

9. $729 - 54x^2 + x^4$

11. $b^2c^2 - a^2$

13. $-4a^2 + 4ab - b^2$

15. $156m^2 - 204mn + 65m - 85n$

17. $9 + 6a + 12b + a^2 + 4ab + 4b^2$

19. $4x^2 - a^2 + 2ay - y^2$

21. $9a^2 - 6ab + 3a - b + \frac{1}{4}$

23. $n^2 - m^2 - 2am - a^2$

25. $16a^2 - 72ab + 81b^2 - 56ac$
$\quad + 126bc + 49c^2$

27. $16x^2 + 24xy + 9y^2 + 40ax$
$\quad + 30ay + 25a^2$

29. $\frac{25}{4} + 10y + 4y^2 - 5x/2 - 2xy + x^2/4$

31. $49a^2 - 14ab + b^2 - 9c^2$

33. $9b^2 - c^2 - 4cd - 4d^2$

35. $81p^2 - 72pq + 16q^2 - 54p + 24q - 16$

37. $361 + 152y + 16y^2 - 64x^2$

39. $4a^2 - b^2 + 6bc - 9c^2$

41. $x^2 - 49y^2 + 56y - 16$

43. $9 - m^2 - 2mn - n^2$

45. $4a^2 + 4ab + b^2 - x^2 - 6xy - 9y^2$

47. $m^2 - 6mn + 9n^2 - p^2 - 14pq - 49q^2$

49. $36a^2 - 24ab + 4b^2 - x^2 + 6xy - 9y^2$

1. $\{1, 2, 3, 4\} =$
$\{x \mid 0 < x \leq 4$ and x is an integer$\}$

3. $\{11, 22, 33, \ldots, 99\} =$
$\{11x : 1 \leq x \leq 9$ and x is an integer$\}$

5. $\{2\} =$
$\{x : \sqrt{2} < x < \sqrt{7}$ and x is an integer$\}$

7. $\{6, 12, 24, 30\} =$
$\{6a \mid 1 \leq a \leq 5$ and $a \neq 3$ and a is an integer$\}$

9. $\{-9, -8, -7, \ldots, 10\} =$
$\{x : -10 < x \leq 10$ and x is an integer$\}$

13. $\{$Conn., Mass., Me., N.H., R.I., Vt.$\}$

15. $\{0, 2\}$

17. $\{2n - 1 : n$ is a positive integer$\}$

19. $\{1/x : x$ is a positive integer$\}$

21. $\{3x : x$ is a positive integer$\}$

23. $\{5x : x$ is a positive integer$\}$

25. $\{4n + 1 : n \geq 0$ and an integer$\}$

27. $\{x^2 : x \geq 0$ and integral$\}$

29. $\left\{ \dfrac{2n - 1}{2n + 1} : n \geq 1 \text{ and integral} \right\}$

31. $\{1, 2, 3, 4, 5, 7\}$

33. $\{1, 2, 3, 4, 5, 6, 7\}$

35. $\{2, 4\}$

37. A

39. A

41. $\{1, 3\}$

43. T

45. T

47. F

49. T

51. F

53. F

55. F

57. F

59. F

61. T

63.

65.

67.

69.

71.

73. Y

75. X

77. $\{2, 3, 4\}$

79. $\{1\}$

1. 1

3. $\varnothing$

5. 1

7. 0, 1

9. $\varnothing$

11. 5

13. 2

15. 3

17. 0

19. 5

21. -27

23. 1

25. 0

27. $\varnothing$

29. $\frac{11}{4}$

31. -3

33. 0.1

35. 0

37. $\frac{3}{10}$

39. 0

41. 21

43. -123

45. 1

47. -178

Exercise 13, page 29

1. 5	**17.** 20	**31.** 1110	**45.** $0.91\bar{6}$
3. 2	**19.** 422	**33.** 1111	**47.** $0.\overline{57}$
5. 196	**21.** 13	**35.** 1000110	**49.** $0.\overline{714285}$
7. 194	**23.** 187	**37.** 101	**51.** $\frac{7}{9}$
9. 256	**25.** 510	**39.** 100	**53.** $\frac{7}{33}$
11. 10	**27.** 10011	**41.** 1111101	**55.** $\frac{58}{99}$
13. 11011	**29.** 100000	**43.** $0.\bar{5}$	**57.** $\frac{34}{333}$
15. $\frac{10}{11}$			**59.** $\frac{73}{90}$

61. (a) iv   (b) i, iii, iv   (c) none

62. (a) yes   (b) no   (c) a is the negative of b
(d) 9   (e) a

63. (a) no   (b) no   (c) 8   (d) 22   (e) no

65. (a) 14   (b) yes   (c) yes   (d) -4
(e) -20 (f) 5

67. (a) 0   (b) 3   (c) 1   (d) 4
(e) 4   (f) 1, 4   (g) no   (h) 3

69. (a) 8   (b) 0   (c) 3   (d) 1   (e) -4
(f) -3 (g) 14   (h) 11   (i) 0   (j) -100

71. (a) 1   (b) -2 (c) all non-integers

Exercise 14, page 35

1. -2	**11.** $1, -5$	**21.** $\frac{1}{3}$	**31.** $3, -3$
3. $-2, 4$	**13.** $14, -8$	**23.** $3, 15$	**33.** $2, -2$
5. $-1, 1$	**15.** $\frac{7}{3}, -\frac{5}{3}$	**25.** $1, -1$	**35.** $0, 2$
7. $-2, 2$	**17.** $6, -6$	**27.** $-\frac{2}{3}, 4$	**37.** $1, -3$
9. $-6, 6$	**19.** $1, -1$	**29.** $-1, 5$	**39.** all integers

Exercise 15, page 37

1. $x > 4$	**9.** $-1 \leq x \leq 6$	**17.** $-2 \leq x < 0$	**25.** $-3 < x < 3$
3. $x \geq 2$	**11.** $x \geq -5$	**19.** $x > -2$ or $x < -4$	**27.** (a) T (b) F (c) T (d) T
5. $x < 3$	**13.** $x \leq 1$	**21.** $2 \leq x \leq 7$	(e) T (f) F (g) T
7. $x \leq 3$ or $x \geq 7$	**15.** $x \leq \frac{1}{2}$	**23.** $1 \leq x \leq 3$	**29.** No, only when $x > 0$.
			31. $x > 0$

Exercise 16, page 39

1. 2

3. 1, 2, 3

5. −1, −2, −3, −4, −5

7. −2 ≤ x ≤ 2

9. x > 2 or x < −2

11. −2 ≤ x ≤ 4

13. x < −1 or x > 5

15. 3 < x < 7

17. no

19. no

Exercise 17 page 40

(A)

1. T

3. F

5. F

7. F

9. F

11. F

13. T

15. T

17. F

19. T

(B)

1. b

3. c

5. c

7. c

9. b

(C)

1. $3ab - 11a^2b + 5ab^2 + 7$

3. 7

5. $3x^2 - 8x + 4$

7. $-x^3 + 2x^2 - 3x + 1$

9. 530, 163, 441, 23

(D)

1. $2a^2 - ax - 3ax^2 - 6xy$

3. $1 - 2x - 2x^2$

5. $x^2 - 3x + 9 - \dfrac{54}{x + 3}$

7. $b^3 - b^2 - b$ by 20

9. F, T, F, F, F

Exercise 18, page 45

1. $36a^2b^2(b^3 - 2a^2b - 3a)$

3. $13aby(ay - 5ab - 3by)$

5. $3p^2q^2(q - p - 3)$

7. $\pi(x - a + b - 1)$

9. $8x^2(8x^4 - 4x^3 + 2x^2 - 1)$

11. $2(a + b)(x + 1)$

13. $(11)(14)(10) = 1540$

15. $-31(172) = -5332$

17. $2x(x + y)$

19. $(x + y)(2a)$

Exercise 19, page 46

1. $(13x + 12y)^2$

3. $(9m - 2n)^2$

5. $(1 - 25p^2)^2$

7. $2a(x + y)^2$

9. $x^2(x - 4)^2$

11. $(4x - 3y)^2$

13. $(a + b - 16)^2$

15. $(a + b + 3c)^2$

17. $(4 + 3m + 3n)^2$

19. $(7 + 3a - 3b)^2$

1. $(15a^2b^3 + 13y)(15a^2b^3 - 13y)$

3. $(12m + 7n)(12m - 7n)$

5. $a^2b^2(a^2 + b^2)(a + b)(a - b)$

7. $5x(x + 5y)(x - 5y)$

9. $2a(4a^2 + 9b^2)(2a + 3b)(2a - 3b)$

11. $3m(m + 6n^3)(m - 6n^3)$

13. $2(2r + 3s^2)(2r - 3s^2)$

15. $32a^2(x^2 + y^2)(x + y)(x - y)$

17. $(x + 3)^2(x - 3)^2$

19. $(12x + 5m + 5n)(12x - 5m - 5n)$

21. $(x^2 + 4m - 4n)(x^2 - 4m + 4n)$

23. $(2x + 4 + 21a)(2x + 4 - 21a)$

25. $(x - 3 + 11y)(x - 3 - 11y)$

27. $(5x + 2a + 2b)(5x - 2a - 2b)$

29. $(2a - 1 + y)(2a - 1 - y)$

1. $(x + 7)(x + 5)$

3. $(x - 6)(x - 1)$

5. $(m + 9)(m + 7)$

7. $(a + 10)(a - 2)$

9. $(x + 9)(x - 6)$

11. $(x^2 - 11)(x^2 - 8)$

13. $(x - 12)(x + 9)$

15. $(x - 14)(x + 11)$

17. $m(m - 13)(m + 6)$

19. $(a^2 - 3)(a + 1)(a - 1)$

21. $(x + 3)(x - 3)(x + 2)(x - 2)$

23. $5(x^2y^2 - 13)(x^2y^2 - 5)$

25. $2(23 + x)(2 - x)$

27. $(p - 9q)(p + 7q)$

29. $(a - 7)(a - 5)$

31. $3a(a - 7)(a + 4)$

33. $4(a^2b - 6c)(a^2b + 3c)$

1. $(2x + 1)(x + 1)$

3. $(2m + 1)(m + 2)$

5. $(2q - 7)(q - 1)$

7. $(2a + b)(3a + 2b)$

9. $(3 - 2x)(1 + 3x)$

11. $(3x - 1)(x + 1)$

13. $(5x - 1)(x - 2)$

15. $(28x - 1)(2x + 1)$

17. $(3x^2 - 2)(2x^2 - 3)$

19. $(2x + 1)(2x - 1)(x^2 + 1)$

21. $(5a - 2b)(5a + 7b)$

23. $y(5y - 2)(2y - 3)$

25. $(3a + 2)(3a - 2)(a + 1)(a - 1)$

27. $(2 - x)(4 - 5x)$

29. $(3a^2b - 2c)(a^2b + c)$

31. $3(5x - 2)(x + 2)$

33. $(4x - 3)(3x - 4)$

35. $(3x + y)(x + 2y)$

Exercise 23, page 52

1. $2(x + y)(a + b)$

3. $(x + 1)^2(x - 1)$

5. $(2a - b)(3x - y)$

7. $5(m - n)(p + q)$

9. $(7 - x)(a + b)$

11. $-b(x - y)$

13. $(a - b - 5)(a - b)$

15. $(a + 1)(a - 1)(x + y)(x - y)$

17. $5(m - n)$

19. $(x - 2)(x + 3)$

21. $(m - n - 1)(a - b)$

23. $(a - b)(x - 2 - y)$

25. $(b - c)(a - 2)(a + 1)$

27. $(x + y + 1)(m + n)$

29. $(3a + 2b)(x - y + z)$

Exercise 24, page 53

1. $(a - b)(a^2 + ab + b^2)$

3. $(2a + b)(4a^2 - 2ab + b^2)$

5. $(y + 3z)(y^2 - 3yz + 9z^2)$

7. $(a + 1)(a^2 - a + 1)(a^6 - a^3 + 1)$

9. $(x - y)(x^2 + xy + y^2)(x + y)(x^2 - xy + y^2)$

11. $(2a - 1)(4a^2 + 2a + 1)$
    $(2a + 1)(4a^2 - 2a + 1)$

13. $(3y^2 - 1)(9y^4 + 3y^2 + 1)$

15. $xy(y - x)(y^2 + xy + x^2)$

17. $a^2(2a + 3b)(4a^2 - 6ab + 9b^2)$

19. $8(2a - b)(4a^2 + 2ab + b^2)$

21. $(2m - 3p)(4m^2 - 6mp + 9p^2)$

Exercise 25, page 54

1. $(x + 8)^2$

3. $(4x + 1)(3x + 2)$

5. $(a - 2)(a^2 + 2a + 4)$

7. $(4x - 9)(x + 4)$

9. $a^2(b + 21)(b - 2)$

11. $(a + 3b)(a + c)$

13. $(p + 4)(p - 4)(p + 1)(p - 1)$

15. $2a(y - b)$

17. $4(a - 2b)(b - c)$

19. $(11a^2 - 2)^2$

21. $(3a + 1)(2a - 1)$

23. $(2x + 1)^2(2x - 1)^2$

25. $(9p - 4)(p - 1)$

27. $(16x - 9)^2$

29. $(8a - 3)(a + 4)$

31. $m^2(m + n + 1)(m + n - 1)$

33. $(2x - 2y + 13)(2x - 2y - 13)$

35. $a^4x^4(a^4 + x^4)(a^2 + x^2)(a + x)(a - x)$

37. $(1 - b)(1 - a)$

39. $(3m - 2n)(3m + 2n + 1)$

41. $x^2(4x - 3a)(3x + 2a)$

43. $p(3p + 5)(p - 2)$

45. $(x^2 - a + 1)(x^2 - a - 1)$

47. $(a - b)(2a - b)$

237

49. $(2x - 2y + 3)^2$

51. $(2a - b)(4a^2 + 2ab + b^2)$

53. $2x(x - y)$

55. $(x + 2)(2x + 1)(x - 1)$

57. $(x - 2)(x^2 + 3)$

59. prime

61. $(3x - 2y)(2x - y)$

63. $(a - 1)(x + 3)(x - 2)$

65. $a(a - 1)$

67. $(x - 3 - a)(x + 3 + a)$

69. $(c + a + b)(c - a - b)$

71. $(x + 1)(x^2 - x + 1)$

73. $(a + 1)^2(a - 1)^2$

75. $(a^2 + b^2)^2$

77. $x(y - 2)(y^2 + 5)$

79. $(a^2 - 2a + 3)(a + 3)(a - 1)$

81. $(x^2 - 3)^2$

83. $xy(x - y)$

85. $(m - 1)(m^2 + 1)$

87. $4a(2a - b)$

89. $2y(x + y)(x - y)$

91. $(3 + x^2y^4)(2 + xy^2)(2 - xy^2)$

93. $(a^2b - x^4)(a^4b^2 + a^2bx^4 + x^8)$

95. prime

97. $(x + y)(x - y)(x + 1)(x - 1)$

99. $(x - y + 4a)(x - y - 4a)$

Exercise 26, page 56

1. $\dfrac{11a^2}{27bx}$

3. a^2

5. $\dfrac{1}{a + x}$

7. $\dfrac{6m - 1}{8}$

9. $\dfrac{a + 3}{4}$

11. $\dfrac{a - b}{4(a + 2b)}$

13. 1

15. $\dfrac{b - 2a}{x + y}$

17. $2x + h$

19. 1

21. $\dfrac{2x + 3}{2(3x - 1)}$

23. $\dfrac{x - a - b}{a - x - b}$

25. $\dfrac{x + 3y}{x - 3y}$

Exercise 27, page 57

1. $\dfrac{28ab - 24ac + 9bc}{12a^2b^2c^2}$

3. $-\dfrac{5}{a + 1}$

5. $\dfrac{8ab}{a + 4b}$

7. $\dfrac{6x^2 + 8x - 4}{x^2 - 1}$

9. $\dfrac{-2x + 13}{(x - 6)(x - 1)(x - 5)}$

11. $\dfrac{5}{m^2 - 4}$

13. $\dfrac{5b^2 + 23ab}{6(a^2 - b^2)}$

15. $\dfrac{-x + 8}{(x - 3)(x - 2)(x - 1)}$

17. $\dfrac{-5a^2 + 16a - 3}{4(a - 1)}$

19. $\dfrac{4a}{(a^2 - 4a - 4)(a + 2)}$

21. 0

23. $-\dfrac{3}{4ab}$

25. $\dfrac{x^2 + 3xy + y}{xy}$

27. $\dfrac{-8x^2 + 6x + 1}{4(2x - 1)^3}$

29. $\dfrac{a - y}{(a - b)(x - y)}$

31. $\dfrac{m^2 - 4m + 2}{m^2(m - 1)^2}$

33. $\dfrac{x^3 + 3x^2 - 7x - 45}{x^2 - 9}$

35. $\dfrac{-2mn}{(m - n)^2(m + n)}$

37. $\dfrac{3b^2 - 7ab + 4a^2 - 2b}{b(a - b)}$

39. $\dfrac{x^2 - 3}{x^2 - 1}$

41. $\dfrac{2a^2 - 9a + 5}{a^2(a - 5)^2}$

43. $\dfrac{a + 2}{a + 1}$

45. $\dfrac{-6a + 7}{a(a - 1)}$

Exercise 28, page 63

1. $\dfrac{7}{8}$

3. $\dfrac{2mx^2}{n}$

5. $-x$

7. $\dfrac{8a(a + 2)}{a - 3}$

9. $\dfrac{ab}{2}$

11. $\dfrac{2(2x - 3y)}{x}$

13. $\dfrac{36a^2}{2a - 3b}$

15. $\dfrac{3x - 1}{(2x + 3)^2}$

17. $x + 2$

19. $\dfrac{-2x}{a^2(a + x)^2}$

21. $\dfrac{n^3}{3}$

23. $3x$

25. $\dfrac{1}{a - b}$

27. $\dfrac{(a - 2)(b - 5)}{(a + 6)(b - 1)}$

29. $\dfrac{(a - b)^2}{a^2}$

31. $\dfrac{a}{b}$

33. 4

35. $\dfrac{a^2}{a - 1}$

37. $\dfrac{(1 - x)(1 + 2x)}{1 + x}$

39. $\dfrac{8m}{m + n}$

Exercise 29, page 67

1. $\tfrac{3}{2}$

3. $a + 2$

5. $\dfrac{6x - 4y}{3}$

7. $\tfrac{3}{5}$

9. $\dfrac{a + x}{2a + x}$

11. $\dfrac{a}{1 - b}$

13. $\dfrac{4a}{a + b}$

15. $1/x$

Exercise 30, page 69

1. $\dfrac{1}{a - b}$

3. $-\dfrac{c}{c + d}$

5. $\dfrac{y^2 - 1}{y}$

7. $\dfrac{-5}{2m + 3}$

9. $\dfrac{x}{a^2 + x^2}$

11. $\dfrac{2(x + y)}{(x - y)}$

13. $\dfrac{4ab}{b^2 + 2ab - a^2}$

15. x

17. $-\dfrac{3a + b}{2a + b}$

19. $1/n$

Exercise 31, page 71

1. 10

3. 1

5. $-\frac{7}{2}$

7. $\frac{11}{10}$

9. 10

11. -2

13. $\frac{39}{5}$

15. 0

17. 14

19. $\varnothing$

21. 2

23. $\frac{5}{8}$

25. 2

27. -2

29. $46\frac{1}{2}$

31. $\frac{1}{10}$

33. $\frac{9}{16}$

35. $\frac{5}{2}$

37. $-\frac{3}{2}$

39. -1

41. $-\frac{7}{2}$

43. $\frac{3}{4}$

45. $\frac{3}{2}$

47. $\varnothing$

49. -1

51. $-\frac{1}{5}$

53. 2

55. $x \neq 2$

57. 6

59. $\frac{1}{4}$

61. $5a$

63. $\dfrac{3a - b}{5}$

65. 4

67. $\dfrac{4a - 2b}{b}$

69. $-b$

71. $\dfrac{m - n}{3}$

73. $\dfrac{m + n}{m}$

75. $-\dfrac{4am + 2an}{mn}$

77. $a + b$

79. $\dfrac{a^2 + b^2}{4ab}$

81. $-\dfrac{3m}{a}$

83. $2b$

85. $b + 2a$

87. 0

89. $\dfrac{b - a}{2}$

91. $-\dfrac{a(a + 3n)}{3a + n}$

93. $\dfrac{a^2}{a + b}$

95. $2m - n$

97. $\dfrac{m^2 + n^2}{m^2 - n^2}$

99. 1

1. $x = 3$
$y = 1$

3. $x = 5$
$y = 3$

5. $x = 4$
$y = -3$

7. $x = \frac{1}{3}$
$y = 1$

9. $x = 3$
$y = 8$

11. $x = 2$
$y = 3$

13. $x = 7$
$y = 1$

15. $x = \frac{7}{3}$
$y = \frac{1}{4}$

17. $x = -6$
$y = -8$

19. $x = -9$
$y = -7$

21. $x = 3$
$y = 7$

23. $x = 6$
$y = \frac{1}{7}$

25. $x = \frac{1}{5}$
$y = -\frac{1}{3}$

27. $x = 8$
$y = 9$

29. $x = -1$
$y = -4$

31. $x = \frac{1}{2}$
$y = \frac{1}{3}$

33. $x = 6$
$y = 4$

35. $x = 7$
$y = 2$

37. $x = 5$
$y = 3$

39. $x = \frac{1}{2}$
$y = \frac{1}{3}$

41. $x = -2$
$y = \frac{1}{3}$

43. $x = -\frac{1}{8}$
$y = -\frac{1}{5}$

45. $x = \frac{1}{3}$
$y = \frac{1}{4}$

47. $x = \frac{1}{8}$
$y = 1$

49. $x = \frac{11}{7}$
$y = 11$

51. $x = m$
$y = -3m$

53. $x = a$
$y = 2b$

55. $x = a + b$
$y = a - b$

57. $x = \dfrac{1}{a}$
$y = \dfrac{1}{b}$

59. $x = \dfrac{1}{b - a}$
$y = \dfrac{1}{a - b}$

61. $x = \dfrac{2ab}{a^2 - b^2}$
$y = \dfrac{b^2 + a^2}{b^2 - a^2}$

63. $x = \dfrac{2}{m - n}$
$y = \dfrac{2}{n - m}$

65. $x = \dfrac{cn - bd}{an - bm}$
$y = \dfrac{cm - ad}{bm - an}$

67. $x = 3m + 1$
$y = 3n + 1$

69. $x = m - n$
$y = m + n$

71. $x = 3m$
$y = 2n$

73. $x = -0.6$
$y = 1.5$

75. $x = 2.4$
$y = 2.0$

77. $x = 2.37$
$y = 0.17$

1. $x = 1$
$y = -1$
$z = 2$

3. $x = 3$
$y = 4$
$z = -5$

5. $x = 5$
$y = 6$
$z = 7$

7. $x = -\frac{3}{2}$
$y = \frac{3}{4}$
$z = 2$

9. $x = 10$
$y = 8$
$z = 6$

241

1. $x = 3$

3. $x = \frac{9}{8}$

5. $x = 18$

7. $a = 2$

9. 9, 12

11. 30, 60, 90

13. 36, 63, 81

15. $2x : y = 14 : 5$

17. W, \$1400; T, \$600; M, \$800

19. $\dfrac{md}{m+n}, \dfrac{nd}{m+n}$

21. 63, 112 or
$\frac{126}{23} \quad \frac{224}{23}$

23. 48

25. -48

27. \$12, \$60

29. (a) $y = kx$; $y_1 : y_2 = x_1 : x_2$

(b) $y = \dfrac{k}{x}$; $y_1 : y_2 = x_2 : x_1$

(c) $y = kx^2$; $y_1 : y_2 = x_1^2 : x_2^2$

(d) $y = \dfrac{k}{\sqrt{x}}$; $y_1 : y_2 = \sqrt{x_2} : \sqrt{x_1}$

31. $V = kr^3$; $V_1 : V_2 = r_1^3 : r_2^3$

33. $P = kh$; $P_1 : P_2 = h_1 : h_2$

35. $A = kr^2$; $A_1 : A_2 = r_1^2 : r_2^2$

37. $I = \dfrac{k}{d^2}$; $I_1 : I_2 = d_2^2 : d_1^2$

39. $F = \dfrac{k}{d^2}$; $F_1 : F_2 = d_2^2 : d$

41. $l = kt$; $l_1 : l_2 = t_1 : t_2$

43. $133\frac{1}{3}$ liters

45. $\dfrac{3\sqrt{2}}{2}m$

47. 5 kg/sq cm; 2.5 cu m

49. $V = \dfrac{kT}{p}$; 74°C

1. $x \geq \frac{19}{3}$

3. $x > \frac{4}{3}$

5. $x \leq 10$

7. $x < -1$

9. $x \geq 12$

11. $x > -20$

13. $x \leq 7$

15. $x < -1$

17. $-5 < x < 1$

19. $x \leq -\frac{13}{9}$ or $x \geq \frac{11}{9}$

21. $\frac{3}{2} \leq x \leq 4$

23. all reals

25. $x \leq -\frac{3}{2}$ or $x \geq \frac{7}{8}$

27. $\varnothing$

29. $x \leq -7$ or $x \geq -1$

31. $x > 0$

33. $\varnothing$

35. $x > 2$

37. $x < 0$

39. $\varnothing$

1. 56, 80

3. \$500, \$700

5. 300, 320, 310 bu

7. $\frac{10}{48}$

9. \$76

11. 786

13. 13, 15, 17

15. $\frac{27}{45}$

1. \$12, \$60, \$90

3. 3, 3, $5\frac{1}{2}$ tons

5. 50 @ \$1.50, 20 @ \$2.25

7. 525 orch., 125 bal.

9. 500, 1250 liters

11. 5 @ \$35, 7 @ \$40

Exercise 38, page 96

1. 90%

3. 27°

5. 2200 kg

7. 3 games

9. 8 games

11. 16 games

Exercise 39, page 98

1. 45, 54

3. $386 @ 5%, $772 @ 6%

5. $4500, $5040

7. $6,200 @ $3\frac{1}{2}$%, $12,400 @ 5%

9. $\dfrac{5m}{11}$, $\dfrac{6m}{11}$ marbles

11. $7620 @ 4%, $9380 @ 5%

Exercise 40, page 100

1. 15, 26m

3. 10, 20 m

5. 18, 8

7. 5, 10 m

9. 16, 20 cm

Exercise 41, page 102

1. 27

3. 41

5. 39

Exercise 42, page 103

1. 4 kph

3. $3\frac{1}{5}$ hrs

5. 9 km

7. $9\frac{3}{13}$ hrs

9. $1\frac{2}{3}$ kph; $6\frac{2}{3}$ kph

11. $\dfrac{abh - am}{b - a}$ km

Exercise 43, page 105

1. 6 liters

3. 35 bu

5. 3 kg

7. 120 liters

9. 28 liters @ 10%; 36 liters @ 5%

Exercise 44, page 107

1. $2\frac{2}{5}$ hrs

3. 10 hrs

5. $3\frac{1}{3}$ hrs

7. 18, 36 days

Exercise 45, page 109

1. 6, 13, 18, 9

3. 15, 45 yrs

5. $5\frac{1}{2}$ m

7. $\frac{7}{19}$

9. $2.30, $2.80, $1.90, $2.10

11. 49

13. $1425

15. 60 kph

17. $(100m - 5d)$ @ 6%; $(6d - 100m)$ @ 5%

19. $(m + 13)$ yrs

21. $\dfrac{2a - b}{8}, \dfrac{3b - 2a}{8}$

23. 5, 6, 7

25. 6, 15 yrs

27. 79, 65 cents

29. 11, 24 cm

31. 335 kmh

33. 55 cents

35. 12, 16 days

37. 7.5, 2.5 tons

39. 12 liters

41. $2500

43. 108, 80 km

45. 35

47. $5000 @ 2%, $20,000 @ 4%

49. 10 dozen

Exercise 46, page 112

(A)

1. 20

3. $2t + 4$

5. $3x + 5y$ hours

7. $y = -33$

9. $x \geq -1$

(B)

1. e

3. d

5. b

7. e

9. e

Exercise 47. page 115

1. $4y^4/a^2$

3. 1

5. m^6

7. ax^6

9. x^2y^8

11. x^{4a}

13. x^{3m+3n}

15. 1

17. x^{20}

19. $a^{2n} - b^4$

21. $a^{3n} - 2a^n + 1$

23. $-27x^6y^{15}/64a^9$

25. 16

27. $x^{3a}y^{3a}/8m^3$

29. $128x^2y^6$

31. $64x^{12}$

33. $32a^{30}$

Exercise 48, page 117

1. a^5

3. x^n

5. $5ab^{n-2}$

7. $a^n b^{n+2}$

9. $(1 - a^2 b^2)/a^2$

11. $72 a^{5n-1} b^{4n-3}$

13. a^2

15. $a^{2n-2} - b^{2n-2}$

17. $m^{n-1} + 2m^n + 2m^{n+1} + m^{n+2}$

19. $9 x^{m-4} a^{m-2}$

21. $a^{n-2} - 10$

23. a^{12x+3}

25. a^{2m^2}

27. x^{mn}

29. x^{ab}

31. $\dfrac{1}{a + b}$

33. 16

35. $\dfrac{mn}{m + n}$

37. 5

39. -5

Exercise 49, page 119

1. $5ab + 3a^{3/2} b^{3/2} - 4a^2 b^2$

3. $x - y$

5. $x^{3/5} + 2x^{2/5} + 2x^{1/5} + 1$

7. $x^{2/5} + x^{1/5} y^{1/5} + y^{2/5}$

9. $\dfrac{64a^2}{b^4 c^3}$

11. $a^2 + 2ab + b^2$

13. $8a^4 b$

15. $a^2 b^{2y}$

17. b^6

19. $x^{2m} y$

21. $a + b$

23. $\dfrac{1}{a + b}$

25. $x^{1/9}$

27. $\dfrac{x^{4/3} y^2}{a^{1/3}}$

29. x^2

31. $x^{n-1} y^{m-1}$

33. 0

35. $\frac{17}{3}$

37. 4

Exercise 50, page 121

No answers

Exercise 51, page 122

1. 11

3. 29

5. 98

7. 6.8

9. 8.7

11. 15.2

Exercise 52, page 122

1. 2.8

3. 4.2

5. 7.1

7. 9.9

9. 12.1

11. 14.14

13. 5.20

15. 22.36

17. 36

Exercise 52, page 122, continued.

19. $\frac{1}{3}$

21. 128

23. $\frac{1}{3}$

25. $\frac{1}{2}$

27. $\frac{1}{8}$

29. $-2x^3y^4$

31. $4a^2c^{2/3}$

33. $a - b$

35. 5

37. $13\frac{1}{2}$

39. 4

41. $\frac{97}{24}$

43. $\sqrt{6}/6$

45. $a\sqrt{a + b}/(a + b)$

47. $\sqrt{a(a - b)}/(a - b)^2$

49. $\sqrt{3x}/x$

51. $a\sqrt{ab}/b^2$

53. $(a - b)\sqrt{a}$

55. $\sqrt{a^2 - b^2}/(a + b)$

57. $\sqrt{a(a + b)}/(a + b)$

59. $3\sqrt[3]{4}/4$

Exercise 53, page 125

1. $4\sqrt{2}$

3. $12\sqrt{2}$

5. 0

7. $4\sqrt{3} - 15\sqrt{2}$

9. $-15\sqrt{2}$

11. $\dfrac{\sqrt{2}}{2}$

13. $\dfrac{21\sqrt{m}}{5}$

15. $2\sqrt{14}$

17. $2a\sqrt{a}$

19. $a\sqrt[3]{2a^2} + \sqrt[3]{25a^2}$

21. 4

Exercise 54, page 127

1. $20\sqrt{3}$

3. $14\sqrt{10}$

5. $2\sqrt{3}$

7. $21a\sqrt{a}$

9. $11ax\sqrt[3]{12ax}$

11. 4

13. $\frac{4}{3}$

15. $\frac{3}{2}\sqrt[3]{4}$

17. 36

19. $\frac{1}{5}$

21. $2\sqrt{6}$

23. $\frac{4}{21}\sqrt[3]{9}$

25. $9\sqrt{3} - 2$

27. $\dfrac{\sqrt{10}}{4}$

29. $-5 - \sqrt{2}$

31. $\dfrac{(a - 2b)\sqrt{a}}{a}$

33. $5 - 2\sqrt{6}$

35. $2a + b + 2\sqrt{a(a + b)}$

37. $3\sqrt{5} - 3\sqrt{2} + \sqrt{30} - 2\sqrt{3}$

39. $-27\frac{1}{2}$

41. $2 - \sqrt[3]{12} + \sqrt[3]{4}$

43. $18 - 10\sqrt{7}$

45. $x\sqrt{x - y} + (x - y)\sqrt{x} + x\sqrt{x^2 - y^2}$

47. $3\sqrt{2} + 1 + 2\sqrt{3}$

49. $2\sqrt{6}$

Exercise 55, page 130

1. $\sqrt{2}/2$

3. $\sqrt{ac}/c$

5. $\sqrt{5}$

7. $\sqrt[3]{25}/3$

9. $\sqrt[3]{3a^2x}$

11. $\sqrt{6} - 2$

13. $-4(2\sqrt{7} + 5\sqrt{2})/11$

15. $\sqrt{x} - \sqrt{y}$

17. $\dfrac{3}{\sqrt{6}}$

19. $\dfrac{a}{\sqrt{ab}}$

Exercise 55, page 130, continued.

21. $\dfrac{2}{\sqrt[3]{18}}$

23. $\dfrac{12}{3\sqrt{2} - 2\sqrt{3}}$

25. $\dfrac{3}{\sqrt{2} - 1}$

27. $\dfrac{1}{\sqrt{x + h} + \sqrt{x}}$

Exercise 56,   page 132

(A)

1. $-12x^{a+1}y^{a+3}$

3. $9\sqrt{15}$

5. $-m^{10}$

7. $5\sqrt{2}$

9. $-y^{3/2}$

11. $\dfrac{1}{5 - 2\sqrt{6}}$

13. $\dfrac{x}{128y^7}$

15. $\dfrac{a^2 + 1}{a}$

17. $\dfrac{20 - 2\sqrt{5}}{19}$

19. $26 + 13\sqrt{3}$

(B)

1. e   **2.** e

3. a   **4.** b

5. b   **6.** d

7. e   **8.** e

9. d   **10.** a

11. c   **12.** d

13. e   **14.** b

15. d   **16.** b

17. b   **18.** d

19. a   **20.** c

Exercise 57,   page 135

1. ± 5

3. $\pm \frac{9}{2}$

5. $\pm 2\sqrt{10}$

7. $\pm \sqrt{3}$

9. $\pm \dfrac{\sqrt{3}}{2}$

11. $\dfrac{\pm a + 1}{a}$ or

13. $\pm \dfrac{b\sqrt{6}}{a}$

15. $\pm \dfrac{m - n}{m + n}\sqrt{m + n}$

17. $\pm (a - 2)$

19. $\dfrac{\pm 3\sqrt{2}}{2}$

Exercise 58,   page 136

1. $0, -4$

3. $9, -3$

5. $.8, -.3$

7. $-23, 2$

9. $-1, -\frac{1}{2}$

11. $2, \frac{4}{5}, 0$

13. $\dfrac{9}{a}, \dfrac{2}{a}$

15. $-a, -b$

17. $a, -3$

19. $4, -7$

21. $4m, -9m$

23. $\frac{2}{3}$

25. $1, -9$

27. $11, -1$

29. $\frac{2}{3}, -\frac{4}{3}$

31. $\frac{11}{4}, -\frac{1}{4}$

33. $\frac{5}{4}, \frac{1}{4}$

35. $1, -4$

37. $-\frac{10}{3}, -\frac{1}{3}$

39. $2, -1$

41. $-5 \pm 3\sqrt{3}$

43. $5 \pm 2\sqrt{6}$

45. $\dfrac{6 \pm \sqrt{2}}{2}$

47. $\dfrac{2 \pm \sqrt{3}}{3}$

49. $a, -7a$

51. $-\dfrac{5}{2a}, -\dfrac{1}{2a}$

53. $1 \pm \sqrt{a}$

55. $\dfrac{3 \pm \sqrt{4a - 135}}{4}$

57. $\dfrac{a \pm b}{2}$

59. $2a \pm \sqrt{4a^2 - 3}$

61. $\dfrac{-b \pm \sqrt{b^2 - 4c}}{2}$

63. $\dfrac{b \pm \sqrt{b^2 - ac}}{a}$

65. $-\frac{1}{2}, -1$

67. $2 \pm \sqrt{5}$

69. $0, -7$

71. $d, -2$

73. $\dfrac{5 \pm \sqrt{6}}{2}$

75. $\varnothing$

77. $\dfrac{-7 \pm \sqrt{97}}{8}$

79. $1 \pm a$

81. $\dfrac{2b}{a}, \dfrac{b}{a}$

83. $\dfrac{1 \pm \sqrt{a}}{2}$

85. $\dfrac{a \pm \sqrt{b}}{m}$

87. $\dfrac{b \pm \sqrt{b^2 - 80ac}}{2a}$

89. $14, -3$

91. $0.6, 0.7$

93. $0, 4$

95. $\varnothing$

97. $(5 \pm \sqrt{61})/6$

99. $\pm(2m - 1)$

101. $\frac{1}{3}, -\frac{3}{2}$

103. $\dfrac{-8 \pm \sqrt{262}}{9}$

105. $\dfrac{1 \pm 3\sqrt{109}}{14}$

107. $\dfrac{-5 \pm \sqrt{33}}{4}$

109. $1.19, -4.19$

111. $2.35, -0.85$

113. $0.36, -0.16$

115. $1.00, 0.29$

Exercise 59, page 142

1. $\pm 1, \pm 2$

3. $\pm\sqrt{3}$

5. $\pm\frac{3}{2}$

7. $1, 3$

9. $\pm 1, \pm\sqrt{2}$

11. -2

13. $4, -\frac{1}{2}$

15. $0, \pm 2$

17. $4, \pm 3, -2$

Exercise 60, page 142

1. $x > 2$ or $x < -2$

3. $x \geq 10$ or $x \leq -10$

5. $-\sqrt{7} < x < \sqrt{7}$

7. $\varnothing$

9. all reals

11. $x < 0$ or $x > 2$

13. $-2 < x < 1$

15. $x < 1$ or $x > 3$

17. $x \leq -1$ or $x \geq 4$

19. $x \leq -2$ or $x \geq 1$

21. $\varnothing$

23. $\frac{1}{2} \leq x \leq 2$

Exercise 61, page 144

1. 81

3. 4

5. $\frac{1}{81}$

7. $\frac{1}{2}$

9. $\frac{1}{25}$

11. $-\frac{2}{3}$

13. 3

15. 7

17. $\frac{1}{8}, \frac{\sqrt{2}}{4}$

19. $0, \frac{1}{2}$

21. 16

23. $\frac{10}{3}$

25. 27/4

27. 2

29. 2

31. $\varnothing$

33. $\varnothing$

35. $\varnothing$

37. $\varnothing$

39. 4

Exercise 62, page 146

1. $(4,3), (3,4)$

3. $(-2,-6), (6,2)$

5. $(3,-7), (-2,-2)$

7. $(5,13), (-1,-5)$

9. $(10,17), (2,1)$

11. $(1,-\frac{1}{5}), (-3,-1)$

13. $(\frac{13}{5},\frac{7}{5}), (-4,-3)$

15. $((-1 \pm 3\sqrt{17})/4, (3 \mp \sqrt{17})/8)$

17. $(3,\pm1), (-3,\pm1)$

19. $(1,2), (\frac{5}{3},3)$

21. $(2\sqrt{7}, \pm\sqrt{7})$

23. $(-5,-\frac{1}{5}), (-\frac{1}{2},-2)$

25. $(2,0), (0,-2)$

27. $(4,3), (3,4)$

29. $(\frac{3}{4},-\frac{5}{4}), (-\frac{1}{3},2)$

Exercise 63, page 148

1. $6, -9$

3. $8, -9$

5. $-4, -3$

7. $6,8$ or $-8,-6$

9. $\frac{1}{8}, 8$

11. $9, 16$ m

13. $5,15$ or $-2,-6$

15. $5,6$ or $-2,-1$

17. $1\frac{1}{3}, 7\frac{1}{3}$ m

19. $\frac{6}{12}$

21. 20 m

23. $3,4$

25. 12

27. $20

29. $7, -4$

31. $5,7$

33. 10

35. 4%

37. 600 m

39. $18,20$ cm

41. $11,40$ m

43. $7,8$ hrs

45. 7.5 m

47. 144 sq m

49. 40

(A)

1. $2, -11$

3. $3 \pm 2\sqrt{2}$

5. $-7 \le x \le 3$

7. $-\dfrac{a + b}{2}, -\dfrac{a - b}{2}$

9. $-9, 8$

(B) True – False

1. T

3. T

5. T

7. T

9. F

(C) Multiple Choice

1. b

3. a

5. d

7. a

9. c

(D) Multiple Choice

1. d

3. a

5. a

7. a

9. e

1. $1, \frac{5}{3}, \frac{7}{3}, -\frac{1}{3}$

3. $0, 0, -\frac{15}{4}$, undefined

5. $-1, 0, \frac{5}{2}, -5$

7. $-3\frac{3}{4}, 15\frac{3}{4}, 53\frac{3}{8}, -9\frac{2}{27}$

9. $2a + 2b + 1, 2a + 2b + 2,$
   $2ab + 1, 4ab + 2a + 2b + 1$

11. $2a^2 + 1, (2a + 1)^2$

13. $4a^2 + 2$

15. $a + 2$

17. $f = \{(0, -1), (1, 1), (2, 3), (3, 5), (4, 7)\},$
   $g = \{(2, 3), (3, 4), (4, 5), (5, 6), (6, 7)\}$
   $D_f = \{0, 1, 2, 3, 4\},$
   $D_g = \{2, 3, 4, 5, 6\}, D_h = \{2, 3, 4\}$
   $h = \{(2, 6), (3, 9), (4, 12)\} =$
   $\{(x, h(x)) : h(x) = 3x \text{ and } x = 2, 3, 4\}$
   $F = \{(2, 5), (3, 7)\} =$
   $\{(x, F(x)) : F(x) = 2x + 1 \text{ and } x = 2, 3\}$
   $G = \{(2, 4), (3, 6)\} =$
   $\{(x, G(x)) : G(x) = 2x \text{ and } x = 2, 3\}$

19. $\{x \in R : x \ne 0\}$

21. $\{x \in R : x \ne -1\}$

23. $\{x \in R : x \ne 1, x \ne -1\}$

25. $\{3, 2, 1, 0, -1, \ldots\}$

27. $\{-2, -1, 0, 1, \ldots\}$

29. $\{1, 2, 3, 4, 5\}, \{0, 3, 8, 15, 24\}, g(t) = t^2 - 1$

31. $4x - 3, 8x - 3, 1, 9, -3$

33. $x \le 5, f(x) \ge 0$

35. $x \in R, f(x) \ge -1$

37. proof

39. $\frac{1}{2}$

41. 1

43. 0

45. $\varnothing$

47. 1

1. Graphs

3. $m = -5, y = -5x$

5. $m = 1, y = x - 4$

7. $m = \frac{1}{3}, 3y = x - 7$

9. $m = -1, y = -x + 6$

11. $m = \frac{8}{11}, 8x - 11y = 191$

13. $m = -1, x + y = 1$

15. no slope, $x = -2$

17. $m = 2, (0, 5), (-2.5, 0)$

19. $m = \frac{2}{3}, (0, -4), (6, 0)$

21. $m = \frac{1}{2}, (0, -2), (4, 0)$

23. $m = -\frac{3}{2}, (0, \frac{5}{2}), (\frac{5}{3}, 0)$

25. $m = \frac{2}{3}, (0, -\frac{5}{3}), (\frac{5}{2}, 0)$

27.

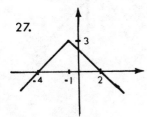

29.

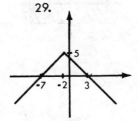

33.

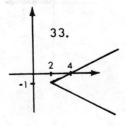

31.

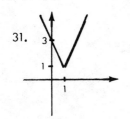

35. $y = -x + 5$

37. $y = 3x - 3$

39. $x + 3y = 11$

41. $3y = 2x + 8$

43. $2x + 7y + 37 = 0$

45. $(1, 5)$

47. $(-1, 2)$

49. $(0, 0)$

51. $(2, -3)$

53. none

55. $x - 2y = 3$

57. $(8, 1)$

59. $(0, 1)$

61. $(4, 2), (-8, 6)$

63. $(6, 0)$

1.

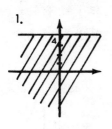

3.

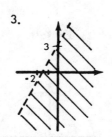

5.

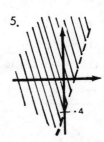

7.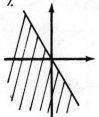

9.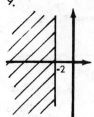

11.

13.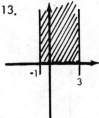

15.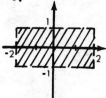

17.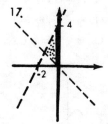

19.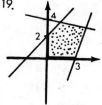

Exercise 68, page 168

1. $x = 0$; $(0, 0)$

3. $x = 0$; $(0, 0)$

5. $x = 0$; $(0, -1)$

7. $x = 1$; $(1, 0)$

9. $x = -2$; $(-2, 0)$

11. $x = 3$; $(3, 0)$

13. $x = -1$; $(-1, 0)$

15. $x = -2$; $(-2, 0)$

17. $x = \frac{3}{2}$; $(\frac{3}{2}, -\frac{1}{4})$

19. $x = 0$; $(0, 4)$

21. $x = 1$; $(1, 0)$

23. $x = 1$; $(1, -1)$

25. $x = \frac{5}{2}$; $(\frac{5}{2}, -\frac{25}{4})$

27. $x = -2$; $(-2, 1)$

29. $y = 0$; $(0, 0)$

31. $y = 2$; $(-1, 2)$

33. $y = -2$; $(9, -2)$

35. $y = -\frac{1}{2}$; $(-\frac{25}{4}, -\frac{1}{2})$

37. $y = 1$; $(-8, 1)$

39.

41.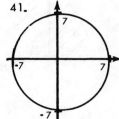

43.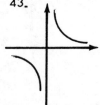

45.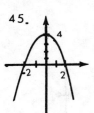

47.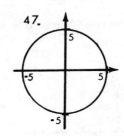

49. $(-2, -1), (1, 2)$
51. $(0, -5), (4, 3)$
53. $(3, -7), (-2, -2)$
55. $(7, 1), (1, 7)$
57. $(2, 5), (-1, -1)$
59. $(4, 3), (3, 4),$
$(-4, -3), (-3, -4)$

Exercsie 69, page 171

1. $x \leq -\frac{2}{3}$ or $x \geq 1$
3. $-5 < x < 3$
5. $x < 3$ or $x > 4$

7.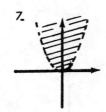

9.

11.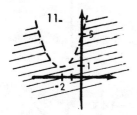

13.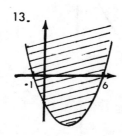

15.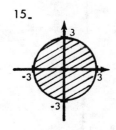

17.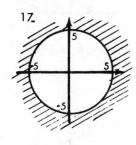

19.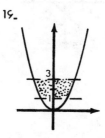

21.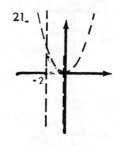

23.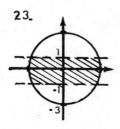

25.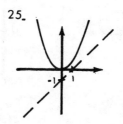

253

1.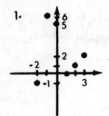

3.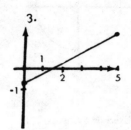

5.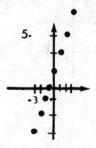

7.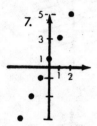

9.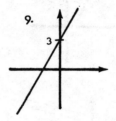

11.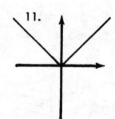

13.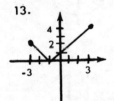

15.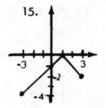

17.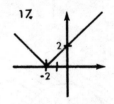

19.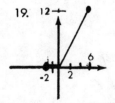

21.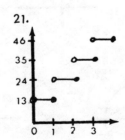

23.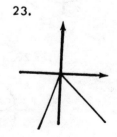

254

25.

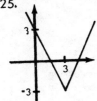

27.

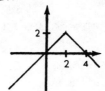

29.

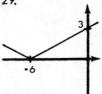

31. $-2 \leq x \leq 2$

33. $x \leq 0$ or $x \geq 3$

35. $x \leq -3$ or $x \geq 1$

37. $-6 \leq x \leq 1$

39. $-2 \leq x \leq 2$

41.

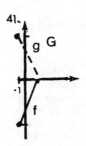

43.

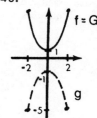

45.

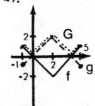

47.

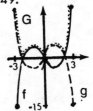

49.

Exercise 71, page 175

1. $2\sqrt{13}$, $\dfrac{2}{\sqrt{13}}$, $3/2$

3. $32/3$, $\dfrac{8\sqrt{7}}{3}$, $3/4$

5. $\dfrac{\sqrt{3}}{3}$, $1/2$, $\dfrac{\sqrt{3}}{2}$

7. $\dfrac{\sqrt{55}}{3}$, $\dfrac{3}{\sqrt{55}}$

9. $2\sqrt{5}$, $4\sqrt{5}$

11. 26, 13, 60°

13. 27, 9, 12

15. 27, 29

17. 63°, 27°, 22

19. 90°, 13

21. 76 m

23. 34 m

25. 18 m

27. 11,430 m

29. 36°

31. 52.5 m

33. 38°, 52°

35. 27°

37. 26°

39. 21.6 km

41. 28° N of W

43. 6°

45. 56°

47. 290 m

49. 6,053 m

255

7. 2, 11, 4, 5.52, probably a child's

9–12. mode 14 yr 2 mo
youngest 13 yr 11 mo
oldest 14 yr 9 mo
range 10 mo
mean 14 yr 3 mo
median 14 yr 3 mo
quartiles 14 yr 1 mo, 14 yr 3 mo, 14 yr 5 mo

13–16. mode 66 in
shortest 59 in
tallest 70 in
range 11 in
mean 64.6 in
median 66 in
quartiles 62, 66, 67

17–20. mode 145 lb
lightest 95 lb
heaviest 175 lb
range 80 lb
mean 136 lb
median 145
quartiles 125, 145, 155

Exercise 73, page 185

Review Exercise (A), page 185

1. (a) $2(2m + 1)(m - 3)$
 (b) $(x + a)(x + b)$
 (c) $(-1, -5)$

2. (a) $(2a - b)(4a^2 + 2ab + b^2)$
 (b) $-\frac{26}{9}$
 (c) $k < -\frac{1}{2}$

3. (a) 230122_4
 (b) 75
 (c) $-\frac{1}{2}$

4. (a) $x \leq 2$
 (b) 67.2 km

5. $x = \frac{1}{2}, y = 7, z = -3$

6. (a) $a^4 + 2a^3b + 3a^2b^2 + 2ab^3 + b^4$
 (b) -4

7. (a) $(x + 2)(x + 1)(x - 1)$
 (b) 12 liters

8. (a) $(2a + 3b - 1)(2a - 3b + 1)$
 (b) $x/(x - 2a)^2$

9. (a) $-1, 2$
 (b) graph

10. (a) $\dfrac{1 \pm \sqrt{7}}{3}$
 (b) $\{0, 1, 2, 3, 4, 5, 6\}$

11. (a) 2
 (b) $2xy\sqrt[3]{2}$
 (c) $(a - 1)/a$

12. (a) 9
 (b) $-a - 2$

13. (a) x^8
 (b) $2 + 2\sqrt{2}$
 (c) $x < -1$ or $x > 6$

14. (a) $7\sqrt{10}$
 (b) $\frac{3}{5}, \frac{4}{5}$

15. (a) $\{1, 2\}$
(b) $m = -1; (1, 0)$

16. (a) $\frac{1}{2}$
(b) proof

17. (a) $\frac{7}{8}$
(b) 69

18. 320, 328 km

19. (a) $x = y = (r + 2)/5$
(b) 3 days

20. (a) yes
(b) $a(b \# c) = ab \# ac$
(c) yes
(d) no

21. graph

23. $1/(1 - x + y)$

22. 12 kph

25. (a) $3/(x - 3)$
(b) $x = \frac{1}{2}, y = -\frac{1}{3}$

24. (a) $A = \$12, B = \$16, C = \$34$
(b) 147 m

Review Exercise (B), page 188

1. (a) $-a^2 + a - 4$
(b) $3x^2 - x - 2$

2. (a) $11x$
(b) $9(a - 2b)(a + 2b)$
(c) -10

3. (a) $(2x + 3y)(4x^2 - 6xy + 9y^2)$
(b) $(a + b + 1)(a - b - 1)$
(c) $2(x - y)(a - 3)$

4. (a) $x \geq \frac{13}{14}$
(b) $1/(2x - 1)$

5. (a) $\frac{2}{3}$
(b) $-4, \frac{3}{3}$

6. (a) Definition
(b) Graph

7. (a) $5a(a + 2b)(a - 2b)$
(b) $(a + x - p)(a - x + p)$
(c) 19

8. (a) $\dfrac{\sqrt{3} - 1}{2}$
(b) $x < \frac{4}{3}$

9. -3

10. (a) Definition
(b) $(2x - 5)^2$
(c) $(5 - 2x)(3 + x)$
(d) 1, 9

11. (a) $27x^7y^6$
(b) HCF = 14, LCM = 2310
(c) -343

12. $2\frac{1}{2}$

13. (a) 11, 13
(b) 60 kg

14. (a) $(2a - b)(4a^2 + 2ab + b^2)$
(b) $9, -2$
(c) $x < 9$
(d) $x + y + z$

15. (a) 1
(b) $2x - 3y = -5$
(c) $x + y = 6, 2x + 2y = 12$

16. \$3900 at 5%, \$3400 at 6%

17. $(3, -1)$

18. -1

19. (a) $V = (1, 4); (-1, 0), (3, 0)$
(b) $y = x + 3$

20. (a) $8\sqrt{3}/3$
(b) $0, -2$

21. (a) 4
(b) 2 days

22. (a) $\sqrt{15}/5, \sqrt{6}/2$
(b) 72 m

Review Exercise (B), page 188, Continued

23. $10\frac{1}{2}$ days

24. (b) (i) T; (ii) F, $\frac{18}{30}$; (iii) F, $x = -1$

25. (a) (i) $\sqrt{2} \cdot \sqrt{8} = 4$
      (ii) $\sqrt{2} + (-\sqrt{2}) = 0$

26. (a) 31
    (b) $(1 \# 2) \# 3 = 5 \# 3 =$
       $23 = 1 \# (2 \# 3)$
    (c) $-\frac{1}{2}$

27. (a) $(x + 6)/(x - 2)$
   (b) $a = 1, b = 4$

28. (a) $\dfrac{-5 \pm \sqrt{13}}{2}$
    (b) $-4.3, -0.7$

29. 20 km

30. (a) proof
    (b) (i) unknown
       (ii) positive
      (iii) unknown
      (iv) negative
      (v) x positive, y negative

Review Exercise (C), page 192

1. d	**2.** a	**27.** b	**28.** e
3. a	**4.** c	**29.** c	**30.** b
5. a	**6.** c	**31.** d	**32.** a
7. d	**8.** d	**33.** a	**34.** d
9. a	**10.** e	**35.** d	**36.** d
11. e	**12.** d	**37.** a	**38.** b
13. a	**14.** d	**39.** d	**40.** e
15. d	**16.** b	**41.** d	**42.** b
17. d	**18.** e	**43.** b	**44.** b
19. b	**20.** a	**45.** d	**46.** d
21. c	**22.** c	**47.** d	**48.** c
23. e	**24.** a	**49.** b	**50.** c
25. b	**26.** e		

Review Exercise (D), page 196

1. c	**2.** b	**11.** b	**12.** c
3. c	**4.** e	**13.** b	**14.** b
5. a	**6.** d	**15.** c	**16.** e
7. d	**8.** d	**17.** b	**18.** a
9. c	**10.** a	**19.** b	**20.** d

Mathematics III Algebra

1. 126 and 72

2. (a) positive   (b) positive
(c) positive   (d) negative

3. (a) −6 (b) −48
(c) − 14 (d) 0

4. (a) 291   (b)760
(c) 0.0057 (d) 10,000

5. (a) $\frac{12}{7}$
(b) Any number x, such as 23.155,
where $23.15 < x < 23.16$

6. (a) Commutativity of multiplication
(b) Commutativity of addition
(c) Distributivity
(d) Associativity of addition

7. (a) −2
(b) All non-zero real numbers
(c) All positive real numbers
(d) No values
(e) All real numbers
(f) No values

8. (a) $n \neq 0$
(b) No restrictions other than
n's being real
(c) $n \neq 7$
(d) No restrictions

9. (a) Any suitable answer such as $2k + 1$
(b) Any suitable answer such as $k - k$
(c) Any suitable answer such as $\dfrac{k}{k}$
(d) Any suitable answer such as $- |k|$

10. −7

11. (a) $7b$
(b) $4.99x^2$ provided $x \neq 0$

12. (a) 59
(b) 4

13. (a) A/h (The fact that $h \neq 0$ is apparent
from the answer and is not stated
as part of the answer by NAIS.)
(b) $\dfrac{P - 2h}{2}$ (c) $\dfrac{2A}{h}$ (d) $\dfrac{2A - ha}{h}$

14. (a) 3   (b) 0 or 4

15. $3 + 2\sqrt{2}$ or $3 - 2\sqrt{2}$

16. (a) $-3 - \sqrt{5}$
(b) $18 - 12\sqrt{2}$

17. (a) $2 + a$ or $2 - a$
(b) a or -1

18. $t \leq -10$

19. graph

20. graph

21. (a) $x = a$ (b) $m < n$

22. graph

23. (2, 1)

24. (a) $x(x + 3)(x - 3)$
(b) $(3 + 7x)(1 - x)$

25. (a) graph
(b) 30 square units
(c) 15 square units

26. (a) $17c - 46$
(b) $1 + rt$ and $p \neq 0$

27. (a) $\dfrac{5}{x}$ (b) $\dfrac{ad}{bc}$ provided $d \neq 0$

   (c) $-\dfrac{5}{2x}$ (d) $\dfrac{x + 20}{5}$

29. (a) $\dfrac{2x + y}{x + y}$ provided $x \neq y$

   (b) $a^2 - 3$ provided $a \neq 2$

31. (a) $a + 2$

   (b) $a \notin \{2, -2, \sqrt{5}, -\sqrt{5}\}$

33. (a) $\dfrac{17\sqrt{6}}{2}$ (b) $\dfrac{\sqrt{2}}{4}$

   (c) $50\sqrt{2} - 25\sqrt{6}$ (d) $\tfrac{1}{3}$

35. (a) 5   (b) $\dfrac{n - 5}{n}$

   (c) $\dfrac{n - 5}{2n - 5}$ (d) 25

37. **53, 20**

39. 28 nickels and 14 dimes

41. 30 shirts

30. (a) $\dfrac{a}{5b + 30}$ provided $b \neq 1$

   and $b \neq 6$ and $a \neq 0$

   (b) -2 provided $a \neq b$

28. (a) $\dfrac{x}{2}$ provided $x \neq -1$

   (b) $-\dfrac{3x}{2}$ provided $x \neq 5$

32. (a) 5 : 4   (b) 1 : 3

   (c) undefined (d) 4 : 1

34. 52, 54, 56

36. (a) The area is quadrupled

   (b) The volume is quadrupled

38. Bob is 15 and George is 20

40. 3.6 hours

Mathematics IV Algebra, page 202

1. $\tfrac{1}{8}$

3. $6x^4 - 9x^3 + 10x^2 - 19x + 2$

5. (a) $(x + 2)(x - 2)(x + 3)(x - 3)$
   (b) $(x - 3)(x - 3 - a)$

7. $x + 1$ provided $x^3 - x^2 + 1 \neq 0$

2. $2x + 3y - 6 = 0$

4. (a) $(x - 13)(x + 7)$
   (b) $2(x + 2)(x + 1)$

6. (a) $x(x + 8)(x - 8)$
   (b) $2(x + 4)(x^2 - 4x + 16)$

8. (a) $\dfrac{x^2 + y^2}{x + y}$

   (b) $\dfrac{2}{2 - x}$ provided $x \neq -2$. (The fact that $x \neq 2$ is apparent from the answer and is not stated as part of the answer by N.A.I.S.).

9. (a) $-\tfrac{3}{5}$ provided $a \neq \dfrac{2b}{3}$

   (b) $\dfrac{y}{4y - x}$ provided $y \neq 0$ and $x \neq -4y$

10. (1) closure for addition

   (2) associativity of addition

   (3) additive inverse

   (4) additive identity

260

11. (a) $\{-3\}$
(b) $\{0, 2\}$

12. (a) $\{1, -1\}$ (b) $\{1, -1\}$
(c) All x greater than 1
(d) All x such that $-1 < x < 1$
(e) All x such that $0 < x < 1$

13. 4

14. 13

15. (a) $\dfrac{2 + 3\sqrt{2}}{2}, \dfrac{2 - 3\sqrt{2}}{2}$
(b) All x such that $3 < x < 4$

16. (a) $\{x : -2 < x < 6\}$
(b) $\{-1, 11\}$

17. $\{(-2, 11)\}$

18. $r = \dfrac{Rf}{F - f}$ and $r \neq 0$ and $f \neq 0$

19. (a) -4 (b) $x \leq 0$
(c) $x > 0$ (d) $x < -2$

20. 2

21. (a) $\frac{1}{3}$ provided $x \neq 0$
(b) 3

22. (a) $\dfrac{1}{a^2 + 1}$ provided $a \neq 0$
(b) $x^2 + 1$ provided x is positive

23. (a) $\dfrac{2 - \sqrt{2}}{2}$
(b) $\dfrac{24\sqrt{7}}{7}$

24. (a) $\frac{2}{3}$

(b) 1

25. (a) $2x^2 - 4x + 3$
(b) $\{x : x \geq 2\}$

26. $b = 0$

27. $\dfrac{2n}{5}$

28. $2a + 3(b + 4a) = 2a + (3b + 12a)$
distributive prop
$$= 2a + (12a + 3b)$$
commut of add
$$= (2a + 12a) + 3b$$
associative of add
$$= 14a + 3b$$
closure of add

29. (a) parallelogram
(b) $(\frac{3}{2}, 2)$

30. $2x - 3y + 9 = 0$

31. graph

32. 3

33. No number has that property

34. Domain $\{p : p \geq -4\}$. Range $\{p : p \geq 0\}$.

35. $f(a) = a^3 - 3a + \dfrac{3}{a} - \dfrac{1}{a^3}$

$$= -\dfrac{1}{a^3} + \dfrac{3}{a} - 3a + a^3$$
(by commutativity of addition)
$$= f\left(-\dfrac{1}{a}\right) \text{ (by definition).}$$
Then use transitivity of equality.

36. 5 problems

37. Between 3 and 6 mph

39. 50

38. {orange, yellow, violet}

40. $\{(x, y) : y \geq \frac{1}{2} |x| + 1 \text{ and } y < 3\}$

Exercise 75

Midyear Examination (A), page 206

1. (a) $7a - 7b + 7$
   (b) $-6x^2y^2 + 7x^3y + 1$

2. (a) 1
   (b) $a^3 + 2a^2 - 4$

3. (a) $(3a + 5b)(2a - 3b)$
   (b) $3(x + 2)(x^2 - 2x + 4)$
   (c) $(2x + 1)(2x - 1)(x + 2)(x - 2)$

4. (a) $m(n - m)$
   (b) $a + b$

5. (a) $p = (2t + 6k)$ft.

   (b) $2x + 2, 2x + 4$

   (c) $\dfrac{tc}{a}$ cents   (d) 23

6. $\dfrac{4a - 5}{(a - 1)(a^2 - 4)}$

7. $700 at 5%; $400 at $3\frac{1}{2}$%

8. 2

9. Donner, 9; Blitzen, 4; Dasher, 16

10. (a) (i) all x; (ii) all x not 0; (iii) $x = 0$
   (b) $-\frac{1}{9}$ (c) 13,480

Midyear Examination (C), page 208

1. $2(y + 3)(y - 3)$

2. $-72x^7y^8$

3. -32

4. $2x^2 + x - 3$

5. 1

6. $x < 4$

7. 14

8. Definition

9. $2x$

10. $(a^2 - 3b)(a^4 + 3a^2b + 9b^2)$

11. 10

12. $-4, 10$

13. $2t + 4$

14. $(3x + 2y)(12x - 7y)$

15. $2\frac{2}{5}$ hrs.

16. -10

17. (a) 7 (b) yes (c) 3, -5

18. $n = 21, d = 10, q = 5$

19. 1

20. 20 mph

1. (a) $-a - b$
   (b) $y - xy$

2. $-a^2c + 5ab$

3. (a) $2x^2 - 4x + 3$
   (b) $2(t + 3)(t - 3)$

4. (a) $c(x + 2)$ cents
   (b) $m/10$ hrs.
   (c) $2x + 2y$ cm

5. 2

6. (a) $(4a - 3b)^2$
   (b) $-10x^7$

7. 21, 26

8. (a) $\frac{36}{11}$
   (b) $x < 6$

9. $2x^5 - 5x^3 + 2x^2 + 2x - 2$

10. (a) $(3a + 7)(2a - 5)$
    (b) -2

11. (1) Identity for Addition
    (3) Multiplication Property for Equality
    (4) Distributive Law
    (5) Identity for Addition
    (6) Subtraction Property for Equality

12. (a) $(2a + b)/ab$
    (b) -8

13. (a) $4x + 6$
    (b) 12, 24

14. (a) $-5 \le x \le 5$
    $2 < x$
    (b) $-5 \le x < 2$
    (c) $\{x \mid x \le 5\}$

Exercise 76. Final Examinations

Final Examination (A), page 212

1. (a) $(3 + x^3)(3 - x^3)$
   (b) $(m + 7)(m - 4)$

2. -2

3. $a^3 + 2a^2 - 4$ with remainder $2a$

4. $-2, 3$

5. (a) $4x$ (b) $\dfrac{a}{a^2 + 1}$

6. $\dfrac{2 - a^2}{a}$

7. (a) $\frac{1}{4}, \frac{3}{4}$ (b) $x \le \frac{9}{2}$

8. $\dfrac{1 \pm \sqrt{19}}{3}$

9. $-1, 8, 4$

10. $3\sqrt{6}$

11. 3, -5

12. $\dfrac{-t}{t + h}$

13. $2 + \sqrt{2}$

14. (a) $(2a + b + c)(2a - b - c)$
    (b) $(y - 2z)(y + 2z + a)$

15. $(0, -2), (3, 0), \frac{2}{3}$

16. -1

17. 7 miles

18. (a) $(3, 5), (6, 3), (9, 1)$
    (b) $(3, 0), (0, -6)$

19. (a) $\sqrt{13}$ (b) $\sqrt{x^2 + y^2} = \sqrt{y^2 + x^2}$
    (c) 0   (d) NO
    (e) 8

263

1. (a) $\frac{1}{5}$, 2
   (b) $(x - y)(x + y - a)$
   (c) $\{3, 5, 7\}$

3. (a) $3 \pm \sqrt{9 - k}$
   (b) 81

5. (a) $a\sqrt[6]{ab^5}$
   (b) $4\sqrt{7} - 10$

7. (a) $2a + 1$
   (b) 9/4

9. (a) (i) $\odot$ distributes over $\oplus$,
   (ii) No, $\sqrt{\dfrac{ab}{c}} \neq \dfrac{\sqrt{ab}}{\sqrt{ac}}$
   (b) 69.7 ft.

2. (a) $7\sqrt{6}/6$
   (b) $\frac{1}{2}$
   (c) $(a^2cb^4)/4$

4. (a) $(0, 12), (6, 0), (-2, 0)$; $V = (2, 16)$
   (b) $x > 5$ or $x < -2$.

6. (a) $(x + y + z)(x - y - z)$ (b) $\dfrac{2a}{b - 2}$
   (c) $\tan B = \frac{1}{3}$, $\cos A = \frac{1}{5}$

8. (a) $\frac{1}{2}$ qt of 60%; $1\frac{1}{2}$ qt of 80%
   (b) $3 \pm 2\sqrt{2}$

10. $a = 20$, $b = 35$ days

1. (a) 8
   (b) $\cos \alpha = \frac{40}{41}$; $\tan \alpha = \frac{9}{41}$

3. (a) (i) 13, (ii) 9, (iii) 37
   (b) $V = (-2, -9)$

5. 35

7. $\dfrac{x}{x - 1}$

9. vertices, $(0, 4)$ and $(4, 2)$.

2. (a) (i) $x(x + y)(x^2 - xy + y^2)$
        (ii) $(x - 4 + y)(x - 4 - y)$
   (b) 129/5

4. (a) $\sqrt{21} - 2\sqrt{5}$
   (b) 4.56 (c) $-2\sqrt[3]{2} - \frac{1}{2}$

6. (a) 12 (b) $x < -7$ or $x > 5$

8. Walk 4 mph; Ride 20 mph

10. $\frac{1}{2}$, 8

1. $3a(\sqrt{2a} - \sqrt[3]{2a})$

3. -2

5. (a) $2(x + 3)(x - 3)$
   (b) $(y - 2x)(3x - 1)$

7. $D = -23$, Solutions are complex.

9. proof

2. $2x - 5y = 0$

4. 50

6. $4 - \sqrt{7}$

8. $(3y)/(4a^2)$

10. (a) less than 0, (b) 0
    (c) $q = p$ (d) less than 0
    (e) $q \leq 0$

Final Examination (F), page 220, Continued

11. $(a + b)/b$

12. $x = \dfrac{2}{a + b}$ $\quad y = \dfrac{2}{a - b}$

13. $t/u = \frac{2}{3}$, $10u + t - 27 = 10t + u$

14. (a) $\frac{3}{2}$
    (b) undefined
    (c) x

15. 59.5 ft.

16. graph

17. $3(\sqrt{2} + 1)$

18. 32, 24 mph

19. (a) graph
    (b) graph
    (c) graph

Final Examination (G),   page 222

1. (a) -4
   (b) $y = 0$
   (c) yes

2. (a) {0, 1, 4, 9, 16, 25, 36, 49, 64}
   (b) {1, 4, 9, 16, 25}
   (c) 31

3. (a) $-5 < x < 8$
   (b) $(\pm 2, 0)$, $(0, 4)$

4. (a) $k < -\frac{1}{2}$
   (b) $-\frac{26}{9}$

5. $x = 12$
   $y = 6$

6. (a) $\frac{14}{11}$
   (b) $3x - y = 6$

7. 145, 148 km

8. (a) $p/5d$
   (b) -4

9. (a) 1
   (b) $(-\frac{16}{3}, -\frac{8}{3})$
       $(0, 8)$
       $(4, 2)$

10. \$12, \$16, \$34

Final Examination (H),   page 223

1. $9(y + 2x)(y - 2x)$

2. $-2ac^6$

3. $x < -1$

4. $(3y - 7)(2y + 5)$

5. $2x + y = 4$

6. 1

7. $(x + 3)(x^2 - 3x + 9)$

8. $x = 2$
   $y = -3$

9. (a) -16
   (b) 5

10. $(a - d)(a + d - 1)$

11. $7x^2 - 2x + 3$

12. 220 km

13. $(a^2 - 3)(a + 3)(a - 3)$

14. $5x + 8$

15. $-\frac{1}{8}$

16. 32 yrs

17. 1 or 3

18. $(-5a^2 - a + 10)/(a^2 - 1)(a - 2)$

19. $(-3, -2)$, $(-3, 9)$, $(0, 7)$

20. 10 liters